D1409803

Connected Geometry

A Habits-of-Mind Approach to Geometry

Connected Geometry is a dynamic, innovative, and versatile geometry program. Developed by Education Development Center, Inc., and funded by the National Science Foundation, *Connected Geometry* is an activity-based program with a problem-solving focus and is firmly grounded in the NCTM *Standards*. Based upon extensive research and field-tested with diverse student populations, *Connected Geometry* is organized around mathematical ways of thinking called "habits of mind."

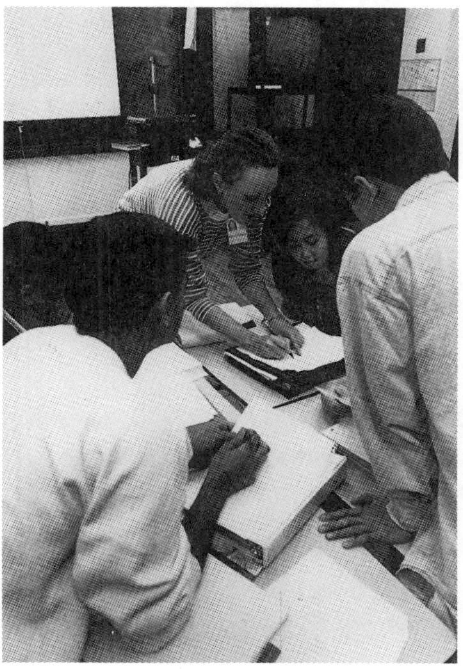

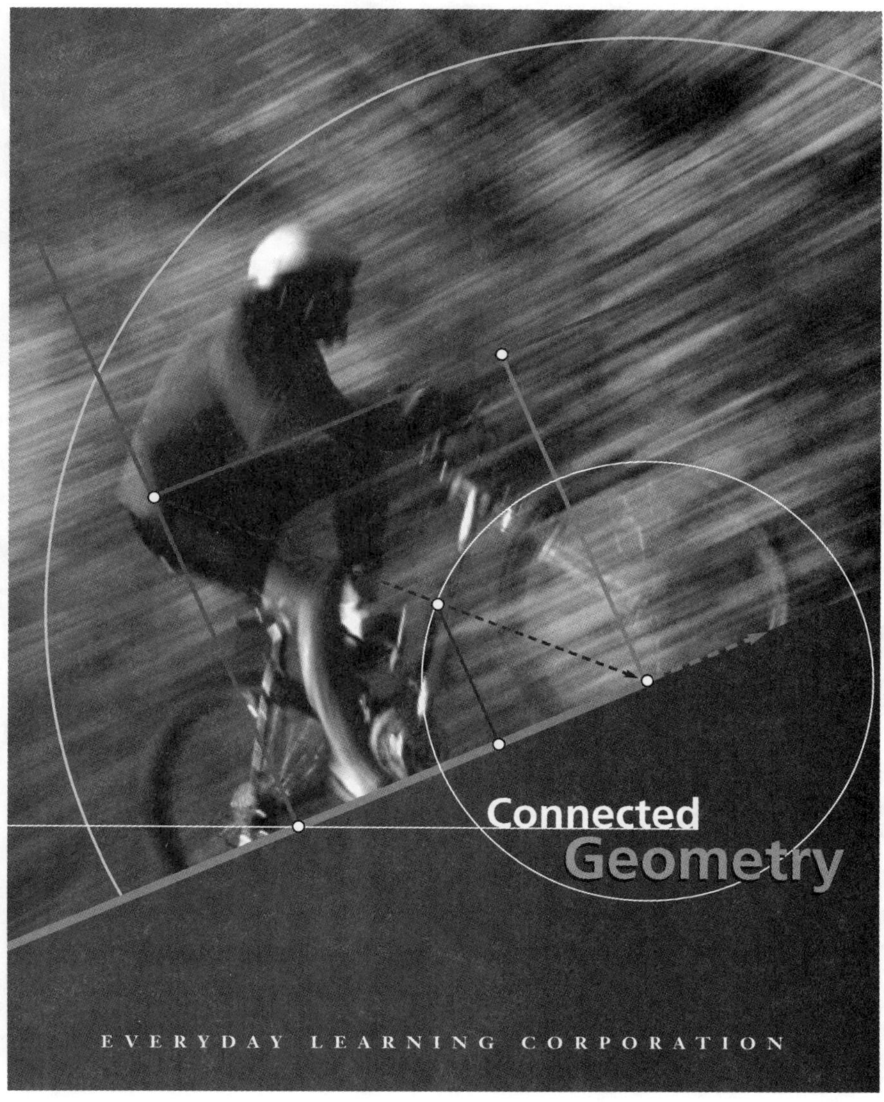

A rich mathematics curriculum and a unique approach

- Emphasizes mathematical habits of mind as students master geometric concepts.
- Contains problem-based lessons that promote active learning and critical thinking.
- Uses technology which enables students to experiment and to explore topics in greater depth.
- Encourages communicating, conjecturing, and mathematical reasoning.
- Brings together ideas from geometry, algebra, and analysis in an investigative way that does not require a specialized background.

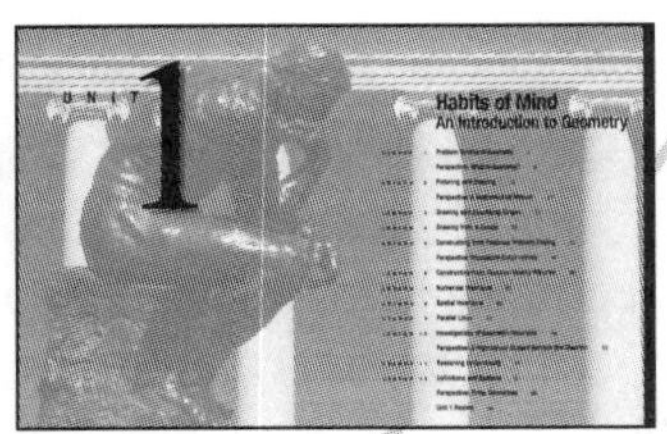

Habits of Mind: An Introduction to Geometry

This first module introduces important mathematical ways of thinking and essential vocabulary for an appropriate classroom culture.

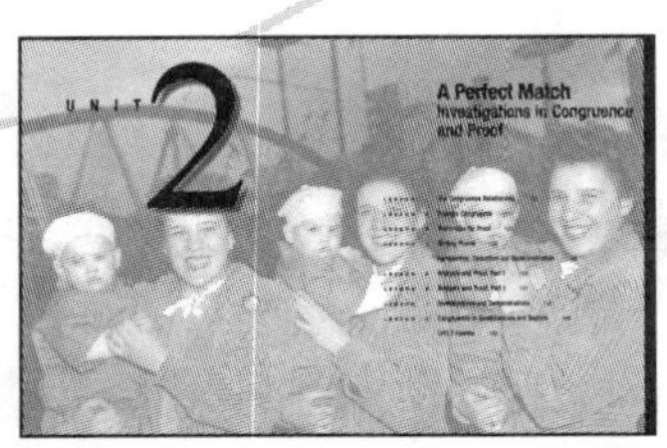

A Perfect Match: Investigations in Congruence and Proof

The focus is on the congruence properties of triangles and the introduction of formal proof.

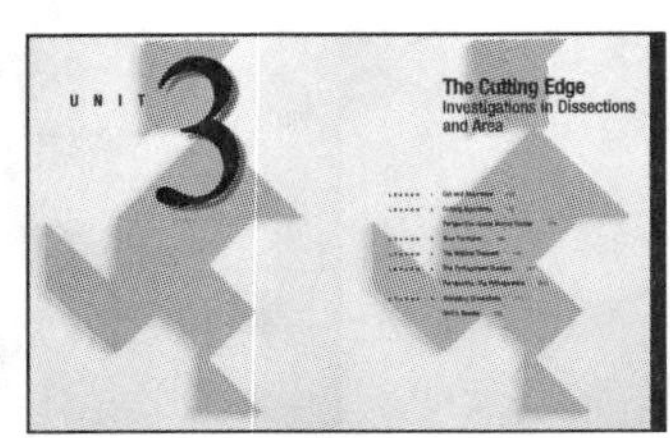

The Cutting Edge: Investigations in Dissections and Area

Dissection algorithms provide a context for learning about area and perimeter and provide more opportunities to work with proof.

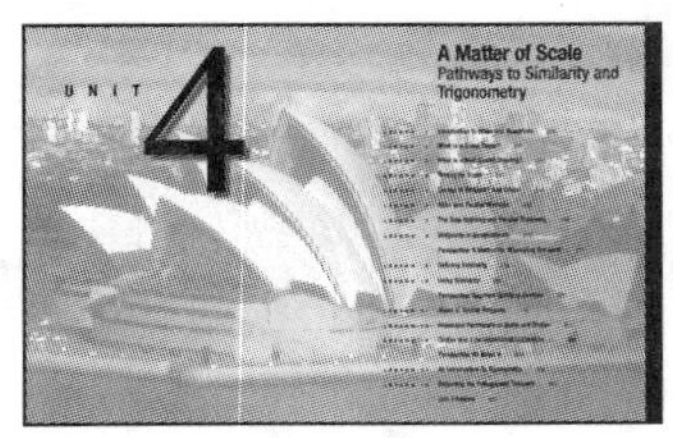

A Matter of Scale: Pathways to Similarity and Trigonometry

This module focuses on three related themes: scale drawing, similarity, and trigonometry. In addition, there are opportunities for proof, applications, and historical connections.

The Language of Coordinates and Vectors: Connecting Geometry and Algebra

Students plot points and locate shapes in a coordinate plane, use algebraic methods to scale and to translate figures, and use vectors to prove some standard geometric concepts.

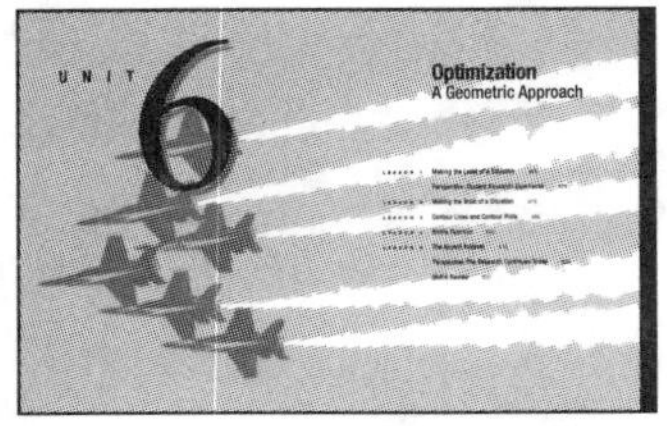

Optimization: A Geometric Approach

The focus is on finding maxima and minima without calculus.

Flexible components meet classroom needs

- Enjoy a substantial program—Student and Teacher text materials provide a complete 10th-grade Geometry curriculum.
- Find plenty of suggestions in the Teacher's Guide—The Teacher's Guide suggests ways to use the materials in the classroom and references investigations of the CD-ROM to supplement the *Connected Geometry* text.
- Enhance any curriculum with the CD-ROM—Use individual modules to replace units of standard texts as part of an integrated curriculum or to provide additional investigations and extensions.
- Extend investigations—The additional investigations and information on the CD-ROM may be used to supplement the text. Use the extended investigations for enrichment, assessment, special projects, or additional practice.
- Take advantage of complete support materials for the curriculum—Solution and Problem Solving Resource, Assessment Resources, and Teaching Resources provide complete support for teachers and students.

Connected Geometry is a full-year course for all students that emphasizes the thoughtful path to the solution.

Providing a full array of support, this resource offers overviews, planning guides, assessment suggestions, pacing suggestions, and detailed teaching notes for the lessons.

Corresponding modules on the CD-ROM provide flexibility in a variety of ways. Use independently or in combination with the text for additional investigations, enrichment, or student projects.

Complete solutions to all problems are accessible to teachers and students. Also included are proofs, statements of theorems, and alternative approaches.

To ensure a complete, balanced, and varied assessment program, developers provide lesson Quizzes, two forms of Mid-Unit Exams, and two forms of End-of-Unit Exams, all with answers.

Blackline Masters for creating overhead transparencies help students organize their work and ease teachers' preparation.

Textbook features that promote student understanding

Lesson Objective

Explore and Discuss
Encourages communication, conjecturing, and mathematical reasoning.

Lesson Activities
Problem-based lessons engage students in interesting and challenging problems that project deep mathematical thinking.

Take It Further
Challenges students with problems that extend the lesson.

Ways to Think About It
Provides insight into problem-solving strategies and helps students connect activities to big problem-solving ideas.

For Discussion
Allows students to discuss their ideas with classmates before writing or orally presenting their conclusions.

Write and Reflect
Requests a response similar to a brief essay, in which students express opinions or provide a carefully thought-out explanation.

Checkpoint
Provides opportunities for students to assess their progress and to clarify results of activities.

Perspective
Includes personal stories or views from mathematicians and some history of major mathematical results.

On Your Own
Includes a rich variety of problems, many of which are open-ended.

Sidenotes
Offers hints, suggestions, and sometimes tidbits of interest from teachers.

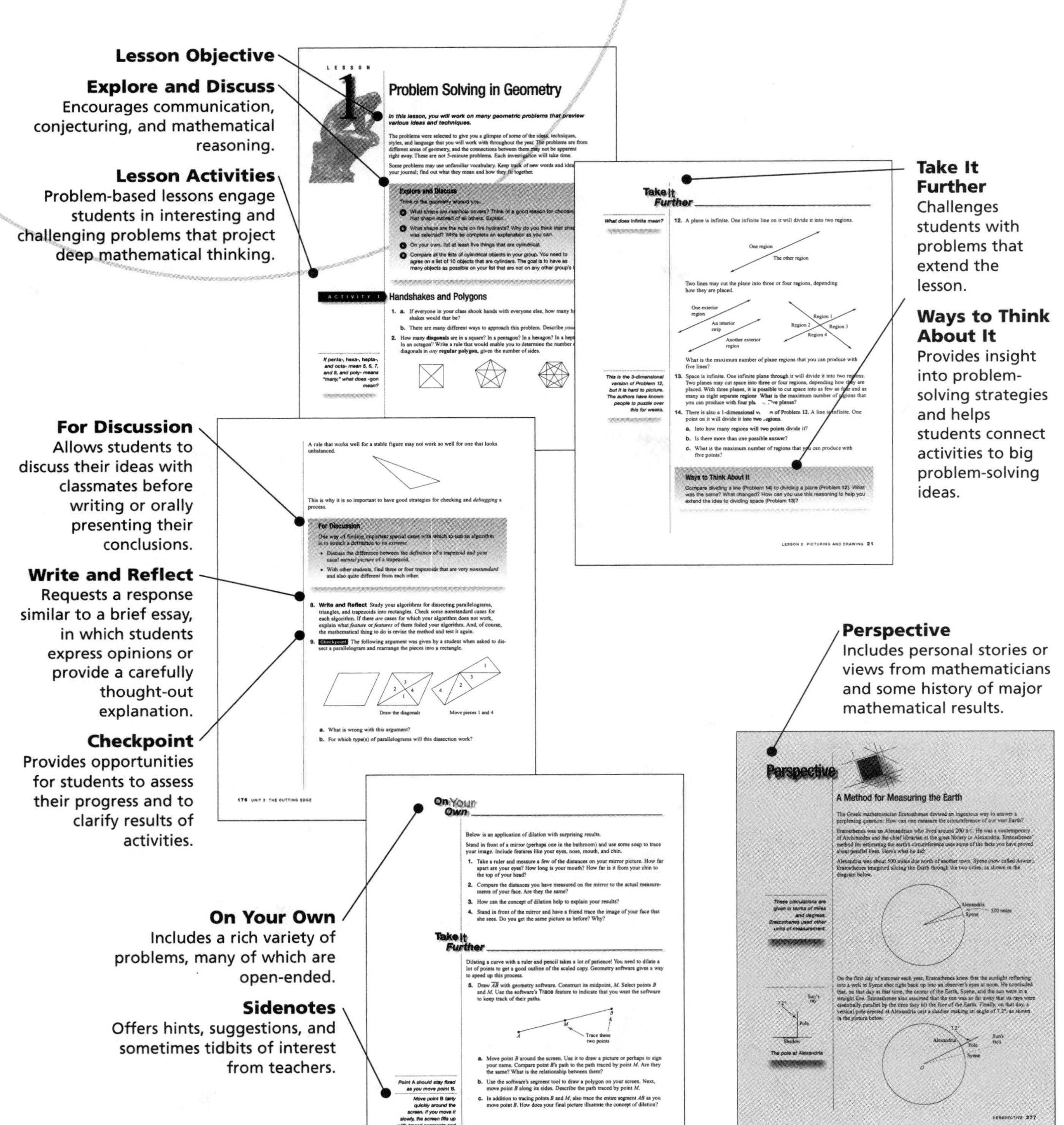

Teacher's Guide

Connected Geometry

Developed by

Education Development Center, Inc.
Newton, Massachusetts

EVERYDAY LEARNING®

Chicago, Illinois

Cover image: Photodisc™

Everyday Learning Development Staff

Editorial: Anna Belluomini, Steve Mico, Carol Zacny

Production/Design: Fran Brown, Annette Davis, Jess Schaal, Norma Underwood

Additional Credits: Herman Adler Design Group, Carlisle Communications, Jody Levine

This project was supported, in part, by the National Science Foundation. The opinions expressed are those of the authors and not necessarily those of the Foundation.

ISBN 1-57039-590-X

Everyday Learning Corporation
P.O. Box 812960
Chicago, IL 60681
1-800-322-MATH (6284)

Visit our website at www.everydaylearning.com

1 2 3 4 5 6 7 8 9 CU 04 03 02 01 00 99

Contents

Acknowledgments

The *Connected Geometry* modules are the result of the efforts of many people besides the project team of the Education Development Center. These people provided support and encouragement throughout the writing, field testing, and final production. A group of teacher advisors and their students provided extremely valuable assistance with feedback on how the lessons worked in their classrooms. They held the first trials of the methods and ideas we use. Both teachers and students offered detailed comments and opinions about how they worked with the material. We, in turn, have incorporated their work as well as what we learned from visiting many of these teachers' classes over the years. **Teacher Advisors and Field Testers:** Jim Barnes, Joan Bryant, Cheri Dartnell, Larry Davidson, Paul DiNolo, Janice Enos, Kathy Erikson, Jane Gorman, Carol Haney, Betty Helm, Felisa Honeyman, Elfreda Kallock, Britt Kleiman, Phil Lewis, Carol Martingnette-Boswell, Barney Martinez, Doug McGlathery, Bill Nevin, Mary T. Nowak, Faye Ruopp, Gary Simon, Jesse Solomon, and Jennifer Takarabe.

We've also benefited greatly from the opportunity to work with an Advisory Board of mathematicians, educators, college professors, and high school teachers. Our Advisory Board members brought us a wealth of resources, and helped us collect material to develop ideas for topics and problems. **Advisory Board Members:** Barbara Adler, Gail Bussone, Douglas Clements, Ed Dubinsky, Joan Ferrini-Mundy, Carol Findell, Hector Hirigoyen, Paul Horwitz, James Kaput, Margaret Kenney, Harvey Keynes, Eugene Klotz, Steven Monk, Bob Moses, Barbara Scott Nelson, Jim Newton, Arthur Powell, Andee Rubin, Deborah Schifter, Marjorie Senechal, Antonia Stone, Ellen Wahl, and Bernie Zubrowski.

We are indebted to our reviewers, who read the drafts of the modules, and to their students. The reviewers used the modules as course material. They pointed out omissions and errors, as well as their favorite problems and other things that they particularly enjoyed. They also shed light on new ways of looking at some of the problems and themes. **Reviewers:** Peter Baunfeld, Larry Davidson, Tommy Dreyfus, Brad Findell, Carol Findell, Wayne Harvey, Jim King, Terry Leveritch, Gary Martin, Barney Martinez, Tricia Pacelli, Libby Palmer, Faye Ruopp, Judy Roitman, Chih-Han Sah, and Hung-Hsi Wu.

We also extend thanks to the following **Special Contributors:** Tammy Jo Ruter, for her illustration expertise, Jim Sandefur for the 120° devise used in *Optimization,* and Jim Tattersall for providing information on segment splitting.

- **Looking for invariants**

  The search for invariants—things that stay put while other things around them are changing—is really the heart of mathematics. As with all of the ways of thinking that are emphasized throughout *Connected Geometry,* looking for invariants is extremely useful outside as well as inside mathematics. When one is trying to understand a situation or phenomenon in just about any field, a useful technique is to look not only for what changes, but also for what does *not* change.

  The solution of the following problem lies in reasoning about proportions, a special and important kind of invariant. Proportional reasoning is a major part of the work in Lesson 8 of *A Matter of Scale.*

  A shape-invariant: when E, F, G, and H are midpoints, regardless of how the quadrilateral ABCD is changed, EFGH will remain a parallelogram. But why?

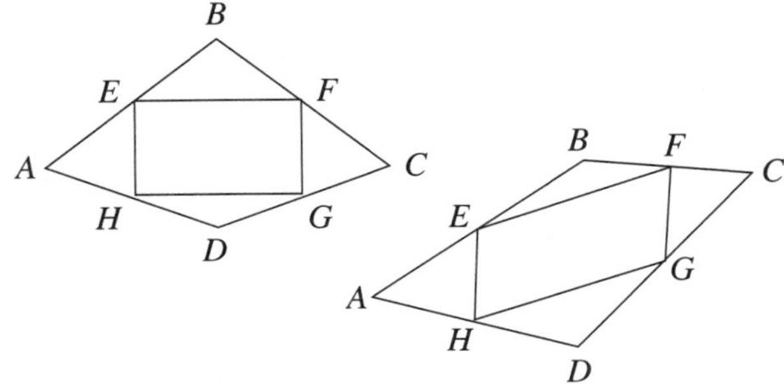

- **Reasoning about processes**

  Algorithms have always been an important part of mathematics. In the computer age, especially, they have become an essential piece of a student's understanding. The *Connected Geometry* materials ask students to work with algorithms frequently. Sometimes, there is an obvious way to check an algorithm: Follow the instructions precisely or run the computer program, and see if the right thing happens. Other times, the process needs to be reasoned out step by step. In Lesson 1 of *The Cutting Edge,* students create algorithms to dissect any paper parallelogram in a way that allows the parts to be rearranged into a rectangle. But before they can draw conclusions based on their algorithm, the students have to check its validity; they cannot be satisfied with something that just "looks like it does the right thing."

  Below, the cut creates two pieces from the parallelogram: a triangle and a trapezoid.

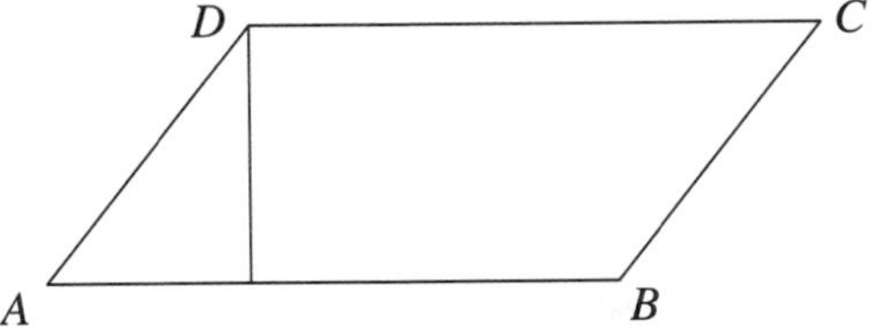

  Then these pieces are rearranged. But what guarantees that the rearrangement has four sides?

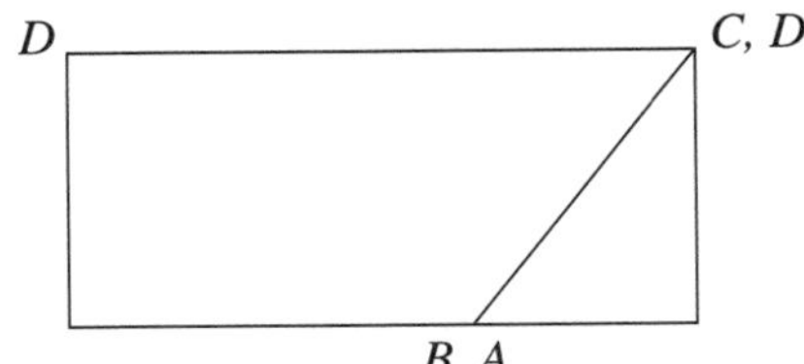

The next two figures show ways that the dissection might fail.

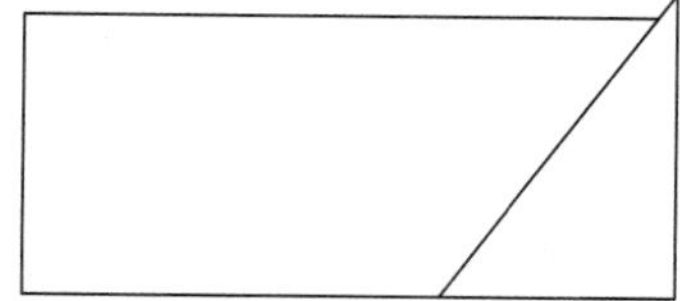

1. *The newly "glued" edges might not match.*

2. *The new sides might be "bent."*

Explain how the properties of a parallelogram assure you that when you slide the triangle to the opposite side of the trapezoid . . .

- *the two pieces* will *fit together exactly, and*
- *the new bottom edge* will *be straight.*

- **Reasoning by continuity**

  Perhaps because a major motivation among early geometers was to describe two- and three-dimensional space, reasoning by continuity has always been an important habit of mind in geometry.

  The theorem about the sum of the distances from an interior point to the sides of an equilateral triangle provides an example of this type of reasoning. Before reading and discussing this theorem in Lesson 5 of *Optimization,* students encounter it in the form of a multiple-choice question from a standardized test.

  Given an equilateral triangle of side 10 and a point D inside the triangle, what is the sum $DR + DQ + DP$ of the distances from D to the sides of the triangle?

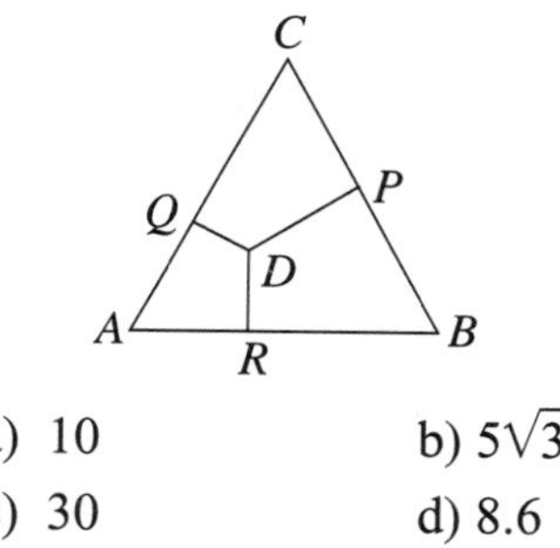

a) 10 b) $5\sqrt{3}$

c) 30 d) 8.6

Given a specific sidelength of an equilateral triangle and four lengths from which to choose, students are asked to find the sum of the distances to the sides. The problem is solved by using a mix of deduction, experimentation, and reasoning by continuity.

- Since there is one correct answer for this multiple-choice question, the sum must be constant no matter where the interior point is located.
- Experimentation with a few different positions for the interior point shows that a location just a short distance away from any one of the vertices will require two very short distances and a third distance that is almost equal to the height of the triangle.

Students Working Together

Group work is powerful, but certainly individual work can be just as valuable. Many students need to think about a problem on their own before they can contribute productively to a group, and many students find the best way to use a group is as a "sounding board" for ideas they have already thought about.

When students work together to solve problems, it can be a powerful vehicle for supporting mathematics teaching and learning. We have seen quite a range of classes working with the *Connected Geometry* materials, and many teachers have found that the mathematical thinking students develop in these activities can at times be enhanced by having students work in groups. The range we have seen includes teachers who have students work together every day, others who do it a couple of times a week, and others who use it to break up a routine of individual learning.

The following pages point out specific aspects of the *Connected Geometry* materials that can be enhanced by group work, provide some tips for the first few times you ask your students to work together on a task, and include a specific example of students working together on a *Connected Geometry* problem.

When Is Working Together Helpful?

Students can work together in any number of situations. You as the teacher—or even your students—should be the judge of whether group work makes sense for a particular activity. What follows is a description of places in the *Connected Geometry* materials where our field-test teachers found it beneficial to ask students to work in groups.

Group work allows students to observe multiple problem solving strategies, which will come in handy later. You may hear things like, "That's a neat way of doing it!"

Group work allows students to accomplish something that may have been beyond the individual capabilities of the students.

You really understand something if you can explain it to someone else.

- **When diverse approaches are helpful.** Some problems in *Connected Geometry* are so different from what students are used to that they really need a variety of ideas to get started. We have found that this is especially true of the early problems in the books. Students find it helpful to try out different things, talk through their strategies, and get feedback. In whole class discussions, it is rare that more than one student can share an idea at a time. Working together in small groups, more students have the opportunity to share their ideas and conjectures, and they can get immediate feedback from their peers. Many teachers feel that students in their classrooms become more actively engaged in the learning process.
- **When the reading is lengthy or difficult.** The *Connected Geometry* materials depend heavily on problems presented in words. Sometimes these are verbal descriptions that must be translated into mathematical diagrams or notation. Other times students may be asked to read a page or two of text—a proof, a story to set up a problem, or a solution to an earlier problem—and then answer questions based on the reading. For some students, such reading (especially about mathematics) is difficult, but when working with other students they can figure out the meaning. Groups of three or four students can read the section aloud to each other, and work together to solve the problems based on the reading.
- **When communicating about mathematics is the point of the problem.** Many *Connected Geometry* problems ask students to write explanations, proofs, or algorithms. A natural way to check these solutions is to see if someone else can read and understand them. This is particularly useful in the case of algorithms: When partners try out each others' algorithms, do they get the results they expect?

- **When modeling the structure of a research team.** When the focus is on a specific problem, as in *Optimization*'s "airport problem," a group of students might function as a research team, critiquing each other's approaches, acting as a forum in which students bounce ideas around, and keeping track of the growing body of partial results and conjectures. The results of such an effort are truly the work of the group, and they members of the group may decide to write up a joint paper describing the results they obtain.

Getting Started

If having students work together on problems is new to you, it is very likely new to most of your students as well. It may take a few classes to get into a flow of productive group work. The following list discusses how to help students work in groups the first few times.

- **Face-to-face, small group interaction.** Having students work with a very small group (3 or 4 students) encourages more of them to talk about the mathematics. This is furthered by making sure that students sit facing each other, not just next to each other. This may be the most important aspect of having students work together.
- **Positive interdependence.** If working together is new for the students, it may take time for them to become accustomed to it. Some teachers in our field-testing group have students choose various roles or jobs to ensure that each member of the group is working on something, making a contribution to the thinking or resolution of the problem. If students are asked to explain their group's work in front of the class, and if you randomly select which student in the group will give that explanation, it will encourage the group members to make sure everyone understands the work they are doing.

Students accustomed to working in groups may need less direction than this.

- **Group composition.** There really isn't one way to do this that works best in all situations. We've worked successfully with teachers who very carefully engineer which students work together, with teachers who set up a system of randomly-chosen groups, and teachers who just leave it up to the students to decide. The important thing here is to decide on a process that is comfortable for both you and your class. See the book *Cooperative Learning in Mathematics* ([2]) for more discussion of this issue.

One teacher used the question of how to form groups to stimulate a class discussion about how students felt they best learned mathematics. They discussed issues including different learning styles and achievement levels as well as the advantages and disadvantages of knowing or not knowing the students in one's group.

- **Materials ready.** One common fear about group work is that students will spend the time on social talk instead of mathematics. We have found that this is minimized if students begin their group work with a clear task and with materials ready. Downtime—while they wait for an explanation, wait to get a paper, etc.—can lead them to start their group interaction around social rather than mathematical talk.
- **Additional problems.** Some groups will finish an activity or problem well before others. If you have follow-up problems ready, these groups are more likely to continue working together productively.
- **Individual accountability.** There are several ways to get information about an individual student's understanding, even when students have worked with others to solve problems. One way is to ask students to write up their work individually, in their own words. Another option is to assign a homework problem that is similar to, or extends ideas from, a problem solved in groups.

One Example

The Triangle Inequality problem from the first activity of the *Habits of Mind: An Introduction to Geometry* book is an example of a lesson in which students might benefit by working together; among other things, they may come up with multiple conjectures. The following is a description of how one teacher taught her class.

The teacher decided she wanted individuals within the groups to have a chance to form their own conjectures about the triangle inequality, but also felt that students could gather data more quickly in groups, and could motivate each other with their conjectures.

Before breaking into groups, she discussed the activity and made sure that the task was clear.

She had a set of three dice and eighteen rods (three rods each of lengths 1 through 6 units) ready for each group of three or four students, and passed them out as the students were arranging their seats to face each other. She wanted the groups to tabulate the results of rolling the number cubes twelve times. (Each time, the students select rods whose lengths matched the numbers on the number cubes, and then attempt to form a triangle with those rods.) She asked students to make conjectures, silently at first, about when triangles can or cannot be formed. She suggested that students might tell the rest of their group whether they thought a particular set of three numbers can form a triangle, without revealing the whole conjecture. In this way she made it clear to the students that she wanted them all to make the effort and have the time to come up with their own conjectures.

After gathering the data, the groups were to discuss their conjectures, to test them out with more triangles, and to come up with a reason why one of their conjectures worked. The teacher asked one student from each group to present that group's findings to the class. She asked them to discuss any interesting conjectures that proved *not* to be true, as well as any conjecture the group decided *was* true, because students often learn from seeing why something doesn't work.

For homework, she assigned the follow-up problem in the *Habits of Mind* unit, where students are asked to extend their triangle inequality (only tested so far on the integers 1-6) to any set of three real numbers. In this way, she was able to see if individual students could picture and explain the triangle inequality.

Bibliography

1. Cohen, Elizabeth. 1986. *Designing Groupwork: Strategies for the Heterogeneous Classroom.* New York: Teachers College Press.
   Pays particular attention to using small groups in heterogeneous classes, and addresses issues of group learning in a bilingual class.

2. Davidson, Neil, editor. 1989. *Cooperative Learning in Mathematics: A Handbook for Teachers.* University of Maryland, College Park: Addison-Wesley.
   Contains different perspectives on small group learning, addresses using computers with groups, and discusses various forms of group composition.

3. Johnson, David W. and Roger T. 1987. *Learning Together and Alone; Cooperation, Competition and Individualistic Learning.* Englewood Cliffs, NJ: Prentice-Hall.
   Describes the basic principles of group learning, with an emphasis on the development of social skills.

Assessing Student Learning

"What's on the test?" This question is the eager student's way of asking what is important to learn. Tests and other assessment tools should always be chosen to assess what we value in learning so that our answer to that student reflects our most important goals.

Historically, the words "assessment" and "testing" were used interchangably. Mathematics assessment was designed to gauge whether students learned and could use a collection of facts, rules, and algorithms. In recent years, many educators, have advocated a deeper focus—the assessment of students' full mathematical power. By focusing on *mathematical habits of mind,* the *Connected Geometry* materials support and encourage students and teachers to do just that.

These educators include the National Council of Teachers of Mathematics [8].

Choosing Assessment Methods and Tools

Connected Geometry is designed to be adaptable to a variety of assessment forms. You can use a traditional, test-based approach, newer forms of problem- and project-based assessment, or some combination to fit the needs of your classes.

Our problems and activities are well-suited to "authentic assessments"—tasks that look and feel like the work students ordinarily do in class and for homework and in which students have the same tools available to them.

Many teachers, attempting to apply new assessment techniques, find themselves overwhelmed and somewhat skeptical. Choosing from among the vast menu of "alternative assessments" can be time consuming, and may leave you *and* your students very unsure about the value and meaning of the assessment. What follows is a list of six possibilities, intended to suggest new ideas, but not intended to be applied in its entirety. We recommend that you read the whole list and choose one or two things that make sense to you. Then develop an assessment plan that combines these with tests and other forms of assessment with which you are comfortable. We encourage you to experiment in finding what works best for you. After the descriptions of individual assessment tools, we present two possible scenarios for a six- to eight-week assessment plan.

The overall goal is for you to have a clear picture of what each student in your class understands. You probably have your own ways to achieve this; those offered here are merely suggestions.

Connected Geometry's Top Six

Our choices for assessment tools which most effectively assess student learning in the *Connected Geometry* books are **Problems from the Text, Discussions, Journals, Portfolios, Presentations,** and **Projects.** For each we have provided a general description, specific application ideas, and suggestions for grading.

1. Problems from the Text. The heart of the *Connected Geometry* materials are its problems. Any really good problem can also function as a really good assessment. We suggest that you use problems from the text as the backbone of any assessment plan. For example:

- All activities contain a "Checkpoint" problem. You can use this as a quiz or self-test.
- Most lessons also include "Take It Further" problems. You might ask students to write a report of their work on one of these challenging extension problems.
- "Write and Reflect" problems appear frequently in all the units. You can use them as homework assignments that are collected for grading.
- Consider assigning a challenging problem as the basis for a series of student journal entries: initial conjectures about the problem, first attempts at a solution, a revised solution, and a summary of the mathematics involved in the problem.
- Another good assessment is to choose a problem from the text that allows a variety of solution methods and then have individuals or groups present their solutions to the class.
- At the end of a unit, you might ask students to choose a set of problems that demonstrate something you wish to assess and include these in their portfolios.
- Returning to a difficult problem. Consider asking students to choose a problem they had trouble with, and work on it again. Have students explain where they had trouble before, and what they have learned that helps them solve the problem.

For example, "Select the five problems which you think were most important to understanding congruence."

Some people are taking the cue from English teachers and instituting a system where a student submits work, receives comments, and revises the work until both student and teacher are happy with it. People who have tried this say it's not as much work as it sounds.

Grading problems that are used for assessment purposes is a more likely stumbling block than selecting them. We suggest these principles:

1. Communicate very clearly to students what is expected before giving the task. Tell them in advance how problems will be scored.
2. Keep the scoring method *very* simple. For example: 1 to 3 points each for clarity of explanation, mathematical correctness, and effective drawings or graphs. A simple check, check-plus, check-minus system might even suffice.
3. Plan ways for students to see high-quality work from other students. Presentations, bulletin board displays, or reading within cooperative groups allows students to see what a good piece of work looks like and helps them develop the skills sought by these new forms of assessment.

2. Discussions. Helping students communicate mathematical ideas can be a major goal for a *Connected Geometry* course. Whole-class and small-group discussions are ideal settings for students to communicate and express ideas, to clarify their thinking, to make generalizations, and to make connections between various results and findings. Most teachers are already experienced in the art of leading a discussion and in finding good topics for these mathematical conversations. For additional ideas please note that key discussion questions labeled "For Discussion" appear frequently in the student materials.

A more difficult task is how to use these discussions as effective assessment tools. Some suggestions follow for those who wish to try evaluating student discussion in a way that gives both teacher and student specific feedback.

A class list with simple column headings for five or six skills works well.

- Have one student or a group of students lead a discussion. Score both the discussion leaders and the class using a short, prepared checklist containing easily observed thinking and communication skills. For example: participates in

Consider having students observe and score a discussion themselves.

If the problem is one of the homework problems to be given that night, it ensures the attention of the rest of the class, as they'll get a head start on their work.

discussion, makes good mathematical points, uses correct mathematical language, asks a good question, makes a strong summary statement.

- Some teachers evaluate group work and discussion skills by conducting a *scored discussion.* One group, sitting in front of the class, has five minutes to work on a problem (usually a fairly difficult one). The goal is not necessarily to solve the problem but to work on it as a group, to find a good approach, and to develop a plan. The rest of the class watches. Score each student in the group based on her participation; students can earn both positive and negative points. Make clear to students that it is not the quantity or volume of their participation but the quality. Do they listen and reflect on what they've heard as well as offering their own ideas?

3. Journals. Journal writing reveals students' understandings and misunderstandings, stimulates reflection, stimulates construction of knowledge, develops students' skills in communicating mathematically, and encourages organization ([2]). We include suggested writing assignments (labeled "Write and Reflect") in most activities. The teaching notes make further suggestions for using writing to enhance each activity. When asking students to keep journals, it is important that they know the criteria on which their journals will be judged.

Having students write up their solutions in the form of research papers is an effective way to get them to polish their thinking.

A student mathematics journal could include:

- Responses to some "Write and Reflect" questions.
- A particularly interesting or important problem, written up in detail.
- A problem that the student had trouble with the first time, reworked and revised, including explanations of what was done differently and why.
- An individual student's explanation of a problem that was worked on in a group during class.
- Lists of conjectures to be verified at a later point.
- List of new vocabulary words and definitions.
- Writing about affective factors, personal reactions to mathematics or to the process of learning mathematics.

Students who keep portfolios over a period of years would be particularly able to trace the growth in their thinking.

4. Portfolios. Portfolios can be an effective means to collect work samples documenting a student's growth and accomplishments over time ([3], [4]). Because portfolios contain a history of the student's work, they are ideal for assessing the development of mathematical habits of mind.

Note the potential for encouraging students to actually keep all their work so they have something to look through.

Note the potential for reflection as well as review.

A good opportunity for sharing ideas about learning and about what matters in mathematics.

Here are some suggestions for using portfolios:

- At the end of each unit (or term) a student looks carefully back through all of his or her accumulated work: a pile of homework papers, tests, projects, unfinished problems, perhaps a journal, or a disk of drawings from the computer lab.
- From this assortment, the student selects the most important things, using criteria you define. Students can be directed to choose favorite work, important proofs, something that was revised and improved, the most difficult problem, or simply what shows best what the student learned.
- The student might then present the portfolio, speaking to you, other students, or parents about the contents. Ask students to write a summary of their reflections on the contents and a short introduction to each piece explaining why it was selected.
- The real assessment opportunity for the student will come from making and maintaining the portfolio. Your work is in setting up the initial requirements, and

evaluating the choices and summary. Individual items in the portfolio will already have been graded earlier in the unit.

5. Presentations. Presentations give students a chance to demonstrate a deeper understanding of a specific problem as well as more general mathematical techniques and understandings. In a presentation, students must organize their thoughts, communicate their ideas clearly, and respond to questions posed by their peers and by the teacher. A presentation may be a report, a demonstration of a problem solution, or even a "student as teacher day," where a student teaches a given topic to the class, including example problems, elicits clear explanations from members of the class, and answers questions.

Problems with multiple solutions (of which there are many in the Connected Geometry *materials) are particularly well suited for presentations. These provide opportunities for students to see how others are thinking and to see different strategies.*

Some suggestions for using presentations:

- Have students submit a written version of the presentation to assure ease in grading and to encourage good preparation.
- Encourage questions. Establish an atmosphere where anyone who is confused about a point in a presentation feels free to say so.
- Consider allowing students to assess each other. One *Connected Geometry* field-test teacher used classroom presentations frequently, and had the students help assess themselves and each other by using different colored note cards for 1, 2, 3, or 4 points. Each card included an explanation of the criteria for that number of points. This system was adapted from the article [1].

This is sometimes difficult for the presenter; fielding questions is (as you know very well) difficult. The trick is to establish a non-threatening climate where it's OK for no one in the room to know the answer to a question.

6. Projects. A major goal for high school mathematics classes can be to teach students research skills in mathematics, including how to work productively on a single problem or idea for a sustained period of time. Projects are an ideal means for developing this skill. In addition, they allow students to explore connections between mathematics and science, art, sports, or other areas of personal interest, and to show off some of their other talents. Two types of projects are suggested:

1. Individual or group projects that enrich the activities and foster exploration of mathematical topics can be assigned at any time. Many suggestions for these projects are given in the activity notes. Project ideas will also emerge directly from the class investigations. The student text also contains numerous historical anecdotes, interviews with mathematicians, and interesting language facts that may spark the curiosity of a student and result in a project.
2. Projects may also be used very effectively as a culminating assessment activity for a book or part. In the project, the student demonstrates mastery of the unit's major mathematical ideas.

Students like to present their work. Think about having your students publish their own mathematics journal. They write the papers (based on their projects), establish an editorial committee, review the papers, do the layout and publication, and distribute the journal in the school. Another idea is to help students present their work at the school science or mathematics fair. Many such fairs are often looking for mathematics projects.

In both sorts of projects, teachers have found that it is helpful to consult with individual students about their projects periodically, to assign intermediate deadlines for accomplishing various parts of the project, and to give students a written explanation of the assessment guidelines.

Bibliography

1. Biggerstaff, Margaret, Barb Halloran, and Carolyn Serrano. 1994. "Use Color to Assess Mathematical Problem Solving." *Arithmetic Teacher,* 41, 6, 307-308 Reston, VA: NCTM.
   This article describes a technique for having students score their own and others' work in-class using color-coded notecards.

2. Countryman, Joan. 1992. *Writing to Learn Mathematics: Strategies that Work.* Portsmouth, NH: Heinemann.
This book elegantly illustrates the connections between writing, thinking, and learning in mathematics. It explains how writing offers insight into students' understanding through journals, math autobiographies, and formal writing. It offers specific suggestions for integrating writing into mathematics class and provides samples of student work.

3. Hart, Diane. 1994. *Authentic Assessment: A Handbook for Educators.* New York: Addison-Wesley Publishing Company.
This book focuses on "authentic assessments" and suggests the use of portfolios, observation, self-assessment, and grading rubrics. It also traces the history of assessment practices.

4. Kuhs, Therese M. 1994. "Portfolio Assessment: Making it Work For the First Time." *Mathematics Teacher,* 87, 5, 332-335.
This article gives practical suggestions on getting started with portfolio assessment. It outlines the rationale behind portfolio use, and then provides specific guidelines for gathering and evaluating student material.

5. Lee, Ellen. 1994. *A Sampler of Mathematics Assessment.* Sacramento, CA: California Department of Education.
This booklet documents the use of open-ended questions in mathematics assessment in California. It provides samples of students' work in grades 4, 8, and 10. To order, contact the publications department of the California Department of Education in Sacramento, California at (916) 445-1260.

6. Mathematical Sciences Education Board. 1993. *Measuring What Counts: A Conceptual Guide for Mathematics Assessment.* Washington, D.C.: National Academy Press.
A conceptual guide to understanding assessment reform, this book clarifies the connections between standards and assessment by outlining three principles: content, learning, and equity. It emphasizes that assessment must not only measure results, but also add to the educational process.

7. Mumme, Judy. 1991. *Portfolio Assessment in Mathematics.* Santa Barbara, CA: University of California.
Focusing on implementation, this booklet addresses the value of using portfolios, questions of what to include, and the logistics of deriving grades from portfolios. It includes examples of student work. Available from the California Mathematics Project, University of California, 522 University Road, Santa Barbara, CA 93106.

8. National Council of Teachers of Mathematics. 1994. *Assessment Standards for School Mathematics.* Reston, VA: NCTM.
This book complements the two other NCTM publications: *Curriculum and Evaluation Standards for School Mathematics* and *Professional Standards for Teaching Mathematics.* It presents six assessment standards and elaborates upon them through commentary, vignettes, and examples of student work. To order, call NCTM in Reston, Virginia at (800) 235-7566.

9. Stenmark, Jean Kerr, ed. 1991. *Mathematics Assessment: Myths, Models, Good Questions, and Practical Suggestions.* Reston, VA: National Council of Teachers of Mathematics, Inc. (NCTM).
This booklet discusses the myths surrounding what math assessment "should" be, then counters these myths by providing suggestions and examples of alternatives. It discusses portfolios, journals, and open-ended questions and includes samples of student work and teacher commentary.

Technology in *Connected Geometry*

Everyone in education has gotten both smarter and more skeptical about the benefits of technology in helping students learn mathematics. We are realizing that using computers as the *poser of problems for students to solve, and as the* possessor *of all the answers to the problems posed, amounts to using them as (very expensive) flashcards.*

The software we use in Connected Geometry *plays the role of a laboratory in physics or a workshop in woodworking.*

What's the best way for you to really understand something? Probably by explaining it to someone else.

Have you ever had a student who took things literally? It can be a challenge.

What it means to bring technology into the mathematics classroom depends largely on the choice of software. Some software programs reward students with flashy video game challenges after solving a specified number of drill questions. Other software serves as an electronically enhanced textbook, providing customized pathways through the material with occasional animated demonstrations of theorems.

Both uses of software embellish the presentation of mathematics without really changing what it means to *do* mathematics. Well designed pieces of software can offer more: they provide new tools and environments for exploring mathematics, for gaining insights otherwise not possible within a paper-and-pencil context, and for developing mathematical habits of mind.

Two mathematical habits of mind that are supported by mathematical software are *reasoning by continuity* and *algorithmic thinking:*

1. **Reasoning by continuity.** So much of geometric thinking involves performing thought experiments in which you envision geometric figures interacting in some way. One way to find the area of a parallelogram is to cut off a right triangle at one end, tucking it into the other end to form a rectangle. *You* can read the previous sentence and picture exactly what we are talking about, but you also know what a difficult time many of your students would have doing that thought experiment, even with overhead transparencies, chalk-talk, or movies. "Dynamic geometry software" (described below) allows students to *perform* experiments like these. Research is underway to see if this kind of activity provides students with a "jump start" so that they can learn to picture such experiments in their minds. We conjecture that this is, in fact, the case.
2. **Algorithmic thinking.** Another form of thought experiment involves giving a precise set of instructions that will produce a result that doesn't yet exist. For example, how would you give a precise set of instructions to someone that would result in that person drawing a regular pentagon? Our experience has been that if you can get a student to explain how to draw a pentagon so well that the instructions are completely unambiguous, then that student has learned a great deal about pentagons *and* about giving precise instructions. Because the computers in this way can be an effective way to get students to think about the essential features of a geometric construction and about how they develop and describe algorithms.

Geometry Software

Geometry Software includes *The Geometer's Sketchpad, Cabri Geometry,* and the *Geometry Inventor.* These programs allow students to take the static images in their textbooks and bring them to life on the computer by manipulating their parts and causing them to move. Aside from being great fun for exploring geometry, this software is a serious research tool used by professional mathematicians. Some of its benefits include:

- With dynamic geometry, a general case can be developed rapidly from a specific one. A triangle drawn on paper allows students to examine just that one triangle. A triangle drawn with dynamic geometry can be stretched and moved to become *any* triangle. Consider a triangle inscribed in a semi-circle, with the diameter as a side. A single picture of this construction hints that the angle opposite the diameter is a right angle. Dynamic geometry expands the experimental data from one to many. Students use the software to drag the triangle vertex around the semicircle, gathering evidence for what seems like infinitely many cases.

Of course, this experiment doesn't replace proof, but our materials strive to integrate proof with experiment.

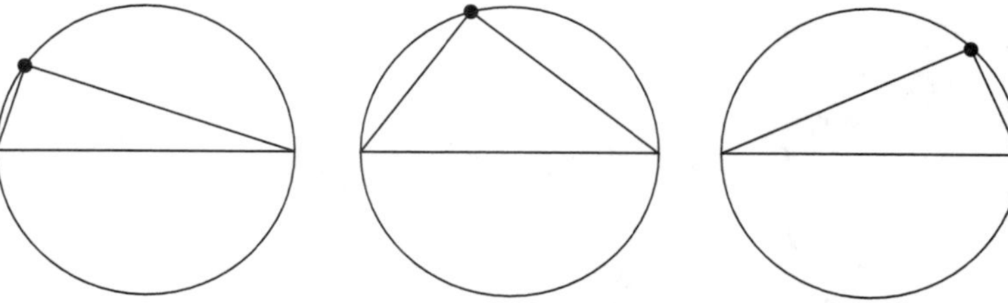

One theorem, several particular cases

- Students often confuse a *construction* with a *drawing*. A drawing is intended to aid our memory, thinking, or communication, and doesn't have to be much more than a rough sketch. A construction is a kind of guaranteed recipe. It shows how a figure can be accurately drawn with a specified set of tools.

  With geometry software you can construct an equilateral triangle in much the same way you would with ruler and compass. The software, though, provides a powerful test to judge the merits of the construction. Tug on a side or vertex of the triangle; it may grow or shrink in size, but the triangle will remain equilateral if it has been properly constructed. If the original triangle was drawn by just eyeballing its angles and sidelengths, it will deform into an arbitrary triangle when tugged.

Colleagues have developed the idea of "messing up." The triangle really is constructed if the teacher (or someone else) can't mess it up by dragging on its parts.

- A ubiquitous problem from algebra and calculus asks students to find a rectangle of a given fixed perimeter that maximizes its area. We'd *like* students to imagine a continuum of rectangles, all with the same perimeter. We'd like them to do a thought experiment starting with a long, thin rectangle that gradually gains height until it is tall and narrow, and we'd like them to imagine that the area is changing in a continuous way throughout the process. We'd even like them to imagine a graph of area against the length of one side developing dynamically. Yet the standard algebraic solution does not require (or even encourage) such thought experiments.

  Geometry software provides a medium in which the primary investigatory tool is continuous variation. Students can model a situation and then investigate how it changes when one feature is dragged around the computer screen. By allowing students to investigate continuous variation directly (without intermediate algebraic calculations), geometry software environments can help students build mental constructs that are useful (even prerequisite) skills for analytic thinking.

By "analytic thinking" we mean the habits of mind underlying calculus and analysis.

Technology in Your Class

Geometry software is central to many of the problems in the *Connected Geometry* materials. For classes without access to computers, we sometimes give alternate experiments that can be carried out by building simple mechanical models or other devices. Nonetheless, having *some* access to computers is highly desirable to get the most from our materials.

If you're new to the software, the introductory computer activities for students in the *Habits of Mind* book will help get you started. For more practice, the bibliography at the end of this piece lists additional resources for learning about the software.

Ryan Morgan, a geometry student at Patapsco High in Maryland, used geometry software to develop a conjecture about triangles that would have been next to impossible to see without the software. Ryan presented his findings to mathematicians and received newspaper coverage, too.

Introducing this technology into your classroom *can* be unpredictable—with the new tools available to them, students may develop conjectures and create mathematical models that you have never seen. Initially this may be a little scary, but it can also be quite exciting. Working together with your students to analyze and understand what they have created is a great way to develop a culture of mathematical exploration in your class.

Additional Resources

The Math Forum on the World Wide Web (http://forum.swarthmore.edu/) is a good source for more information about software geometry and contains downloadable demo versions of both *Sketchpad* and *Cabri.* You'll also find many of the geometry sketches mentioned in our books available for downloading at *Connected Geometry's* Web site: http://www.edc.org/LTT/ConnGeo/.

Bibliography

1. Baulac, Y., Bellemain, F., and Laborde, J.M. 1994. *Cabri Geometry II.* Dallas, Texas: Texas Instruments. Software.
   To obtain ordering information for the software, call 1-800-TI-CARES.
2. Brock, C. F., Cappo, M., Dromi, D., Rosin, M., and Shenkerman, E. 1994. *Tangible Math: Geometry Inventor.* Cambridge, Massachusetts: Logal Educational Software and Systems. Software.
3. diSessa, A. A., Hoyles, C., and Noss, R. 1995. *Computers and Exploratory Learning.* New York: Springer-Verlag.
4. Jakiw, Nicholas. 1995. *The Geometer's Sketchpad.* Berkeley, California: Key Curriculum Press. Software.
   To obtain ordering information for the software, call 1-800-995-MATH.

Connected Geometry and Traditional Geometry Content

Scope and Sequence

Connected Geometry students master all of the topics encountered in a traditional geometry course and newer topics as well. Some topics are resequenced, but field testing has shown that the focus and style of this program has helped many students to develop a better grasp of these ideas than in traditional programs, and that students feel more success at solving both traditional and novel problems.

The following table illustrates where the major geometric topics fit within the framework of the *Connected Geometry* modules.

	Habits of Mind	A Perfect Match	The Cutting Edge	A Matter of Scale	The Language of Coordinates and Vectors	Optimization
Basic Objects	Secondary Focus				Primary Focus	
Parallels and Perpendiculars	Primary Focus	Primary Focus	Primary Focus	Primary Focus	Secondary Focus	Secondary Focus
Properties of Triangles and Right Triangles		Primary Focus	Secondary Focus	Primary Focus	Secondary Focus	Secondary Focus
Congruence	Secondary Focus	Primary Focus	Secondary Focus	Secondary Focus	Secondary Focus	
Proof		Primary Focus	Primary Focus	Primary Focus	Primary Focus	Primary Focus
Pythagorean Theorem			Primary Focus	Secondary Focus	Secondary Focus	
Properties of Quadrilaterals	Secondary Focus	Primary Focus	Secondary Focus	Secondary Focus		
Similarity	Secondary Focus			Primary Focus	Secondary Focus	
Polygons and Polyhedra	Secondary Focus	Primary Focus	Primary Focus	Secondary Focus		Secondary Focus
Coordinates and Vectors					Primary Focus	
Length, Perimeter, Area, and Volume			Primary Focus	Primary Focus		Secondary Focus
Circles and Spheres	Primary Focus	Secondary Focus	Secondary Focus	Primary Focus	Secondary Focus	Secondary Focus
Axiomatic Systems	Secondary Focus	Secondary Focus				
Functions and Mathematical Modeling				Secondary Focus		Primary Focus

Primary Focus

Secondary Focus

Connected Geometry and the NCTM Standards

Process Standards

Mathematics as Problem Solving

Problem solving is central to the *Connected Geometry* curriculum; the modules are organized around sets of interesting and challenging problems that have been carefully crafted so that important mathematical ideas emerge from working them. Unlike many texts, the problems are not sequenced to exercise recently acquired facts and skills. This is like "real life," which doesn't check first to see what chapters you've studied, doesn't make sure the numbers come out even, and where a problem may have multiple solutions and may be approached with a variety of strategies.

Mathematics as Communication

Connected Geometry provides a variety of situations that call on students to reflect upon, critique, and communicate their ideas and the ideas of others. The investigations include "Write and Reflect" prompts, which ask students to explain ideas clearly, to relate two or more concepts to each other, or to reflect in writing on some problem or technique. The investigations support whole-class and small-group discussions with "For Discussion" suggestions. Students also read mathematics: essays about mathematicians, historical essays, and mathematical arguments.

Mathematics as Reasoning

In the *Connected Geometry* materials, students are encouraged to use reasoning as a research tool, to form conjectures based on experiments, to explain and justify their conjectures, and to develop these conjectures into proofs. The program discusses the different ways proofs can be presented, different types of proofs (including counterexamples and proof by construction), and the sometimes messy ways one comes up with a proof.

Mathematical Connections

This standard addresses the very foundations of *Connected Geometry.* The curriculum brings together ideas from geometry, algebra, and analysis (calculus) in ways that do not require any more background than is typical for early high school. The program also points out places where these ideas are used in nonmathematical endeavors.

Unit 5: The Language of Coordinates and Vectors Students who already have a good understanding of coordinates, midpoints, and distance can begin this unit with Lesson 3 or 4. See the *Connected Geometry* CD ROM, Investigation 5.3 for a concise review of these topics. For students who need the review that Lessons 1 to 3 offer, spend time on these lessons and consider ending this unit after Lesson 6, Adding Points and Scaling Points.

Unit 6: Optimization This unit consists of a few lessons that are very accessible to all levels of students (Lessons 1 to 3). More advanced classes should be able to dig into Lessons 4 and 5, each of which is an extended investigation of a single challenging problem.

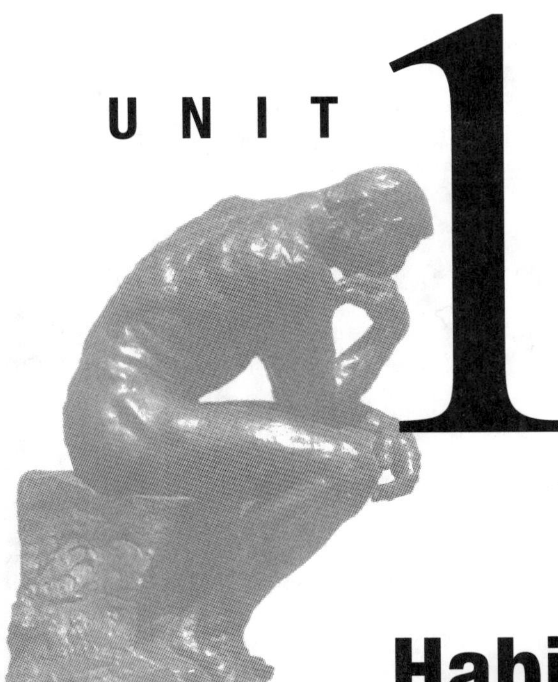

UNIT 1

Habits of Mind
An Introduction to Geometry

Unit Overview

Since what counts *most* is students' thinking, this unit begins not with definitions and review but with problems. The problems require no special background or prior knowledge, but they do require thought and persistence.

Before students can be expected to reason deeply about the properties of geometric objects, they must learn to *see* these objects geometrically. That is, they must be able to dissect them visually, to reproduce them in sketches, and to describe the parts and their relationships clearly and precisely.

Similarity is one idea introduced informally in this unit: Students draw triangles specified by angle and discover that their triangles are not identical, although certain ratios are invariant.

This unit is designed to introduce important mathematical ways of thinking through the study of geometry and assumes no prior geometric knowledge. Using a problem-based approach, it introduces essential vocabulary, ideas, tools, and drawing techniques that students will need throughout their mathematical learning. Students also encounter many geometric facts and concepts in this unit that will be developed more fully later.

Beyond developing students' language, background knowledge, and skills, this unit helps to build a classroom culture of puzzling over problems, asking questions, starting to figure them out, and making tentative conclusions for later investigation.

Moreover, just within the scope of this introductory unit, students *prove* over 20 theorems derived from their own investigations. In contrast to more familiar approaches in which the theorems appear in the student text, virtually all of the conjectures and proofs that give rise to theorems in *Habits of Mind: An Introduction to Geometry* are contained in students' responses to problems. Therefore, the definitions and theorems that one normally expects the authors to have written into the student text appear primarily in the solutions manual. In a sense, the students are writing the textbook themselves!

Learning Goals

1. Name, describe, and construct several standard geometric shapes, including regular polygons.
2. Follow directions to create shapes by hand and with geometry software; create directions based on constructions.
3. State the Triangle Inequality.
4. Given three side lengths or three angle measures, decide if such a triangle exists.
5. Define what an invariant is and describe several examples of geometric invariants.
6. Look at sum, product, difference, and ratio for invariants, and look for shape invariants, collinearity, and concurrence.
7. Argue that the angle sum in a triangle is constant and that the angle sum in polygons is dependent only on the number of sides.
8. State a conjecture about angle sums in polygons based on the number of sides.
9. Know about concurrence of perpendicular bisectors, angle bisectors, and medians in triangles.
10. Have an initial understanding of continuous change and the Mean Value Theorem (though this term is not used).

Assessment Opportunities

Quizzes and Informal Assessment

- If sketching graphs is an important component in your curriculum, assign homework that requires students to draw and label their graphs.
- If this is your students' first exposure to constructing triangles, assign more practice problems for homework.

Journal Ideas

Students keep writing assignments in a journal. Possible assignments:

- Lesson 1, *Write and Reflect* Problem 10. Explain the Triangle Inequality and extend it to noninteger lengths.
- Perspective: Impossible Constructions, *Write and Reflect* Problem 7. Investigate attempts to trisect angles.
- Lesson 6, *On Your Own, Write and Reflect* Problem 11. Write directions for creating unmessupable figures with geometry software.
- Lesson 7, *On Your Own,* Problem 7. Argue for constant angle sum in polygons based on an assumed result about triangles.
- Lesson 8, Problem 11. Summarize results about concurrence in polygons.
- Lesson 8, *Write and Reflect* Problem 15. Explain concurrence of perpendicular bisectors in triangles.

Students who know how the All-Star lineups are done in baseball might explain how each team member runs out and shakes hands with all the others who are already in the line.

Teacher-to-Teacher

One teacher did a nice classroom activity based on the second strategy. Everybody got up, shook hands with everyone else, and counted the times that they, personally, shook hands. The teacher's students thought of multiplying the number of handshakes they counted $(n - 1)$ by the number of people who were counting (n). After testing their solution on a class with only two people, they knew what to do. The result: $\frac{n(n-1)}{2}$.

The third strategy involves drawing a picture. If there are n people in the room, then the handshakes can be modeled by a regular n-gon with all the diagonals drawn in; that is, every person corresponds to a vertex, and every vertex is connected to every other vertex exactly once. This makes a nice connection to Problem **2.**

ACTIVITY 2

Nets *(Student page 3)*

You may want to provide students with Blackline Master 2, scissors, and tape to make the nets.

ACTIVITY 3

The Triangle Inequality *(Student pages 3–4)*

Have students work in small groups. Encourage discussion among students.

You may need to set some rules as to how the rods meet at the corners.

PROBLEM 8 A powerful strategy for figuring out what triples will make a triangle is to keep one side constant and check what fits with it. Some students may have difficulty organizing their work. Entering their results in a table might help. Blackline Master 3 can be copied to provide structure for your students if you think they will benefit from it.

End the activity with a whole-class formal statement of the Triangle Inequality.

ACTIVITY 4

Angles Inscribed in Semicircles *(Student pages 4–5)*

PROBLEM 15 Have a class discussion about this problem. Encourage students to explain their answers.

ACTIVITY 5

Cross Sections *(Student page 5)*

PROBLEMS 17–20 Various materials will work. A very thick mixture of gelatin was used quite successfully in some of our test classes and is especially good for "seeing inside" the solid before making the cut. One college class used Play Doh® (preschool or kindergarten teachers can supply easy recipes). Potatoes, sponges, and clay slabs also work well. Most of these materials can be turned into ink stamps at the end. Students must first cut their material into cubes. They need not be perfect cubes, but they should be close. Students will need several cubes to work with. Dental floss works better than knives for making planar slices through clay.

See "Teacher-to-Teacher" on page 9 for a gelatin recipe.

PROBLEM 20B It is unusual to find ellipses brought up so early in mathematics classes. This lesson introduces the shape, shows some places where it is found, and gives it a name early. As it makes appearances later on, it will be recognized as a familiar figure, and its properties can become part of the study. While recognizing the reappearance of the ellipse and knowing its name are important, naming the other conic sections is optional at this point; sketching them is enough.

On Your Own *(Student pages 6–8)*

These problems provide students with the opportunity for individual practice.

PROBLEM 2 Blackline Master 4 can be given to students to help them investigate diagonals in quadrilaterals.

PROBLEM 7 Blackline Master 5 can be copied for students to help them explore which shapes fold up into 3-dimensional figures.

Take It Further *(Student page 8)*

PROBLEM 13 Think of a cone as the surface generated by a line (a generator) that rotates about another intersecting line (the axis of the cone).

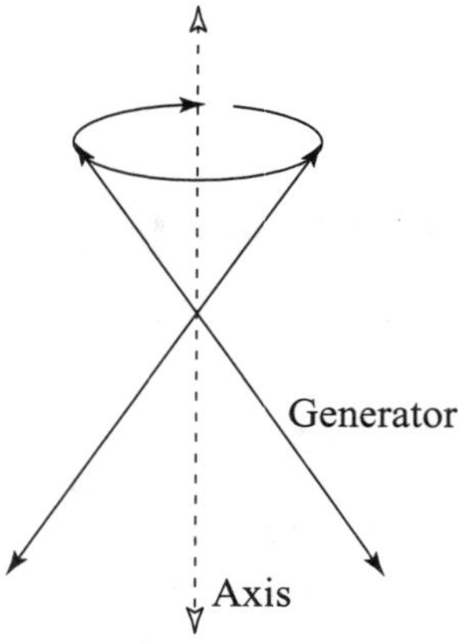

A plane perpendicular to the cone's axis cuts circular cross sections. Tilting the plane from the perpendicular position elongates the cross section to an ellipse. In these positions, the generator of the cone is never parallel to the intersecting plane: Picture it rotating around the cone's axis and constantly cutting the plane. As the plane tilts further, the ellipse lengthens—it takes longer and longer for the intersecting plane to "get back out" of the cone after it has entered. The generator is still always intersecting with the plane, but as it becomes "close to parallel," its intersection with the plane gets quite far away, lengthening the cross section.

If the plane is tilted exactly to the point at which it makes the same angle with the cone's axis that the cone's generator does, then there is exactly one position of the generator that is parallel to the plane. What used to be the "other end of the ellipse" is pushed out to infinity—the plane never gets back out of the cone—and the cross section, formerly elliptical and still approximately elliptical at the "near end," is therefore unending. This cross section is called a *parabola.*

Note the para *in both* parabola *and* parallel. *How many positions are there?*

If the plane tilts still further, then there is more than one position in which the generator is parallel to the plane as it rotates around the cone's axis. The plane cuts through both branches of the cone, and the cross section therefore has two separate parts which are hyperbolic cross sections.

Perspective: What Is Geometry? *(Student pages 9–11)*

Assign this perspective as an in-class reading or as homework.

Options and Extensions

Resources

SAFE-T Products (P.O. Box 692, LaGrange, IL 60525) sells scissors that will cut paper but not skin or hair, compasses without sharp points, and protractors and rulers that will not break and do not have sharp corners.

Teacher-to-Teacher

Here is a recipe for gelatin from Barney Martinez in Daly City, California. He got it from Bev Bos, a preschool teacher who does workshops around the country.

1. Mix 32 packets of Knox gelatin with 22 cups of hot water.
2. Using containers of various shapes—cubes, cones, cylinders, or paper cups—spray the inside with a vegetable oil spray, like Pam.
3. Fill the containers with gelatin, chill, and remove the hardened gelatin from the molds. They will last 2 to 3 days without refrigeration.

PROBLEM 8B This problem can be fun and yet challenging for students. Invite them to share their guidelines with the class. For each presentation, encourage the class to name the famous person.

ACTIVITY 3

Analyzing and Drawing Three-Dimensional Figures *(Student pages 14–17)*

In addition to the ideas presented in this activity, you may want to talk about perspective drawing, generating fractals from mathematics, or any other art-geometry connection.

PROBLEM 9 Drawing from a partially-covered picture helps students separate out the geometric features from the overall gestalt of the figure. Drawing from memory exercises the student's ability to hold these features in mind and to recall how they are assembled into a whole. In reproducing an impossible picture and describing what is wrong with it, students attend to various attributes of the representation of two and three dimensions, such as parallel lines, parallel planes, and how things fit together.

ACTIVITY 4

Using Pictures to Explain Ideas *(Student pages 17–18)*

Some students, including some who have apparently done quite well with graphing, seem to have no idea where to start in interpreting this picture—perhaps it is too unlike graphs they have worked with.

Have students work in small groups on Problems **17–19.** Each group will be asked to explain its ideas about one of the problems to the class. Students should complete the Checkpoint problem individually.

PROBLEMS 17–18 Students who have had experience in algebra may find these visual proofs quite enlightening. For students who have not had enough experience in algebra to understand the pictures' captions, you may adapt the problems by using specific numbers.

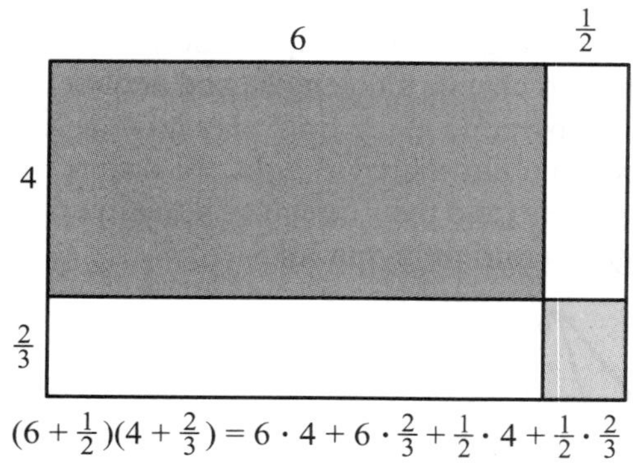

$(6 + \frac{1}{2})(4 + \frac{2}{3}) = 6 \cdot 4 + 6 \cdot \frac{2}{3} + \frac{1}{2} \cdot 4 + \frac{1}{2} \cdot \frac{2}{3}$

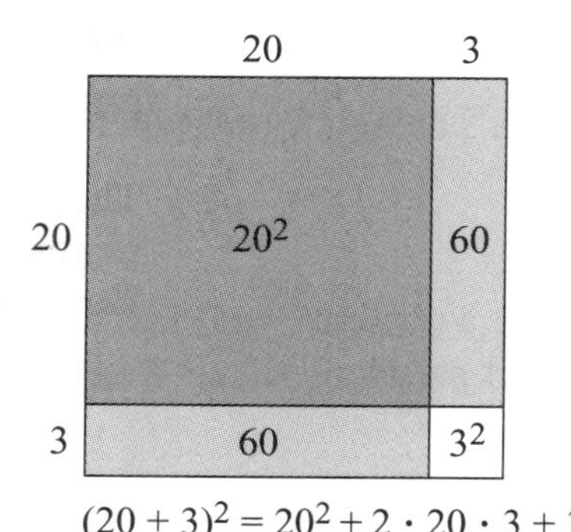

$(20 + 3)^2 = 20^2 + 2 \cdot 20 \cdot 3 + 3^2$

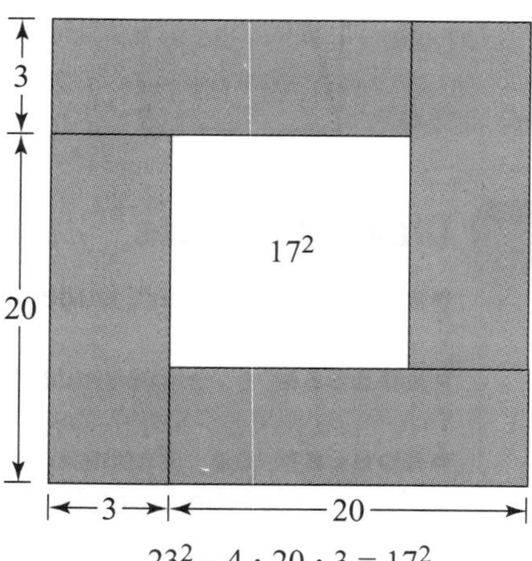

$23^2 - 4 \cdot 20 \cdot 3 = 17^2$

PROBLEM 19 Encourage students to tell a plausible story connected with the graph. There is no question at all about the relation between terror and time—only a question about where *other* events, such as the exam itself, fall along the time axis.

PROBLEM 20 Here are some guidelines to help you assess students' understanding: Are the axes labeled? Do the labels make sense? Are the conventions (independent variable on the horizontal axis, dependent variable on the vertical) observed? Does the graphed relationship make sense? Does the student's explanation of the graph account for it well?

On Your Own *(Student pages 18–20)*

These problems provide students with the opportunity for individual practice.

One group argued about whether circles could be faces and about the edges of cylinders.

PROBLEM 10 Asking students to identify vertices, faces, and edges on impossible figures may seem strange, but when students do this problem in small groups, they generate very interesting discussions. Their understandings and misunderstandings come to light.

Take It Further *(Student pages 21–22)*

PROBLEM 12 Any new line will cut some of the previously-existing regions into two separate regions each. To maximize the number of regions created by *five* lines, we must start with an arrangement of *four* lines that creates the most regions and place the fifth line in such a way that it cuts the largest number of these regions into two parts. The fifth line cannot cut all of the regions. How many can it cut?

When a line is placed so that it cuts across some regions, each of the regions "covers" a portion of the line: The regions divide the line into lengths, just as the line breaks the regions into subregions. So the question boils down to this: Into how many lengths can this line be divided? It is divided into lengths by intersecting with the other lines—only four of them—that have already been placed. Those four intersection points divide the new line into five lengths, and each of these lengths is the boundary between two new regions that used to be one. Therefore, the *line* divides five previously existing regions into 10 regions. Thus, if four lines divide the plane into 11 regions, then five lines can divide the plane into 16 regions.

PROBLEM 13 If students investigate how the *arrangement* of planes affects the number of regions, they may quickly see that parallel planes divide space into fewer regions than intersecting planes and that when several planes intersect along the same line, they divide space into fewer regions than planes that intersect pairs. This is similar to the result with lines in the previous problem. Students can generally visualize how *three* planes can be arranged to divide space into as few as four and as many as eight regions. However, it is so difficult to picture multiple planes in space that few people can visualize the effect of even one more plane. To know what happens with five planes, one must adopt a different strategy, one that is only partially visual.

The strategy developed in Problem **12** can be moved up a dimension. When a new plane cuts n chunks of space into twice that number of regions, it is *itself* cut into n regions, each of which is the dividing wall separating the two new regions of space. Thus, to figure out how many new regions a fourth plane can create, one must look at how the three prior planes can intersect it. Each one intersects the fourth plane in a line, and those three lines can divide the fourth plane into, at most, 7 regions (from

Problem **12**). So, if three planes divide space into 8 regions, then four planes can divide space into at most seven more, or 15 regions.

The idea can be summarized in a table like the one below.

3 planes can divide space into 8 regions.

3 lines can divide a plane into 7 regions.

So, 4 planes can divide space into 7 + 8 regions.

Number of planes dividing space	1	2	4	8	15	26	42	64
Number of lines dividing a plane	1	2	4	7	11	16	22	29
Number of points dividing a line	1	2	3	4	5	6	7	8
Number of objects of one dimension that divide an object of one higher dimension	0	1	2	3	4	5	6	7

PROBLEM 17 This optional project may appeal to students who have a special interest in art. The following are some good references on M.C. Escher:

- Bool, F.H. *M.C. Escher—His Life and Complete Graphic Work.* Harry Abrams (publisher), 1992.
- Ernst, Bruno. *Magic Mirror of M.C. Escher.* Random House, 1995.
- Escher, M.C., and Vermeulen, J.W. *Escher on Escher.* Harry Abrams (publisher), 1989.
- Schattschneider, Doris. *Visions of Symmetry: Notebooks, Periodic Drawings and Related Work of M.C. Escher.* W.H. Freeman & Co., 1992.
- "World of Escher" Web site: http://www.texas.net/escher.

Options and Extensions

Teacher-to-Teacher

Here's a very nice activity from Ros Welchman of Brooklyn College. For each group of four students in your class, prepare a set of small cards: 3" × 5" cards, cut in quarters to make 1.5" × 2.5" cards do very well. Each set of cards contains the following terms, with one term per card: angle, base, circle, cone, corresponding, cross section, cube, cylinder, cylindrical, diagonal, endpoint, equilateral, equilateral triangle, face, heptagon, hexagon, hexagonal, horizontal, inscribed, invariant, line, net, nonrectangular, octagon, octagonal, parallel, parallelogram, pentagon, pentagonal, perpendicular, point, polygon, polygonal, pyramid, quadrilateral, radius, rectangle, rectangular, regular, segment, semicircle, sphere, square, trapezoid, triangle, triangle inequality, vertex, and vertical.

Give each group a set of terms and ask students to sort the cards in some meaningful way. You can leave the task otherwise open, or you can restrict students to at most six categories. Have students explain their categories, and list the terms they included in each. Then ask: Did any terms seem not to fit *any* category?

There are many reasonable ways to sort the terms. Students might, for example, classify *circle* and *cube,* along with other objects, as Shapes. Alternatively, 2-dimensional objects like *circle, net,* and *cross section* might be classified separately from *cube.* Or a curvilinears might be distinguished from straight-line figures. Students often discuss which terms describe *objects* and which describe *qualities* or *relationships.* Among the objects, students also sometimes discuss whether "elementary parts," such as angle and point, are to be kept separate from objects built from them.

Mathematics Connections

The following paragraph was part of Marion Walter's essay, but we thought it would be more interesting for teachers than for students to read:

> The academic thing that I remember best about this school was its projects. These involved the whole school for what I think was a week, though it may have been only a few days. Each year a different topic was chosen. I recall two of them: grains and birds. Grains was the topic when I was nine. What fascinated me were the pie-charts showing different amounts of grain grown locally and in different countries. I don't recall what my contribution was, though I know that *everybody,* whatever age, contributed. "Birds" I recall because I "had" the nightingale, and I had to make a small presentation. Can we learn something from the fact that these projects really stand out 50 years later?

Constructions are often described as if they were just very precise drawings, but precision isn't the issue. The essential element of a construction is that it is a kind of "proof"—a demonstration of how, *in principle,* certain figures can be accurately drawn with the permitted tools. We say "in principle," because mathematics deals with abstract tools, not real ones. A construction executed with real tools (instead of the abstract "tools of the mind") cannot be perfectly accurate: Pencil thicknesses, straightedge unevennesses, and the inability to copy a distance precisely with a compass, all contribute to the real-life inaccuracies and make this "actual" construction no more accurate than a meticulously made drawing. And a construction knocked-off carelessly on a chalkboard is no less a construction. It shows *how* the drawing can be made precisely, even though it, as a drawing itself, is rough and crude.

LESSON

Drawing and Describing Shapes

Lesson Objective

This lesson is designed to help students develop clear language for describing shapes.

Content Overview

Students learn to use names, features, and recipes (algorithms) to describe shapes exactly.

Planning Guide

Pacing	Activity	Materials	Homework Suggestions
Day 1	*Explore and Discuss* (SE p. 26) Activity: Shadows and Directions (SE p. 27)	• clay, sponge, dough, other material (optional) • overhead projector (optional)	*On Your Own,* Problems 1–5

Program Resources

- *Connected Geometry* CD-ROM, Module 1: Investigation 1.3
- *Solution and Problem Solving Resource,* pages 24–25

Preparation and Prerequisites

If students have already worked on the problems about shadows in Lesson 2, they will easily be able to get started on the *Explore and Discuss* section and the activity.

Teaching the Lesson

This is a very short lesson, taking only one or two days of class time. Students can work in groups to make the shapes from clay.

ACTIVITY

Shadows and Directions (Student page 27)

For Problems 1–3, an overhead projector can be used to demonstrate the shadows cast by various objects in these problems.

That "common tool" is the tip of a screwdriver.

PROBLEM 3 Here is a hint for students: There is a common household tool that has this shape.

PROBLEM 4 Any geometric recipe, just like any cooking recipe, assumes some knowledge on the part of the person following the recipe. For example, calling for a cup of flour assumes that the reader knows to use a measuring cup and not a teacup.

To encourage class discussion, you might ask: "When is it reasonable to interpret such nonspecific statements as *turn right* to mean *turn 90° right?*" You may want to draw students' attention to the fact that the way we give and receive directions has a lot to do with our previous experiences and with the context at hand.

On Your Own (Student page 28)

These problems provide students with the opportunity for individual practice. See the lesson Planning Guide for homework recommendations.

Options and Extensions

Resources

Zubrowski, Bernie. *Shadow Play: Making Pictures with Light and Lenses.* New York: Morrow, 1995. Containing interesting ideas for extensions, this book describes investigations with shadows and light, explains the difference between shadows from the sun (parallel rays) and those from most artificial sources (diverging rays or diffuse light), shows how to make a "shadow box" for experiments, and more.

LESSON

Constructing from Features: Problem Solving

Lesson Objective

Students construct various shapes by describing features and using hand construction tools.

Content Overview

In this lesson, students learn

- about some hand construction tools and how to use them;
- the difference between a construction and a drawing;
- the historical importance of constructions in geometry;
- the properties of triangles, including SSS for congruence, AAA for similarity, constant ratios in similar triangles, impossible specifications (violation of triangle inequality, angle sum $\neq 180°$, and so on), and two equal angles imply two equal sides; and
- to see more than one way to solve a geometric problem.

Planning Guide

Pacing	Activity	Materials	Homework Suggestions
Day 1	*Explore and Discuss* (SE p. 32) Activity 1: Constructing Triangles (SE pp. 32–34)	• compasses • paper • protractors • rulers	On Your Own, Problems 1, 4, and 5
Day 2	Activity 1: Constructing Triangles (SE pp. 32–34) Activity 2: Compasses, Angles, and Circles (SE pp. 34–35)	• compasses • paper • rulers	*On Your Own,* Problems 6, 7, and 9
Day 3	Activity 3: More Construction Problems (SE pp. 35–36)	• compasses • paper • rulers	*On Your Own,* Problems 8, 10, and 11 *Take It Further,* Problems 13 and 15
Day 4	Activity 4: Group Thinking (SE p. 37)	• BLM 7A–7D, pp. 8–11 • BLM 8, p. 12 • compasses • index cards • paper • rulers	*On Your Own,* Problems 2 and 3 *Take It Further,* Problem 12

Program Resources

- *Connected Geometry* CD-ROM, Module 1: Investigations 1.5–1.7
- *Solution and Problem Solving Resource,* pages 29–46
- *Teaching Resources,* pages 8–12
- *Assessment Resources,* Quiz 4 Lesson 5, page 5

Preparation and Prerequisites

A lot of vocabulary is introduced here in the context of constructions. This vocabulary helps students process definitions more effectively than by simply reading them. The vocabulary is *not* a prerequisite for the activity.

Teaching the Lesson

Explore and Discuss *(Student page 32)*

Students should complete the *Explore and Discuss* problems. Follow the problems with a class discussion about the method used to do the construction and the reading of Hand Construction Tools.

Note: Paper folding is an often-overlooked construction tool. The symmetry of folds provides an ideal way to construct midpoints (match the two endpoints and fold; the crease is at the midpoint) and angle bisectors (match the two rays and fold; the crease is itself the angle bisector). Paper folding also allows you to create 90° angles by bisecting a straight angle.

ACTIVITY 1

Constructing Triangles *(Student pages 32–34)*

You may want to have a class discussion about the various tools and what they do, addressing such questions as, "How do you make a circle with a compass?" The problems in this activity may be worked on individually or in small groups.

PROBLEM 5 The triangle in Problem **5d** cannot be drawn on a plane but *can* be drawn on a sphere! Let vertex A be on the equator. Let vertex B be $\frac{1}{4}$ of the way around the globe from A and also on the equator. Let the third vertex be at the North Pole. Three 90° angles!

ACTIVITY 2

Compasses, Angles, and Circles *(Student pages 34–35)*

You might ask students to work on these problems individually. Then come back together as a class for a discussion of Problems **12** and **14.**

ACTIVITY 3

More Construction Problems *(Student pages 35–36)*

Place students in small groups and assign a couple of constructions to each group. Have students present their constructions and methods to the class.

PROBLEM 19B The *Solution and Problem Solving Resource* explains only why the result has half the area. If you also care to prove that the result is square, the easiest argument is probably by symmetry: Any way the creased figure is rotated, all of its parts (including all of the angles) match up, because they have all been created in the same way from a set of original parts that are all identical.

This problem implicitly asks students to construct the length $\sqrt{2}$. What about the constructability of irrational lengths? You may start students thinking about that issue now by asking them: "Compared to the original square, what is the length of the sides of the new square?" Define the length of a side of the original square as 2 units; then the legs of the corner triangles (outside the half-sized square) are 1 unit long. The Pythagorean Theorem then says that the length of the hypotenuse is $\sqrt{2}$. This could also be reasoned by area. If the original square's sides are defined as 2 units each, its area is 4 square units. The half-sized square's area is therefore 2 square units, so its side must be $\sqrt{2}$ units.

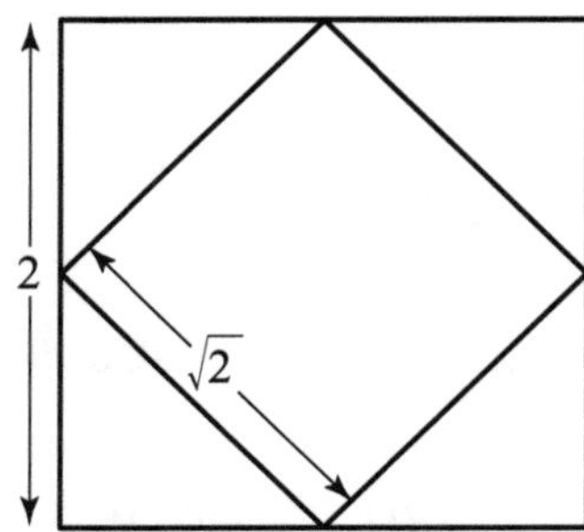

Now you have a method of constructing one irrational length. Not all irrational lengths *can* be constructed, and the proof of that is also the proof of the impossibility of squaring the circle and many of the other classic impossible constructions.

PROBLEM 27 One student found a clever shortcut: Drawing the three medians of the large triangle automatically finds all of the midpoints. Once you have drawn a smaller triangle, the intersections of its sides with the medians are the midpoints, so connect them to draw another triangle. The intersections of *its* sides with the medians are the midpoints, so connect them, and so on.

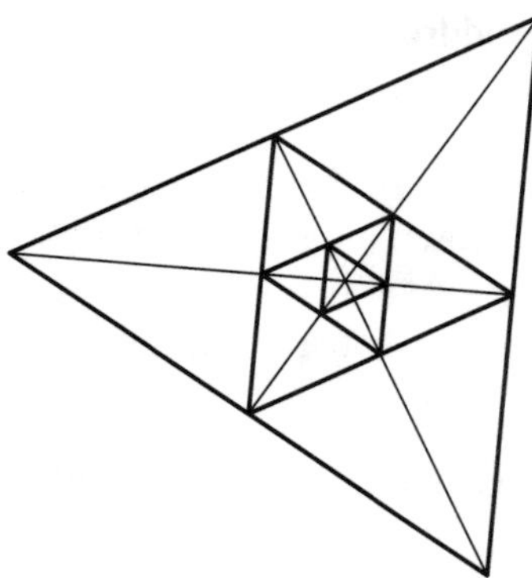

ACTIVITY 4 Group Thinking *(Student page 37)*

Make copies of Blackline Masters 7A–7D. Paste or tape clues on index cards. Divide the class into groups of four to six students. Pass one card to each group, dividing the cards among the group members. If there are fewer than six students in a group, you can give some students two cards. When a group completes its puzzle, group members can work on another one.

PROBLEM 28 Place objects from Blackline Master 8 on index cards. Distribute the cards to students. Students who finish quickly can be given another object to work on while the rest of the class finishes. Alter the list of objects to suit the needs of your class. Polygons, arcs of circles, and midlines of quadrilaterals are all possibilities. You can also include on each card a list of "illegal words" that cannot be used in the students' step-by-step directions.

After students complete this problem, there are many avenues for discussion. Some questions you can pose include:

- Which objects from the index cards were easy to draw just by knowing the definitions?
- Which objects were hard to draw, even though you knew what they should look like?
- Were any of the objects impossible to draw with only a straightedge and compass?
- If any of the objects was not reproduced correctly by the partners, discuss why. What additional directions would have helped?

On Your Own *(Student pages 37–39)*

These problems provide students with the opportunity for individual practice. See the lesson Planning Guide for homework recommendations.

Take It Further *(Student page 39)*

Note that the section on "trisecting an angle" is more open and hence might be more difficult for some groups to get started on. You may take that difficulty into consideration in your assignments.

PROBLEM 12 It is often easiest to draw the figure first, write all the directions, and then find a good way to split them up.

Perspective: Impossible Constructions *(Student pages 40–42)*

This reading is a good follow-up activity to Lesson 5. You can proceed with the entire class working through two or three of the "impossible constructions." Alternatively, you can divide the class into groups, with each group working through *one* section and presenting its results.

Options and Extensions

Supplementary Angle and Protractor Activities

Students often face problems with the use of protractors. The following supplementary activities require students to measure angles accurately and to make drawings that require protractor use. The activities may help your students gain familiarity with angles and skill with using the protractor. They are not all mathematical, but students can have fun with them while learning how to use protractors.

Familiarity with angles Students brainstorm everything they know about angles. They may list words like *obtuse, right,* and *degrees* and try to explain their meanings through other words, pictures, or actions. For example, a person may turn halfway around to show 180°.

Computing angles from the full circle Students find the angle measurement for each angle on pattern blocks by placing several of the same kind of vertex around a point to complete the 360 degrees and counting how many blocks it takes. Then they divide to find the angle measure for that vertex. Some of the angle measures are not factors of 360, so students must use some ingenuity to find those measures.

Some students may call out an angle measurement like 2,000°, which leads to a nice discussion of angles as rotations. Students generally figure out to sweep out a full circle for every multiple of 360°.

Estimating angles In pairs, students are called up to the front of the room. Each student in the pair is given a "ray" (a wooden dowel or yardstick). The class will give the students an angle measurement, and they show that angle with the two "rays." Students should come up with a way to distinguish 360° from 0°.

Measuring angles with a protractor Draw several angles on the board. Give students protractors and ask them to measure the angles without any further directions on using the protractor. Because they already have an idea of how to estimate the size of an angle, students have a basis for trying to figure out a way of getting that result.

Writing directions for the use of a protractor Alone or working together, students write directions on how to use a protractor.

Things to measure might include the angle a chair leg makes with the floor, angles on signs up on the walls, and so on.

Protractor scavenger hunt In groups of 3 or 4, students are given a protractor and asked to measure several angles around the classroom and the building.

The chair Place a folding chair on a desk. Ask students to use their protractor to measure every angle they can find on the chair. They must clearly describe each angle and write down its measurement.

It is actually important to rip rather than cut the corners off. Ripping allows you to keep track of what was a vertex of the triangle and what was not.

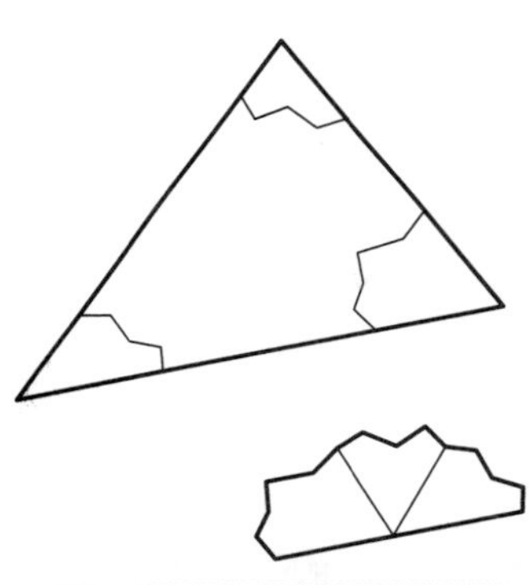

Shapes If your students have not had this experience in earlier grades, let them rip off the corners of a triangle and arrange them so that the vertices meet at a point to show their sum. They end up forming what appears to be a straight line. Provided that they recognize a line as a straight angle (180°), students may then conjecture that the angle sum of a triangle is 180°, confirming protractor results. Is this a proof for all triangles? No. That fact will come later. Similarly, students can rip the corners off of any quadrilateral and fit them around a center point to fill 360 degrees. With concave quadrilaterals, however, students may have difficulty figuring out how to place the vertices.

Resources

The Mirror Puzzle Book. Tarquin Publications, England 1985. (Published also in Chinese, Korean, and French.) (Honorable Mention, New York Academy of Science Children's Book Award Program)

Pattern Blocks are available from many distributors of mathematics manipulatives including

Creative Publications	1-888-MATHFUN
Didax	1-800-458-0024
Cuisenaire	1-800-872-1100

Goniometers (the "gon" is the same root, meaning angle, as in pentagon and hexagon) are another angle measuring device. Built out of two pieces hinged together with something like a protractor at the hinge, goniometers can be used more easily than protractors in many situations. The goniometer can be opened or closed to match some angle to be measured—for example, the angle of bend at your knee—and the angle can then be read directly from the attached goniometer.

Many companies sell scissors that will cut paper but not skin or hair, protractors and rulers that won't break and don't have sharp corners, and compasses without the sharp points. SAFE-T Products (P.O. Box 692, LaGrange, IL 60525) is one.

Teacher-to-Teacher

For what fractions $\frac{m}{n}$ is it possible to fold a square with area $\frac{m}{n}$ of the original? For which fractions is this impossible? It turns out that, for all $\frac{m}{n} < 1$, you can construct a square with area $\frac{m}{n}$ using just folding techniques (assuming you start with a square paper of area 1).

One honors class at Brookline (Massachusetts) High School explored this problem for a week and came up with the following proof:

Lemma 1: You can n-sect the side of your square, so you can create a length of $\frac{m}{n}$ for all $m \leq n$.

You can choose the length of these equal segments, so you can be sure of fitting n of them along the diagonal for any n.

The class decided that folding the paper over on itself, though it works to trisect segments, was unworkable for general n. The students came up with a method to n-sect the side by using parallels. First, construct the diagonal of the square, and mark off n equal lengths along the diagonal (lengths are easily copied by folding). Connect the last endpoint to a vertex of the square not touching the chosen diagonal. Fold parallels to this segment from each mark along the diagonal. This will n-sect the side of the square.

Most methods for folding parallels require folding a perpendicular (not shown here).

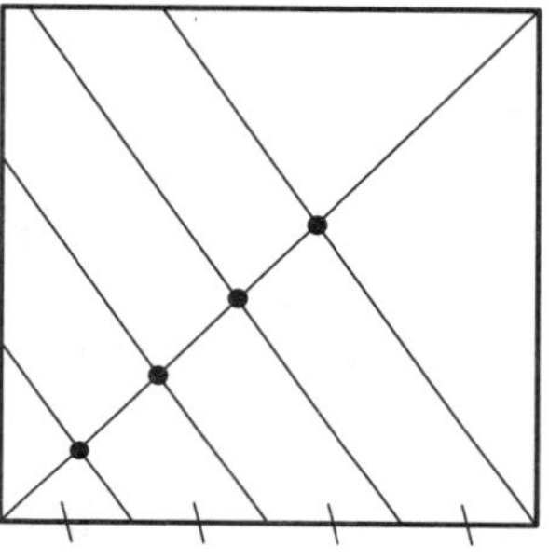

Lemma 2: You can form a length of $\frac{\sqrt{n}}{n}$, which is the same as $\frac{1}{\sqrt{n}}$.

This is possible because of Lemma 1: Simply n-sect two adjacent sides of the square and join up the first marks of each.

If we create a right triangle with leg lengths of $\frac{1}{n}$ and $\frac{1}{n}$, we can use the Pythagorean Theorem to find the hypotenuse: $(\frac{1}{n})^2 + (\frac{1}{n})^2 = \frac{2}{n^2}$, so the hypotenuse has length $\frac{\sqrt{2}}{n}$.

Now we can create a right triangle with leg lengths of $\frac{1}{n}$ and $\frac{\sqrt{2}}{n}$. Again, we can use the Pythagorean Theorem to find the hypotenuse: $(\frac{1}{n})^2 + (\frac{\sqrt{2}}{n})^2 = \frac{3}{n^2}$, so the hypotenuse has length $\frac{\sqrt{3}}{n}$.

One can continue this process, as long as the lengths fit on the 1×1 square. In particular, one can form the length $\frac{\sqrt{n}}{n} = \frac{1}{\sqrt{n}}$ by repeating the process $n - 1$ times.

Lemma 3: You can form a length of $\sqrt{\frac{m}{n}}$.

A similar procedure allows you to form a length of $\sqrt{\frac{m}{n}}$. First, create the length $\sqrt{\frac{1}{n}}$ as described in Lemma 2. Next, create a right triangle with both legs of that length. Calculate the length of the hypotenuse: $(\sqrt{\frac{1}{n}})^2 + (\sqrt{\frac{1}{n}})^2 = \frac{2}{n}$. So, the hypotenuse has length $\sqrt{\frac{2}{n}}$.

Now create a right triangle with legs of length $\sqrt{\frac{2}{n}}$ and $\sqrt{\frac{1}{n}}$. The hypotenuse will have length $\sqrt{\frac{3}{n}}$. In this way, you can create any length of $\sqrt{\frac{m}{n}}$, as long as it fits on the 1×1 square.

Theorem: Once you create the length of $\sqrt{\frac{m}{n}}$, simply copy that length to two adjacent sides of your square. Fold a square with that sidelength. Its area will be $\frac{m}{n}$.

LESSON

Constructing from Features: Moving Pictures

Lesson Objective

Students learn the basics of geometry software while exploring the features necessary to determine some familiar shapes.

Content Overview

***Technology:** See "Getting Started with Geometry Software" in these notes.*

Geometry software constructions can be directly compared to constructions on paper with ruler and compass and can often use the same algorithms. However, the software usually has more tools and more usable strategies available. It is the strategy that counts. In each case, students must look for crucial geometric characteristics of the requested figure.

The main ideas in this lesson include:

- essential properties of a rectangle, square, parallelogram, equilateral triangle, and rhombus;
- exploration of geometry software; and
- introduction to thinking about similar figures.

Planning Guide

Pacing	Activity	Materials	Homework Suggestions
Day 1	*Explore and Discuss* (SE p. 44)	geometry software	*On Your Own,* Problem 6
Day 2	Activity 1: Geometry Software's Basic Tools (SE pp. 44–45)	geometry software	*On Your Own,* Problems 1 and 2
Day 3	Activity 2: Drawings vs. Constructions (SE pp. 45–47)	geometry software	*On Your Own,* Problems 3, 4, 7, and 8
Day 4	Activity 3: Drawing UnMessUpable Figures (SE pp. 47–48)	geometry software	*On Your Own,* Problems 9, 11, and 12
Day 5	Activity 4: A Scavenger Hunt (SE p. 49)	geometry software	*On Your Own,* Problems 5 and 10

Make sure students do not delete objects that they have used to specify the characteristics of other objects. When a line is used to create a perpendicular or is used as the basis for a segment, but the final sketch will not show the original line, many students are tempted to delete the line as *unnecessary* to the final sketch. *Hiding* the line preserves the necessary relationship, but *deleting* the line will free up the objects based upon it or may even cause them to disappear.

Length, area, and angle measure are always provided, along with simple calculations on these values. Some software provides other measures and more advanced calculations (for example, slope, arc length, and trigonometric functions), ways to represent values in tables or graphs, and analytic geometry tools, including coordinates and equations.

The ability to drag a point and watch the entire construction respond dynamically to that change is the feature that defines dynamic geometry. What can be dragged varies greatly with the various software available.

As objects move, they can leave a trace of where they've been. This is often useful in analyzing the behavior of a construction.

Geometry software also allows you to add and may allow you to change the appearance (thickness and color, for example) of objects to help make a diagram more understandable or attractive.

Which software features to use and which to avoid While there are genuine *mathematical* advantages to learning how to use the software, there are also features of the software that, at certain stages in students' learning, may be more distracting than advantageous. In particular, for the problems in this section, it is best *not* to make use of whatever transformational tools (rotation, translation, dilation) your software provides. However, introducing these tools may be appropriate if transformations have already been an important part of your students' prior study or if transformational ideas are to be seriously studied with materials that supplement the problems in this book.

It has been our experience that introducing these transformations for the first time at this point tends to be a distraction from the geometry and tends to be seen by students as features of the software rather than as features of the mathematics. Also, the kinds of errors that students tend to make when using these tools for the first time are often difficult to explain in terms of the *mathematics*.

Mathematics Connections

Sometimes in the hunt for invariants, it is relatively easy to perform experiments "in your head." Squares, for example, are so familiar and regular that a rough sketch is often sufficient. But there are other times—when the objects to be studied are more complex than squares or come in far greater variety—when it is not so easy to perform experiments in your head. In these cases, models are useful for more than just focusing attention; experiments may be performed directly on the models. If the models are to be used in *this* way, they had better not be inaccurate in any important details; they must be built so that they contain the necessary features. It also helps if the model is *variable*—not just *one* triangle, for example, but something that can give you insight into *all* triangles.

Consider how you might explore the properties of triangles. With pencil and paper, you can draw a single triangle and measure its angles and sidelengths. You will find that the angles sum to 180°. Is this an invariant for all triangles? You can start to check by drawing more triangles, but that gets tiresome quickly. Using geometry software, you have to construct only one triangle and instruct the software to sum its angle measures. As you drag one of the triangle's vertices or sides around, the sum of its angle measurements will be updated automatically, and you will be free to examine as many different triangles as you like. While this work doesn't constitute a *proof*—you can't look at every possible example—it is strong confirmation that here is a phenomenon worthy of logical explanation or proof. Sometimes, such experiments give insights that can help you find the proofs.

PROBLEM 13 The solution provided in the *Solution and Problem Solving Resource* concludes with the mysterious statement: "Connecting the four points as shown does *most* of the job." The *rest* of the job may not be at all obvious, is debatably necessary if noticed, and cannot be done anyway! The problem lies in the definition of a quadrilateral. Plane geometry (but not some other geometries) generally restricts the meaning to a figure that does not intersect itself, but no geometry software makes it easy, or, as far as the authors know, even possible, to construct such a figure.

For certain classes, this may be a good opportunity to explore the *purpose* of definition (to help make communication reliable, to help make mathematical reasoning secure) and what particular restrictions students want to place on the definitions of *quadrilateral, vertex,* and *point.* For example, by what arguments or for what purposes should all of the figures below be considered quadrilaterals, and by what arguments or for what purposes should quadrilaterals be restricted more narrowly? What definition would exclude cases 3 and 5 without excluding the others? What definition would include all of the figures below but rule out such four-segment shapes as "M" or "#"?

Is D a vertex in case 3? Is it a point? What about the intersection of $\overline{AB}$ and $\overline{CD}$ in case 5?

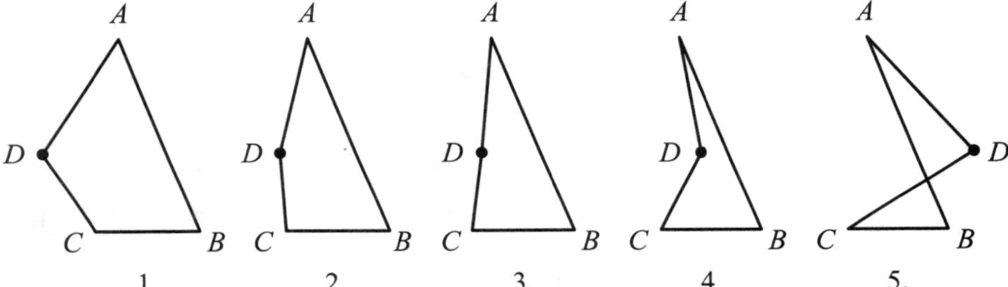

These are issues that are settled not by mathematics but by one's purpose within the mathematics. In plane geometry, cases 3 and 5 are generally *not* considered quadrilaterals, nor is *D* considered a vertex in case 3. Designating one or more of the points along the sides of a triangle as a new vertex doesn't make the triangle into a quadrilateral, or a pentagon, or . . . . But graph theory considers *D* a vertex in all of these figures and does *not* consider the intersection of $\overline{AB}$ and $\overline{CD}$ in case 5 a vertex. Projective geometry considers all five of these cases to be quadrilaterals.

LESSON

Numerical Invariants

Lesson Objective

This lesson introduces students to the hunt for numerical invariants: constant measure, sum, product, ratio, and difference.

Content Overview

In this lesson, students

- look for constant sums or products (for example, if two quantities have the same sign and change in the opposite direction);
- look for constant differences or ratios (for example, if two quantities have the same sign and change in the same direction);
- construct a 90° angle inscribed in a semicircle;
- use a fixed segment as a constant length;
- discover sums of angles in polygons;
- explore the power of a point (informal exploration); and
- learn that any line parallel to the base of a triangle cuts the other sides proportionally.

Planning Guide

Pacing	Activity	Materials	Homework Suggestions
Day 1	*Explore and Discuss* (SE p. 53) Activity 1: Geometric Objectives (SE pp. 54–55)	geometry software	*On Your Own,* Problems 1 and 2
Day 2	Activity 1: Geometric Objectives (SE pp. 54–55)	geometry software	*On Your Own,* Problem 3 *Take It Further,* Problem 10
Day 3	Activity 2: Searching for Patterns (SE pp. 55–56)	No special materials needed.	*On Your Own,* Problems 4, 5, and 6
Day 4	Activity 3: Constant Sum and Difference in Geometry (SE pp. 56–57)	geometry software	*On Your Own,* Problem 7
Day 5	Activity 4: Constant Product and Ratio in Geometry (SE pp. 57–58)	• geometry software • nails (optional) • string (optional) • wooden boards (optional)	*On Your Own,* Problem 8

Program Resources

- *Connected Geometry* CD-ROM, Module 1: Investigations 1.14 and 1.15
- *Solution and Problem Solving Resource,* pages 56–63
- *Assessment Resources,* Quiz 6 Lesson 7, page 7

Preparation and Prerequisites

Students should be familiar with geometry software. Be sure students understand the term *invariant.*

Teaching the Lesson

Explore and Discuss *(Student page 53)*

Problems in this section can be completed individually or in groups.

ACTIVITY 1

Geometric Objects *(Student pages 54–55)*

See the "Without Technology" section on page 35 for an alternative to Problem **5.**

ACTIVITY 2

Searching for Patterns *(Student pages 55–56)*

PROBLEM 7 Assign this problem to individuals or have students work in pairs. Encourage students to share their solutions with the class.

ACTIVITY 3

Constant Sum and Difference in Geometry *(Student pages 56–57)*

PROBLEMS 13–14 These problems are important if your students will be using geometry software later in the course—since they teach one way to create fixed total length—but can be skipped otherwise.

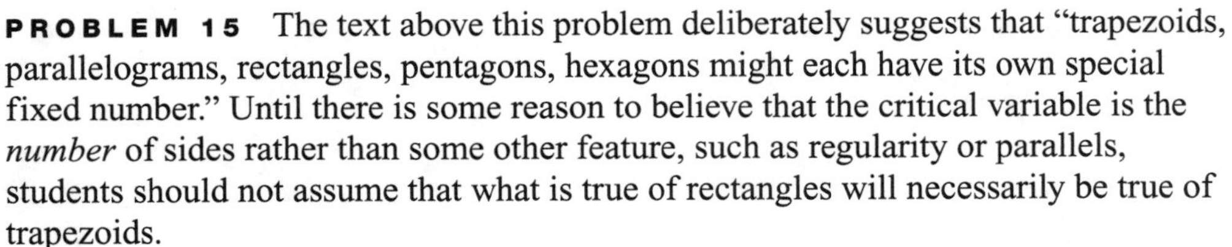

PROBLEM 15 The text above this problem deliberately suggests that "trapezoids, parallelograms, rectangles, pentagons, hexagons might each have its own special fixed number." Until there is some reason to believe that the critical variable is the *number* of sides rather than some other feature, such as regularity or parallels, students should not assume that what is true of rectangles will necessarily be true of trapezoids.

This problem can be time-consuming and is well suited for group work. Students may divide up the tasks and share their findings in order to build a table and look for a pattern. Some students may prefer working with geometry software. Others may prefer paper-cutting or drawing-and-measuring approaches.

The triangle paper-ripping activity from Lesson 5 can be extended to quadrilaterals, completely surrounding the point at which the corners match up:

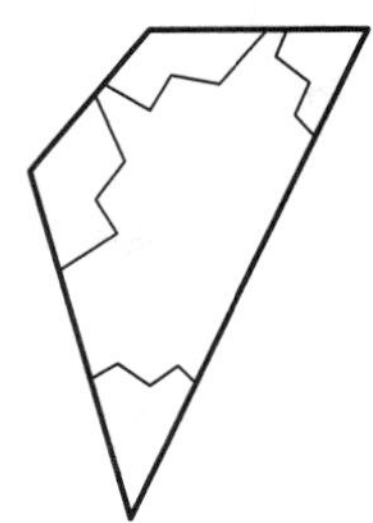

LESSON

Spatial Invariants

Lesson Objective

This lesson introduces students to the hunt for spatial invariants: shape, collinearity, and concurrence.

Content Overview

The main ideas in this lesson include

- invariants don't have to be numbers or relationships between numbers—they can be shapes or relationships between shapes as well;
- connecting midpoints of a quadrilateral in order produces a parallelogram;
- concurrencies of perpendicular bisectors and angle bisectors in a triangle;
- concurrencies in regular and cyclic polygons; and
- collinearity of points equidistant from two fixed points (perpendicular bisector).

Planning Guide

Pacing	Activity	Materials	Homework Suggestions
Day 1	*Explore and Discuss* (SE p. 62) Activity 1: Shape: A Geometric Invariant (SE pp. 62–63)	geometry software (optional)	*On Your Own,* Problem 6
Day 2	Activity 2: Concurrence: A Geometric Invariant (SE pp. 63–66)	• BLM 9, p. 13 • geometry software	*On Your Own,* Problems 4 and 5
Day 3	Activity 2: Concurrence: A Geometric Invariant (SE pp. 63–66)	• BLM 9, p. 13 • geometry software	*Take It Further,* Problem 7
Day 4	Activity 3: Collinearity (SE pp. 66–67)	• BLM 10, p. 14 • geometry software (optional) • large sheet of paper • overhead projector (optional) • scissors • transparencies (optional)	*On Your Own,* Problems 1, 2, and 3

Program Resources

- *Connected Geometry* CD-ROM, Module 1: Investigation 1.16
- *Solution and Problem Solving Resource,* pages 64–70
- *Teaching Resources,* pages 13–14
- *Assessment Resources,* Quiz 7 Lesson 8, page 8

Preparation and Prerequisites

Making the required constructions in this lesson can be time-consuming if students are not already comfortable with using the geometry software.

Teaching the Lesson

ACTIVITY 2

Concurrence: A Geometric Invariant *(Student pages 63–66)*

PROBLEM 5 Distribute Blackline Master 9 to students. Be sure students draw all of the diagonals for each polygon.

PROBLEMS 6–7 These two problems are difficult. You may want to ask questions about the point of concurrence. In each case, what might be special about that point? For the perpendicular bisectors, it must be equidistant from all five vertices, so it must be the center of the circumcircle. For the angle bisectors, the point of concurrence must be equidistant from all of the sides. This would be the center of the incircle.

PROBLEMS 11–14 You may want pairs of students to choose *one* of these problems and present the results to the class. If everyone does all four problems, you will want to allow at least three days for this sequence.

ACTIVITY 3

Collinearity *(Student pages 66–67)*

PROBLEM 18 Blackline Master 10 is provided in the *Teaching Resources.* As an alternative to cutting out discs from paper, you can distribute one overhead transparency to each student and instruct him or her to draw one accurate circle and its center on the transparency. Make sure that circle size varies across the class. On an overhead projection screen, mark two points and then have students come up one-by-one to lay their circles onto the screen so that their circle's circumference touches the two points. When all of the transparencies are laid one on top of the other, the centers of the circles will lie on a line.

On Your Own *(Student pages 67–68)*

These problems provide students with the opportunity for individual practice.

PROBLEMS 1–2 Suggest a minimal kind of consolidation of new words and ideas. You may want to do more with your class. The class might, for example, make an illustrated list, book, or bulletin board display including the following items:

- ways to find numerical invariants
- spatial invariants students have observed
- definitions
- conjectures and theorems
- open questions

Take It Further *(Student page 68)*

This problem will lead students in new directions or will challenge them to apply what they already know.

Options and Extensions

Mathematics Connections

The three medians of a triangle, like the perpendicular bisectors and the angle bisectors, are concurrent. The reasoned argument about why this is true is more difficult than those for the other two. Here is one area-based argument:

Begin with a triangle, $\triangle ABC$, and two of its medians. In the picture below, M_1 is the midpoint of $\overline{CB}$, and M_2 is the midpoint of $\overline{AB}$. The medians intersect at point P, so connect B to P.

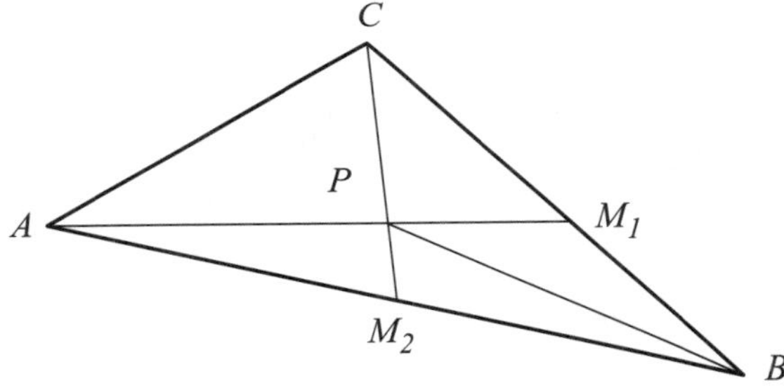

A median bisects area: The base is half the original, and the height remains constant.

Comparing areas, we know that both $\triangle CM_2B$ and $\triangle AM_1B$ have half of the original triangle. Removing the area of quadrilateral PM_1BM_2 from both, we see that the areas of $\triangle CM_1P$ and $\triangle AM_2P$ are equal.

Look at $\triangle BPC$. Its area is bisected by $\overline{PM_1}$. Likewise, the area of $\triangle APB$ is bisected by $\overline{PM_2}$. So the following four triangles have equal area: $\triangle CPM_1$, $\triangle APM_2$, $\triangle BM_1P$, and $\triangle BM_2P$. In fact, each area is $\frac{1}{6}$ the area of $\triangle ABC$, since three of these equal-area pieces make up $\triangle CM_2B$, which is one half of $\triangle ABC$.

Now, connect P to M_3, the midpoint of $\overline{AC}$. One cannot just assume that $\overline{BP}$ and $\overline{PM_3}$ lie on the same line, but if they *do,* that is what you have to show.

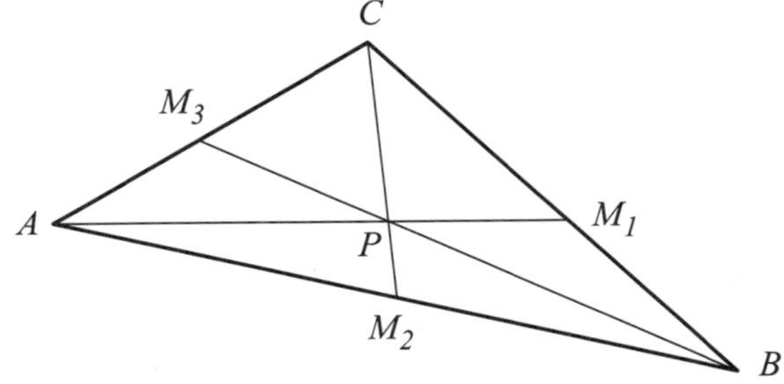

The area of $\triangle APC$ is $\frac{1}{3}$ the area of the whole triangle, and $\overline{PM_3}$ bisects the area of $\triangle APC$. So the areas of $\triangle CPM_3$ and $\triangle APM_3$ are $\frac{1}{6}$ the area of $\triangle ABC$.

Now, the shape of BPM_3C has exactly half $\triangle ABC$'s area because it contains three smaller triangles, each with $\frac{1}{6}$ the area of $\triangle ABC$. You know that if you draw the median $\overline{BM_3}$ it bisects the area of $\triangle ABC$.

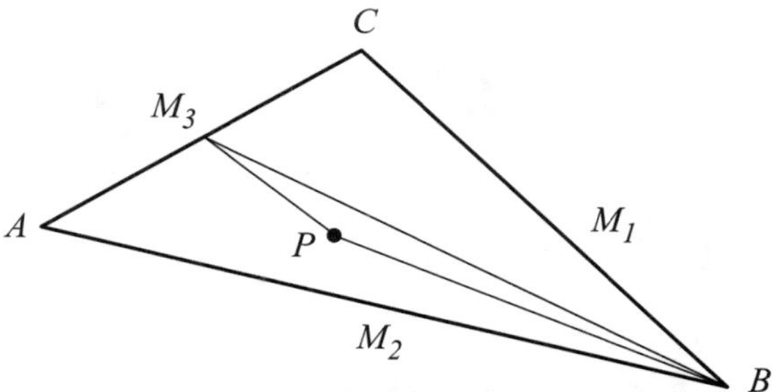

The areas of BPM_3C and $\triangle BM_3C$ are the same—one half the area of $\triangle ABC$. So P must lie on $\overline{BM_3}$, meaning the three medians are concurrent, intersecting at P.

LESSON

Parallel Lines

Lesson Objective

In this lesson, students learn some essential standard geometry content while they continue to hone their "invariant hunting" skills.

Content Overview

The results about parallel lines and angles are essential throughout geometry study. (This knowledge is prerequisite for the units *A Perfect Match, The Cutting Edge,* and *A Matter of Scale.*) The main ideas in this lesson include

- definition of parallel;
- angle relationships in parallel lines;
- *proof* that the sum of the angles in a triangle is 180°; and
- looking for invariants.

Planning Guide

Pacing	Activity	Materials	Homework Suggestions
Day 1	*Explore and Discuss* (SE p. 69) Activity: Explorations (SE pp. 70–71)	geometry software	*On Your Own,* Problems 1, 2, and 3
Day 2	Activity: Explorations (SE pp. 70–71)	geometry software	*On Your Own,* Problem 4 *Take It Further,* Problem 6

Program Resources

- *Connected Geometry* CD-ROM, Module 1: Investigation 1.17
- *Solution and Problem Solving Resource,* pages 71–74

Preparation and Prerequisites

Because the focus of this lesson is not on making constructions but on investigating them, it helps if students are facile at using geometry software to construct parallel lines, measure lengths and angles, and manipulate objects on the screen once they are constructed.

LESSON

Investigations of Geometric Invariants

Lesson Objective

This lesson is designed to present more open investigations for students to practice "hunting for invariants."

Content Overview

In Activity 1, students investigate a shape invariant and a numerical invariant, and they explore informal ideas on similarity. In Activity 2, students look at extreme cases, explore a shape invariant, learn that a perpendicular bisector is equidistant from two endpoints of a segment, and investigate the number of sides a polygon might have, given placement of a point *P.* In Activity 3, students construct a segment to be used as constant total length, construct a circle to be used as constant distance from a given point, and define an ellipse as the set of points at a constant total distance from two points. In Activity 4, students construct a figure that has a specified invariant, independence of perimeter from area, invariant ratios of perimeters, invariant ratios of areas, constant perimeter, constant area, and so on.

Planning Guide

Pacing	Activity	Materials	Homework Suggestions
Day 1	*Explore and Discuss* (SE p. 74) Activity 1: Midlines and Marion Walter's Theorem (SE pp. 74–75)	geometry software	Activity 1, Problems 5, 6, and 7
Day 2	Activity 1: Midlines and Marion Walter's Theorem (SE pp. 74–75) Activity 2: Folding Investigations (SE pp. 76–77)	• geometry software • rectangular sheet of paper • square sheet of paper	*On Your Own,* Problem 1 Activity 2, Problems 11 and 12
Day 3	Activity 3: Circle Intersections (SE pp. 78–79)	• circular piece of paper • geometry software	*On Your Own,* Problems 2 and 3
Day 4	Activity 4: Constructing Invariants (SE pp. 79–80)	geometry software	*On Your Own,* Problem 4 Perspective: A High School Student Extends the Theorem

Program Resources

- *Connected Geometry* CD-ROM, Module 1: Investigation 1.18
- *Solution and Problem Solving Resource,* pages 75–81
- *Assessment Resources,* Quiz 8 Lessons 9 and 10, page 9

Preparation and Prerequisites

Students should have the facility with geometry software: ability to construct midpoints, move constructions around by dragging, and take measurements. Students should be familiar with the properties of quadrilaterals: squares, nonsquare rectangles, and parallelograms. A lot of vocabulary, such as perpendicular bisector, equidistant, and various names for polygons, will be presented. The vocabulary can be developed as students work on the problems. If students have done paper folding before, they will have a better idea about what the folds are doing. Experience with paper folding is not, however, essential.

Teaching the Lesson

Explore and Discuss *(Student page 74)*

Students should work in small groups to extend the list that has been started.

ACTIVITY 1

Midlines and Marion Walter's Theorem *(Student pages 74–75)*

Some software provides tools to subdivide a segment into any number of pieces. If yours does not have such a tool, your students will need some way to do this. You can create a script that will trisect a segment, or you can teach your students the general method and allow them to create their own scripts. In any case, the "parallel" method is probably the easiest way to create the trisection.

Begin with a segment.

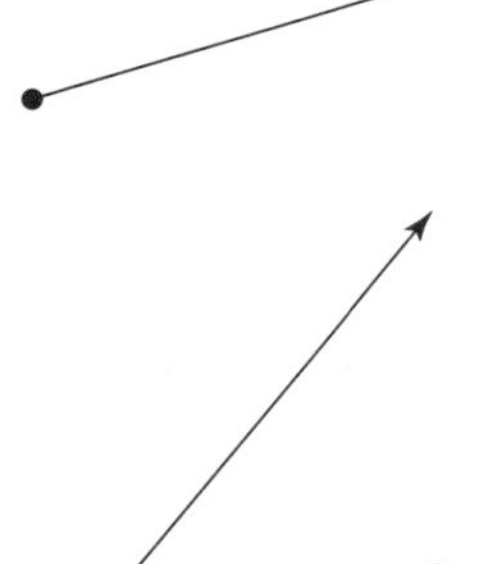

Construct a ray that does not coincide with the segment from one of the segments endpoints.

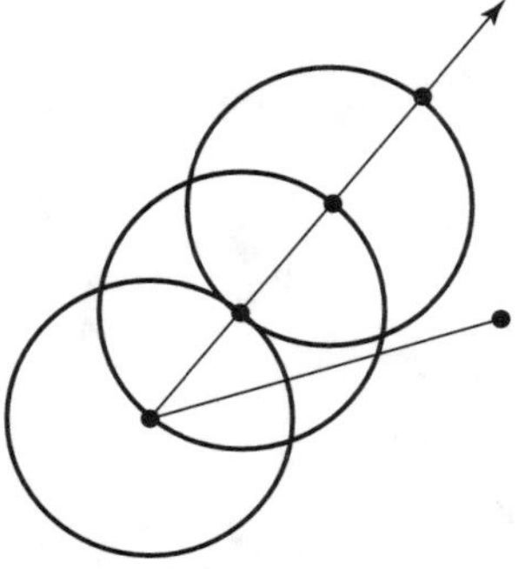

Mark off n equal lengths along that ray using circles. In this case, we want three equal lengths, but the method works for any n.

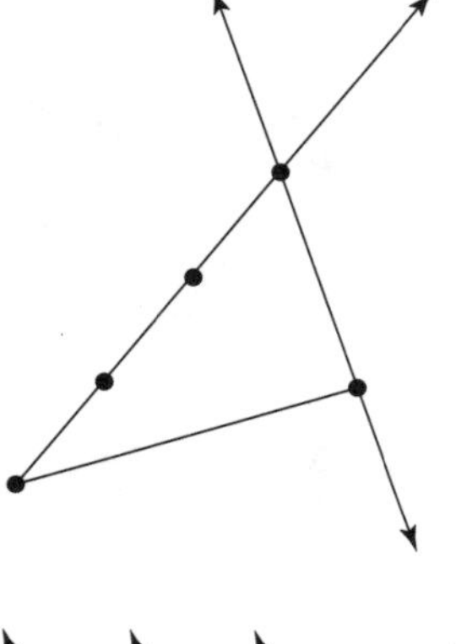

Connect the last mark on your ray to the other endpoint of your segment.

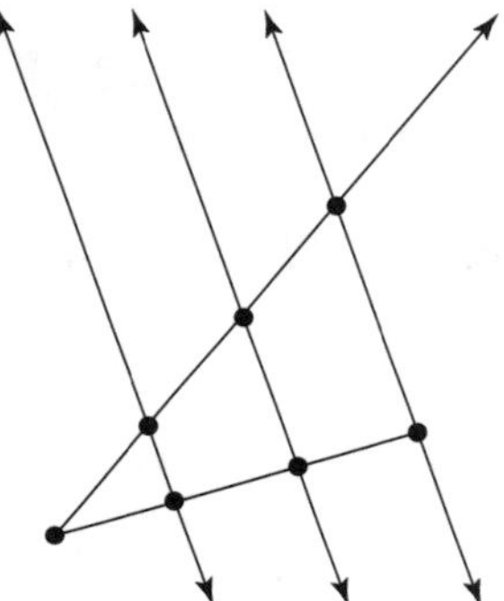

Construct parallels to that line through each of the other marks on your ray. Those parallels divide your original segment into n equal pieces.

You can assign the reading of "A High School Student Extends the Theorem" after students complete Activity 1.

ACTIVITY 2 Folding Investigations *(Student pages 76–77)*

Encourage students to perform the experiment several times. Have them share their results with the class.

ACTIVITY 3 Circle Intersections *(Student pages 78–79)*

This activity should take about two days. Have students work straight through the problems. After the first day, you may want to hold a class discussion about the results from Problem **15.**

PROBLEM 15 The thing that is invariant about all of the traced points is that they all lie on the same shapes. What's the name for the shape they trace out? Ask the class if anyone checked special cases like C at the midpoint of your segment?

PROBLEMS 16–17 After the second day, you may want to hold a class discussion on the results of these problems. If necessary, introduce students to or remind them of the term *ellipse.* Analyze the construction and the definition of an ellipse to see why that shape is created.

An ellipse is the set of points whose total distance from two fixed points, called the foci of the ellipse, is a constant.

Even though they have encountered this idea before, you may need to remind students that naming $\overline{BC}$ as the radius of a circle does not mean it must be attached to the circle.

ACTIVITY 4

Constructing Invariants (Student pages 79–80)

You may want to take two days to complete the problems in this activity, stopping now and then to have students share their written directions with the rest of the class. If there is a problem that no one in class has been able to solve, you can provide step-by-step directions for students who want to make a construction that contains the invariant.

PROBLEM 20 Because there are many different ways to solve this problem, you might challenge some students to invent ways that they think are particularly "elegant" (simple constructions) or "unusual" (approaches they think few others will find) or that have ratios other than $\frac{1}{2}$ or $\frac{1}{4}$.

On Your Own (Student pages 80–81)

These problems provide students with the opportunity for individual practice. See the lesson Planning Guide for homework recommendations.

Options and Extensions

Without Technology

Activity 2 makes no use of the computer, and parts of Activity 4 are quite suitable as non-technology activities too. Virtually *any* geometric questions *can* be pursued without the computer. However, the purposes in Activities 1, 3, and 4, at this point in a student's learning, are largely lost amidst the details and distractions of drawing and measuring if they are pursued without computer.

Problems **19–21** can be done without the computer. If students know enough about area and perimeter of shapes, they can see from a hand drawing that the invariant is independent of the size of the drawing or how it is moved around.

$C_2 = 2\pi r_2 = 2C_1$

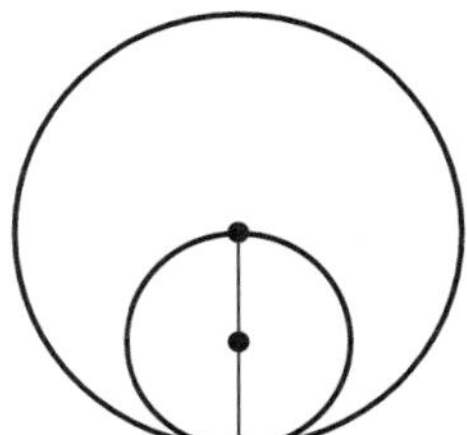

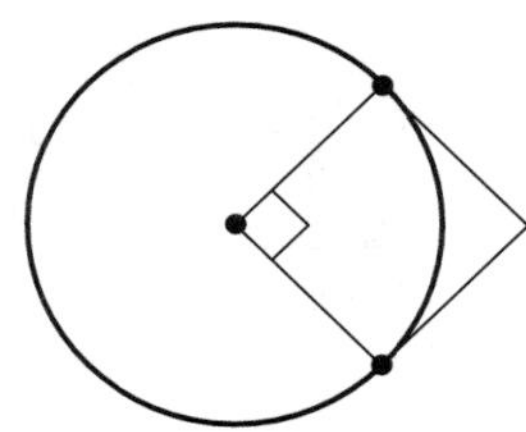

Area of circle is πr^2. Area of square is r^2.
The constant ratio is π.

Resources

Patty paper is available from many publishers of mathematics manipulatives, including Key Curriculum Press. You might also ask a local butcher to sell you the paper, which is used to separate hamburger patties. Waxed paper makes nice creases, but it is a bit harder to handle, and you must cut it into squares. Origami paper also works, but it can be expensive.

LESSON

11 Reasoning by Continuity

Lesson Objective

Students examine the difference between continuous and discrete change and learn to use some big ideas of continuity to solve problems.

Content Overview

Students are introduced to the Mean Value Theorem (not named, but the ideas are used). They also notice when a situation does or does not change continuously.

Planning Guide

Pacing	Activity	Materials	Homework Suggestions
Day 1	*Explore and Discuss* (SE p. 84) Activity 1: Continuous Change (SE pp. 84–85)	No special materials needed.	*On Your Own,* Problems 2 and 3
Day 2	Activity 2: The Box Problem (SE pp. 85–86)	• index cards • M&M's® candies or other small items to be used as counters	*On Your Own,* Problem 4
Day 3	Activity 3: The Ham Sandwich Problem (SE pp. 86–88)	BLM 11, p. 15	*On Your Own,* Problem 1 Activity 3, Problems 16 and 17
Day 4	Activity 3: The Ham Sandwich Problem (SE pp. 86–88)	BLM 11, p. 15	Activity 3, Problems 19 and 20

Program Resources

- *Connected Geometry* CD-ROM, Module 1: Investigation 1.20
- *Solution and Problem Solving Resource,* pages 82–89
- *Teaching Resources,* page 15

Preparation and Prerequisites

"The Box Problem" discusses volume. To explore the problem, students need to have at least an informal notion that volume measures "how much stuff a box will hold." If

$V = x(4x^2 - 26x + 40)$

background of the class, students may set up the function, graph it, and approximate the maximum volume.

People can learn to perform experiments like these in their head—mathematicians call them "thought experiments"—but very few people have had the opportunity to develop these visualization/analysis skills. One way to gain experience is by doing the experiments physically. The emphasis on geometry software is intended for the same purpose—not to generate the *answers* so much as to let students see with their eyes the kinds of continuously changing systems that they will later learn to recreate, modify, and extend in their minds.

Problem **14** asks students how they can know if they have been successful at bisecting irregular shapes. The fact is that they cannot know. There is no area measuring device to check the areas, and no handy way to compute the areas of the two halves. Students need the theory to tell them that it is even possible, and then the best they can do is approximate.

Using Technology

The box problem is nicely modeled with geometry software. If students realize that the volume is simply three lengths on their sketch multiplied together, they can have the software calculate it for them dynamically and graph the volume vs. size of cutout. One of the authors' favorite sketches shows a dynamically changing rectangle with cutouts, box, and graph, all on the same page. You can visit the authors' Web page at http://www.edc.org/LTT/GAMT/box.html to see a sample of the sketch.

Mathematics Connections

From looking at these samples, you might think that if a function has a continuous domain, then it is continuous. This is, of course, not true. Consider the function that assigns 1 to every rational number and 0 to every irrational number. The domain is continuous, but the function is not. This is a tricky point and probably not worth bringing up in most classes. If you want to challenge your students, however, you might ask them to graph this function (it's impossible, but you can get an idea of what it looks like by trying) and to decide if it is continuous or discrete.

LESSON

12 Definitions and Systems

Lesson Objective

This lesson introduces students to geometric systems other than the familiar Euclidean geometry.

Content Overview

Students learn that what is true in one system may not be true in another. This idea is extremely important, even for students who will not continue the studies of axiomatics or alternative systems.

This is a fun, hands-on lesson that includes a fanciful story.

Planning Guide

Pacing	Activity	Materials	Homework Suggestions
Day 1	*Explore and Discuss* (SE p. 92) Activity 1: Life on a Sphere (SE pp. 92–93)	• sphere models • string	*On Your Own,* Problems 1 and 2
Day 2	Activity 2: Parallel Lines and Spheres (SE p. 93)	• sphere models • string	*Take It Further,* Problems 5, 6, 7, and 8
Day 3	Activity 3: Building Up from Rules (SE p. 94)	• beads • wires	*On Your Own,* Problems 3 and 4 Perspective: Finite Geometries

Program Resources

- *Connected Geometry* CD-ROM, Module 1: Investigation 1.21
- *Solution and Problem Solving Resource,* pages 90–97
- *Assessment Resources,* Quiz 9 Lessons 11 and 12, page 10

Preparation and Prerequisites

Students should have enough experience with Euclidean geometry so that this lesson and its contrasts have meaning for them.

Teaching the Lesson

Explore and Discuss *(Student page 92)*

Read the introductory page. In groups, have students come up with answers to the problems in this section. End the section with a discussion about the meaning of *straight* on the surface of a sphere.

ACTIVITY 1

Life on a Sphere *(Student pages 92–93)*

PROBLEM 1 Here are some questions to ask students before you begin this problem. What is straightness? Is it the path that light travels? What about on the surface of the earth? Perhaps it is a vertical projection onto the surface from the path that light travels. What about a person or vehicle with right and left feet (or wheels) traveling the same distance? Or is a *straight* path the shortest path between two points?

Students should be encouraged to use string, held at the two points and pulled taut, for both Problems 2 and 3.

PROBLEM 3 Working in pairs or groups is important because it is difficult to work individually with the sphere models and string.

Students who use the globe as their model of a sphere may be confused by the geographical use of "parallel" as in "the 49th parallel." The senses of nonintersecting and everywhere-equidistant are preserved.

PROBLEM 5 Problem **1** has already hinted that any two *straight lines,* as they have been defined on a sphere, cannot remain the same distance apart and must eventually intersect. Thus, parallel lines do not exist on a sphere. Later in this section students will see that, while parallel lines cannot exist on a sphere, perpendiculars can. This fact leads to a rather startling conclusion and leaves room for a lively debate about the existence of squares on a sphere. One side of the debate correctly argues that four equal-length line segments can be constructed and that it is possible even to build in a right angle. That argument conforms to one definition of a square. But squares, at least in plane geometry, are also a very special kind of parallelogram, and parallelograms *cannot* exist on a sphere because parallels cannot exist on a sphere! How can this be resolved? One must make a decision about which properties to use in *defining* squares for the purpose of doing geometry on a sphere.

If one decides to define a square as an equilateral four-sided polygon, then squares exist on a sphere, but their properties are not the same as those on the plane. For example, they have no parallel sides and no right angles. If one decides, equally reasonably, to define a square as a kind of parallelogram, then a square cannot exist on a sphere.

Goniometers are angle measurers. Built out of two pieces hinged together with something like a protractor at the hinge, goniometers can be used more easily than protractors in many situations.

PROBLEM 6 This problem asks students to investigate the angles in triangles on a sphere. Students will probably need help with the idea of measuring these angles. Goniometers or other such devices are usually preferable to protractors, but even with a protractor, students can get an idea of the angle measure with some help. It's probably best that they work in pairs on this problem, as well as on all the problems using spherical models, so that they can negotiate the difficult points with someone else rather than struggling alone.

ACTIVITY 2

Parallel Lines and Spheres *(Student page 93)*

Have models of spheres available for students to work with individually or in groups.

PROBLEM 12 There are many possible directions that the explorations might take. Students who are interested in *definitions* may find that the problems of redefining objects on this new surface do not end with lines (great circles) and squares (see the discussion on the previous page). One must even reconsider what a *point* is. In the plane (and, for that matter, in 3-dimensional space), two intersecting lines define a single point and two distinct points completely determine a unique line. These are such natural ideas that one would want them to be true in other geometries as well as on the plane. But the ideas appear *not* to be true on a sphere. Two distinct lines (great circles) intersect at *two* antipodal points. And, while most pairs of points on a sphere determine a single great circle, there are many pairs of points (*any* pair of antipodal points) through which an infinite number of lines passes. To maintain the orderliness that feels so natural in Euclidean geometry, spherical geometry defines its (spherical) points differently: A pair of antipodal Euclidean points is considered *one* (spherical) point. So any pair of lines intersects at a single point, and any two distinct points determine a single line. Students who are interested in *phenomena that remain invariant under changes from plane to sphere* may explore some of the concurrences and collinearities they have seen in earlier problems.

This is a rather short activity but students can spend time working on Problem **12,** which asks them to compare properties of shapes in both planar and spherical geometry.

ACTIVITY 3 Building Up from Rules *(Student page 94)*

Pass out the beads and wires (or similar materials). Write the four rules on the board. Students work in pairs or small groups to create the described objects. Groups draw their creations on the board and discuss similarities. Then invite students to work on Problems **14–16.**

PROBLEMS 14–16 In these problems, students are asked to explore a new system: the seven-point geometry. Students may come up with different models of this geometry, but they should all be isomorphic. That is, they must have the *same structure* even if they have different appearances. Two geometric models A and B are *isomorphic* if there exists a one-to-one correspondence between their points P (on A) and P' (on B) and a one-to-one correspondence between the lines, such that P lies on l (of A) if and only if P' lies on l' (of B). Students do not need to know the exact definition of *isomorphism,* but they should check to see that the different models they invent have the *same structure* despite possibly different appearances. So, for example, all the models should have seven beads and seven lines; no more or fewer. Below is one possible model.

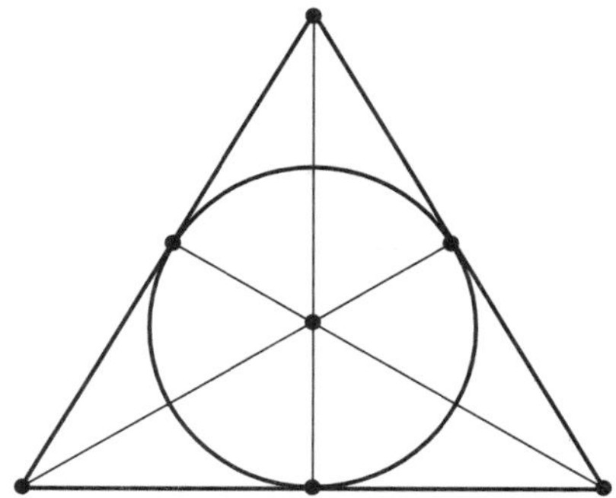

PROBLEM 4 This problem asks students to create directions for drawing a given figure. One set of directions follows. Students should be judged on whether their directions work and are clear rather than if they match the ones below.

- Construct two circles that pass through each other's centers.
- Connect the two centers to each other and to one of the intersection points.
- Erase or hide the two circles.
- Label the vertices of the remaining triangle A, B and C.
- Construct a circle centered at A with radius $\overline{AB}$. Erase all of the circle except the smaller of the two arcs between points B and C.
- Construct a circle centered at B with radius $\overline{AB}$. Erase all of the circle except the smaller of the two arcs between points A and C.
- Construct a circle centered at C with radius $\overline{AC}$. Erase all of the circle except the smaller of the two arcs between points A and B.
- Erase or hide the labels of the points.

The shape drawn is a famous curve of constant width called the Reuleaux triangle. As with a circle, you can make a wheel from this shape and a car would roll steadily.

PROBLEM 5 Students will state the Triangle Inequality in their own words. They should write something like the following: *The sum of the lengths of the two sides of a triangle is always greater than the length of the third side.*

PROBLEM 6 This problem simply asks students to apply the Triangle Inequality in straightforward ways.

a. yes

b. no

c. yes

d. no

e. yes

PROBLEM 7 Students should write something like the following: *An invariant is something that doesn't change in a given situation or construction.*

PROBLEM 8 Answers will vary. Possible answers:

- The sum of the angles in a triangle is invariant.
- In triangles, medians are concurrent, perpendicular bisectors are concurrent, and angle bisectors are concurrent.
- If you connect the midpoints of the sides of a quadrilateral, the shape formed is a parallelogram.
- If you connect the midpoints of two sides of a triangle, the segment is half as long as the third side.

PROBLEM 9 This problem asks students to reconstruct the proof that the sum of the interior angles in a triangle is 180°.

PROBLEM 10 Students should know that the sum of the interior angles of a polygon with n sides is $(n - 2) \cdot 180$.

PROBLEM 11 In triangles the medians are concurrent, the perpendiculars are concurrent, and the angle bisectors are concurrent. Examples in other shapes include the diagonals of regular polygons with an even number of sides, the angle bisectors of circumscribed polygons, and the perpendicular bisectors of inscribed (or cyclic) polygons.

PROBLEM 12 Many examples were given throughout the book, and students should be able to pull examples of continuous and discrete change from their own lives.

PROBLEM 13 This problem asks students to make an informal statement of the Mean Value Theorem. The idea is that if $f(a) = A$ and $f(b) = B$ then a and b must take on every value between A and B.

PROBLEM 14 The graph shows that for continuous change there are no gaps in the graph, and for discrete change it should be a discrete set of points.

- Lesson 4, Problems 1 and 2. Explain experimental and deductive proof of the vertical angle theorem.
- Choose the most difficult proof you did in Lesson 4. Explain your solution and why it was difficult.
- Write up an analysis of a proof from the *On Your Own* section in Lesson 5.
- Analyze a proof in more than one way or find a proof that previously seemed too difficult and show how to analyze it now.
- Lesson 8, *Write and Reflect* Problem 12. Write a convincing argument.

UNIT 2 Planning Guide

Lessons	Learning Goals	Assessment Opportunities	Suggested Pacing	Materials
LESSON 1 *The Congruence Relationship*	1	*Checkpoint,* Problems 13 and 19 Quiz 1, *Assessment Resources,* p. 48	2 days	• BLM 12, p. 16 • BLM 13, p. 17 • rulers • protractors
LESSON 2 *Triangle Congruence*	1	*Checkpoint,* Problems 4, 9, and 12 Quiz 2, *Assessment Resources,* p. 49	3 days	• BLM 14, p. 18 • BLM 15, p. 19 • BLM 16, p. 20 • compasses • envelopes • note cards (optional) • protractors • rulers • small slips of paper
LESSON 3 *Warm-Ups for Proof*	4	*Checkpoint,* Problem 4	1 day	No special materials needed.
LESSON 4 *Writing Proofs*	1–3	*Checkpoint,* Problems 4 and 8 Quiz 3, *Assessment Resources,* p. 50 Mid-Unit Exam, *Assessment Resources,* pp. 53–64	4 days	geometry software
LESSON 5 *Analysis and Proof, Part 1*	1–4	*Checkpoint,* Problems 3 and 6	3 days	• BLM 17, p. 21 • globe (optional)

LESSON 6 *Analysis and Proof, Part 2*	1–4	*Checkpoint,* Problems 7 and 11	3 days	No special materials needed.
LESSON 7 *Investigations and Demonstrations*	1, 3	*Checkpoint,* Problems 3, 5, and 7 Quiz 4, *Assessment Resources,* p. 51	6 days	• compasses • cups, glasses, or cans to trace • cutouts of triangles to trace • geometry software (optional) • protractors • rulers
LESSON 8 *Congruence in Quadrilaterals and Beyond*	3, 4	*Checkpoint,* Problems 13, 18, 24, 31, and 41 Quiz 5, *Assessment Resources,* p. 52	6 days	• BLM 18, p. 22 • BLM 19A and 19B, pp. 23–24 • BLM 20, p. 25 • protractors • rulers • geometry software (optional) • color pencils (optional)
UNIT 2 REVIEW		End-of-Unit Exam, *Assessment Resources,* pp. 65–72	3 days (including testing)	No special materials needed.

LESSON

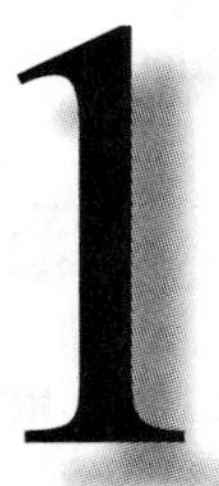

The Congruence Relationship

Lesson Objective

This lesson introduces the notion of congruence as meaning *same shape and size.* Students learn standard mathematical notation used for communicating about congruent figures.

Content Overview

The following two questions are the focus of the lesson:

- If two figures are congruent, must corresponding parts of the figures have equal measures?
- If two figures have certain measures that are equal, what do you know about the congruence of the figures?

In the lessons ahead, students will start writing proofs and determining congruence for particular triangles. To move ahead successfully, students will need to accomplish these objectives:

1. Understand that measurement equality is required for congruence.
2. Understand the meaning of *corresponding parts.*
3. Read and write statements about congruent figures using correct notation.

Planning Guide

Pacing	Activity	Materials	Homework Suggestions
Day 1	*Explore and Discuss* (SE p. 102) Activity 1: Length, Measure, and Congruence (SE pp. 103–105)	• protractors • rulers	*On Your Own,* Problems 1–8
Day 2	Activity 1: Length, Measure, and Congruence (SE pp. 103–105) Activity 2: Corresponding Parts (SE pp. 105–107)	• BLM 12, p.16 • BLM 13, p.17 • protractors • rulers	*On Your Own,* Problems 9–12

On Your Own *(Student pages 115–118)*

These problems provide students with the opportunity for individual practice. See the lesson Planning Guide for homework recommendations.

PROBLEM 12 Blackline Master 15 can be copied to help students explore the diagonals of various quadrilaterals.

Take It Further *(Student pages 118–119)*

Before starting Problems **20–23,** distribute Blackline Master 16 to students.

The "Cutting up, Congruently" problems are fun for students to do because they seem like puzzles. At the same time, however, the problems will help assess whether students know what it means for two figures to be congruent. To use the problems as an assessment tool, have students present their solutions to the class and justify why they think the pieces are congruent, or have students write justifications for their solutions.

Options and Extensions

Using Technology

The envelope game can be done on the computer fairly easily using geometry software. Instead of drawing the triangles using hand tools, students can construct them on the computer. The constructions themselves are a challenge, but the capabilities of the geometry software allow students to stretch each constructed triangle out of shape.

Mathematics Connections

See the book *How Does One Cut a Triangle* by Alexander Soifer (published by the Center for Excellence in Mathematics Education, Colorado Springs, 1990) for more of the triangle dissections. Among other results, the book shows how a generalization of the Midline Theorem allows you to divide any triangle into n^2 congruent pieces by dividing each side into n pieces and connecting the points of division so that segments are parallel to the sides.

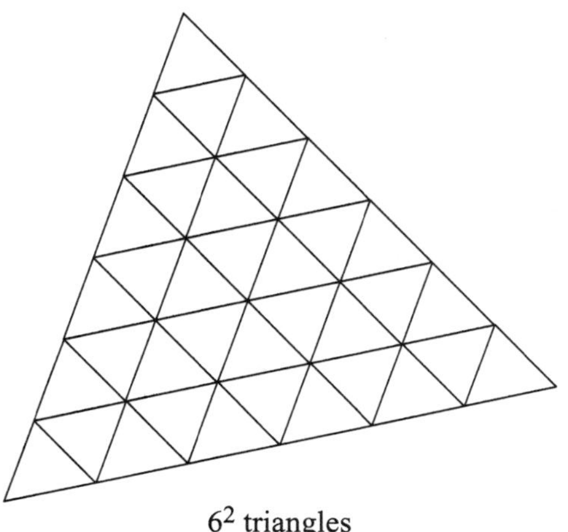

6^2 triangles

LESSON

Warm-Ups for Proof

Lesson Objective

Students construct both mathematical and nonmathematical arguments.

Content Overview

This lesson presents five problems in which students are asked to make arguments, four of them in a mathematical context. The idea is for students to move from thinking about specific cases to thinking about general proofs.

Planning Guide

Pacing	Activity	Materials	Homework Suggestions
Day 1	*Explore and Discuss* (SE p. 120) Activity: Mathematical Arguments (SE pp. 120–121)	No special materials needed.	*On Your Own,* Problems 1–4

Program Resources

- *Connected Geometry* CD-ROM, Module 2: Investigation 2.6
- *Solution and Problem Solving Resource,* pages 120–123

Preparation and Prerequisites

None

Teaching the Lesson

Explore and Discuss *(Student page 120)*

Students can work on this section individually at first and then share their arguments with their group or the class. Students should discuss which arguments are most convincing and why.

ACTIVITY

Mathematical Arguments *(Student pages 120–121)*

Encourage students to discuss their solutions and present them to the class. Have them talk about which arguments are convincing and why.

On Your Own *(Student pages 121–122)*

These problems provide students with the opportunity for individual practice.

PROBLEM 4 This problem is particularly interesting; students are asked to assume one fact in order to prove another.

LESSON

Writing Proofs

Lesson Objective

Students read and write proofs in many different styles.

Content Overview

This lesson includes two very important discussions that attempt to put proofs into context for students.

- What are proofs? What do they look like? How do you write them?
- Why are proofs necessary in mathematics or any other context?

The lesson begins with a discussion of how varied proofs can be, how they differ from experiments, and how they fit into the world of mathematics. A short tutorial on writing congruent triangle proofs is followed by samples of proofs written in several styles.

Planning Guide

Pacing	Activity	Materials	Homework Suggestions
Day 1	*Explore and Discuss* (SE pp. 123–124)	No special materials needed.	Perspective: Deduction and Experimentation *On Your Own,* Problem 1
Day 2	Activity 1: Why Proof? (SE pp. 124–125)	geometry software	*On Your Own,* Problems 5 and 6 (optional)
Day 3	Activity 2: A Beginner's Manual (SE pp. 125–126)	geometry software	*On Your Own,* Problems 2 and 3 (optional)
Day 4	Activity 2: A Beginner's Manual (SE pp. 125–126)	geometry software	*On Your Own,* Problems 4 and 7 (optional)

Program Resources

- *Connected Geometry* CD-ROM, Module 2: Investigation 2.7
- *Solution and Problem Solving Resource,* pages 124–127
- *Assessment Resources,* Quiz 3 Lessons 3 and 4, page 50

Preparation and Prerequisites

This lesson assumes that students understand the meaning of congruence and have been convinced that SSS, SAS, ASA, or AAS will prove triangle congruence but have not actually written formal proofs. Have on hand a supply of congruence proofs that seem suitable for your class. Encourage students to try writing the proofs for these examples in different styles.

The Student Edition includes examples of proofs written by students who have studied in other countries. Before beginning this lesson, talk to your international students and see if any of them have already learned about congruent triangles and proofs in their home countries. If so, you might feature some of their work in class.

Teaching the Lesson

Explore and Discuss (*Student pages 123–124)*

The introductory reading and *Explore and Discuss* are meant for reading, reflection, and discussion. Students should ponder the question, "Why prove things?" and appreciate different styles for presenting proofs.

Begin with a class discussion about different styles of proof. Use student experts from other countries to enrich this discussion. While the primary focus of the discussion is on how many ways there are to write a proof, it is also important to make sure that everyone understands the proof itself.

ACTIVITY 1

Why Proof? *(Student pages 124–125)*

Have the class work on the vertical angle problem. Make sure that there is a full discussion of the difference between the results one gets from experimentation and those one gets from deduction. (Many students are convinced of a result of this sort if a single example measures correctly.) Have students present their results to the class.

ACTIVITY 2

A Beginner's Manual *(Student pages 125–126)*

Remember that these are the first proofs students will have tried. Allow time for ideas to develop and for students to gain some confidence in writing the proofs.

Own Your Own *(Student pages 126–127)*

These problems provide students with the opportunity for individual practice. See the lesson Planning Guide for homework recommendations.

Options and Extensions

Is it important for your class to learn to write congruent triangle proofs in a particular style? The problems in the Student Edition are written assuming that students will read and write in many different styles. If you prefer one style, augment these problems with additional practice in that style.

Using Technology

No computer use is required, but a major focus of this lesson is on the comparison of results obtained by experiment and those obtained by proof. This is a perfect place to introduce students to some questions for exploration using geometry software. Below are some examples.

1. Using geometry software, draw a triangle, a quadrilateral, a pentagon, a hexagon, and several other polygons. For each polygon, measure the sum of the interior angles. Record all of the sums in a chart like the one below.

Number of Sides	Sum of Angle Measures
3	180°
4	
5	
6	

2. Does the angle sum change if the polygon changes its shape but keeps the same number of sides?
3. Find a pattern or rule for finding the sum of the angles if you know the number of sides in the polygon.
4. Use your rule to predict the angle sum for a decagon (10-sided polygon).
5. On the basis of your experimentation, would you conclude that this rule is always true? Explain any exceptions to the rule that you have found or that you might expect to find.
6. Assume for now that your rule is, in fact, always true. Write a proof or a deductive argument that proves your rule. (For an example of a deductive argument, look in the Student Edition at the arguments that prove that vertical angles are congruent.)

For this problem, assume that the sum of the angle measures in a triangle is 180° and prove your conjecture for other polygons.

LESSON

Analysis and Proof, Part 1

Lesson Objective

This lesson is designed to give students the "whole picture" of proof: how to analyze the structure, how to fit parts together, and how to search for missing pieces in some organized fashion.

Content Overview

For a beginner, doing proofs can seem like putting together a jigsaw puzzle that has no picture. If you don't know what the final picture is supposed to look like, you search randomly for tiny pieces that seem to be the right shape or color to match another tiny piece you are looking at. Although individual pieces might lock together successfully, it is difficult to know where they fit in the big picture.

When you do know what the whole picture looks like, you can see each piece as a part of the whole, build bridges from section to section, place finished subsections in their approximate positions, and even frame the whole puzzle before you fill in the interior.

Planning Guide

Pacing	Activity	Materials	Homework Suggestions
Day 1	*Explore and Discuss* (SE p. 129) Activity 1: The Visual Scan (SE pp. 129–131)	No special materials needed.	*On Your Own*, Problems 1, 2, and 3
Day 2	Activity 1: The Visual Scan (SE pp. 129–131) Activity 2: The Flow Chart (SE pp. 131–132)	BLM 17, p. 21	*On Your Own*, Problems 4 and 5 *Take It Further*, Problem 9
Day 3	Activity 2: The Flow Chart (SE pp. 131–132)	• BLM 17, p. 21 • globe (optional)	*On Your Own*, Problems 6 and 7 *Take It Further*, Problems 8 and 10

Program Resources

- *Connected Geometry* CD-ROM, Module 2: Investigation 2.8
- *Solution and Problem Solving Resource,* pages 128–133
- *Teaching Resources,* page 21

Preparation and Prerequisites

When students begin this investigation, they should know how to write a basic congruent triangle proof using SSS, SAS, ASA, and AAS. A number of proofs is provided, but you might want to prepare an extra worksheet for your class.

You may want to spend two or three days on this lesson, allowing students to work on the proofs together and spending time discussing the *On Your Own* problems.

Teaching the Lesson

Explore and Discuss (*Student page 129*)

Read the *Car Talk* dialogue as a class and discuss what medical diagnosis, automobile repair, and mathematical proof have in common. Throughout the discussion, students should begin to *think about their thinking.* What kinds of things do they do when they analyze a problem?

ACTIVITY 1

The Visual Scan (*Student pages 129–131*)

You can simply explain this technique or have the class read along as students take turns reading aloud. After the explanation, it is important to write out the proof that goes with the problem just analyzed. Students should clearly see how the analysis relates to the actual finished proof.

The Student Edition also contains a brief explanation of CPCTC. You might want to add a few more proofs to allow the class to practice with CPCTC while using the visual scan and/or the flow chart.

For Discussion (*Student page 130*)

The CPCTC statement is a technique used in proofs; first show that two triangles are congruent, and then make use of that fact to show that certain corresponding parts of the two triangles are congruent. Think of CPCTC as a type of proof strategy. On the other hand, SSS, SAS, and other tests, are postulates which are used to conclude that two triangles are congruent. They stand for known results. For example, if all three pairs of corresponding sides of two triangles are congruent, then the two triangles are congruent.

ACTIVITY 2

The Flow Chart (*Student pages 131–132*)

Again, you can explain the technique or have students read the explanation aloud. Blackline Master 17 provides you with a copy of the flow chart. The two important points to emphasize in the flow chart are the following: write everything you know or can conclude and then trace a sensible path through the chart. If students are having difficulty, try an easier idea, such as Activities during the Day, Getting to School, and so on.

On Your Own *(Student pages 133–134)*

These problems provide students with the opportunity for individual practice. See the lesson Planning Guide for homework recommendations.

Take It Further *(Student pages 135–136)*

These problems will lead students in new directions or will challenge them to apply what they already know.

Options and Extensions

Additional ideas for this lesson include:

- Suggest that students use a highlighter to color the parts of each flow chart that will make up the final proof. You will be able to read the proof by following the highlighted pathway through the flow chart.
- Have students look for flow charts in other settings (computer programming, debate, organizational flow charts, and so on) and ask them to bring these charts to share with the class.

LESSON

Analysis and Proof, Part 2

Lesson Objective

The goal of this lesson is to get students started in translating statements into hypothesis/conclusion form.

Content Overview

Two extremes emerge as you teach students about proof. At one extreme are the few students who can look at a statement, see it as a hypothesis and conclusion, and, after some thought, offer the outline of a proof. The fully-developed proof seems to appear almost magically. What goes on in the mind before the emergence of the proof is a bit of a mystery, especially to the students at the other extreme, who simply do not see how to do the proof and who beg their teachers to return to the study of algebra and its algorithmic forms.

What *is* going on in the mind as someone tries to come up with a proof? The thought process can be flow-chart style, discussed in the last lesson. Just as likely, there is a type of backwards analysis that goes something like this: "If I want to prove that this animal is a porcupine, then I am going to have to show that it has spines. Now where am I going to find some spines?"

The authors call this analysis form the *reverse list* and treat it in this lesson as a learnable skill. Since this method begins with the question: "What am I trying to prove?" Lesson 6 starts with an explanation of hypothesis and conclusion, followed by practice in translating statements into hypothesis/conclusion form. The *reverse list* method is then described, with examples and practice problems provided.

Planning Guide

Pacing	Activity	Materials	Homework Suggestions
Day 1	*Explore and Discuss* (SE pp. 137–138) Activity 1: What Am I Trying to Prove? (SE p. 138)	No special materials needed.	*On Your Own,* Problem 9
Day 2	Activity 2: The Reverse List (SE pp. 139–141)		*On Your Own,* Problems 1–4
Day 3	Activity 2: The Reverse List (SE pp. 139–141)		*On Your Own,* Problems 5–8

Program Resources

- *Connected Geometry* CD-ROM, Module 2: Investigation 2.9
- *Solution and Problem Solving Resource,* pages 134–141

Preparation and Prerequisites

Students should have a working knowledge of triangle congruence and some experience with proofs. The focus here is on developing analysis skills with more complex proofs. In preparation for teaching the investigation, it is helpful to check the problems given in the *Student Edition*. If they seem too difficult, too easy, or if there aren't enough of them for your class, supplement with problems from any standard geometry text.

Teaching the Lesson

Explore and Discuss *(Student pages 137–138)*

Conduct a class discussion on the terms *hypothesis* and *conclusion.* After the *Explore and Discuss* problems have been discussed, have students go on to Activity 1.

ACTIVITY 1

What Am I Trying to Prove? *(Student page 138)*

Problems **1** through **6** can be assigned for cooperative group work. Assign each group one of the problems to present to the class. Note that finding the hypothesis and conclusion for each statement should take only a short time, but the proofs and counterexamples may be difficult for some students.

ACTIVITY 2

The Reverse List *(Student pages 139–141)*

You should begin this activity with a full explanation of the reverse list technique. First, carefully examine the example that is presented in the *Student Edition*. Then analyze one or two more examples as a full class. It is important to choose proofs that will *not* be obvious to students. They should see how they can use this technique to actually figure something out that they couldn't figure out by just looking at the proof. You may want to give a reverse list in incomplete form and ask students to complete it.

On Your Own *(Student page 141)*

These problems provide students with the opportunity for individual practice. See the lesson Planning Guide for homework recommendations.

Take It Further *(Student page 141)*

These problems will lead students in new directions or will challenge them to apply what they already know.

Options and Extensions

By the end of this lesson, students will have worked with three analysis techniques. Encourage comparisons. Which works best for them? Which was the easiest to learn? Is there another technique they use that is different from these?

As you work through the sample problems with the class, discuss strategies for dealing with dead-end situations, where the choices made aren't leading anywhere. It is important for students to see that backtracking, regrouping, and starting over are integral parts of working on proofs.

Mathematics Connections

PROBLEM 11 This problem is very difficult to prove. What follows is a proof worked out by one of the authors that uses complex numbers and trigonometry.

Here is the basic idea:

> Show that longer sides have shorter angle bisectors. So, if two sides are not congruent, the angle bisectors to these sides are not congruent.

One way is easy: If the triangle is isosceles, the bisectors of the base angles are congruent. The other way isn't so simple.

In other words, you want to express the length of an angle bisector in terms of the lengths of the sides of the triangle. Then you can work with the algebra instead of with the geometry. Here is one version of this idea.

The angle bisector in terms of the sides Suppose the sidelengths of a triangle are a, b, and c. As usual, let the vertices of the triangle be A, B, and C. Let t_s be the length of the angle bisector to side s.

This is somewhat unusual notation (b is opposite A, and so on), but the authors started like this and didn't bother to change it.

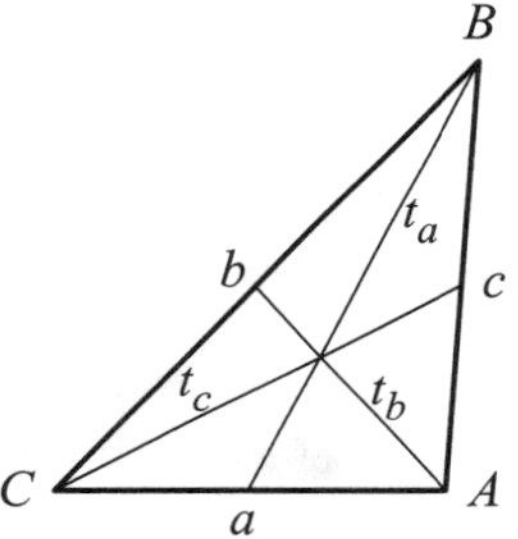

Let's concentrate on t_c and put the whole thing on the complex plane, with C at the origin and A along the real axis. Then let $\theta = \frac{1}{2}m\angle C$ and let $\zeta = \cos\theta + i\sin\theta$. Then $B = b\zeta^2$, $C = 0$, and $A = a$ as in the following picture:

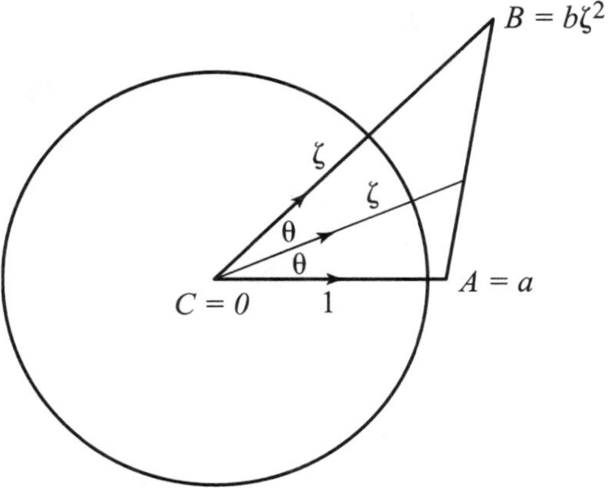

Also, the intersection of the bisector of $\angle C$ with $\overline{AB}$ is $P = t_c\zeta$. But P is also between A and B, so $P = a + r(b\zeta^2 - a)$ for some real r. Hence, you need to solve the equation

$$\begin{aligned} t_c\zeta &= a + r(b\zeta^2 - a) \\ &= a - ra + rb\zeta^2. \end{aligned}$$

If $\zeta = \cos\theta + i\sin\theta$, then $\zeta^2 = \cos 2\theta + i\sin 2\theta$ by DeMoivre's Theorem.

This is really two equations (one equating the real parts, the other equating the imaginary parts) in two unknowns (t_c and r):

$$t_c(\cos\theta + i\sin\theta) = a - ra + rb(\cos 2\theta + i\sin 2\theta).$$

Setting real = real and imaginary = imaginary, you get

$$\begin{aligned} t_c\cos\theta &= a - ra + rb\cos 2\theta \\ t_c\sin\theta &= rb\sin 2\theta = 2rb\sin\theta\cos\theta. \end{aligned}$$

The double angle formulas are used for sine and cosine here.

The second equation implies that $t_c = 2rb\cos\theta$. Substitute this in the first equation and find that

$$\begin{aligned} 2rb\cos^2\theta &= a - ra + rb\cos 2\theta \\ &= a - ra + rb(2\cos^2\theta - 1) \\ &= a - ra + 2rb\cos^2\theta - rb. \end{aligned}$$

You know you are on the right track when things start canceling.

This implies that

$$r = \frac{a}{a+b}.$$

Since $t_c = 2rb\cos\theta$, then

$$t_c = \frac{2ab\cos\theta}{a+b}.$$

Check out the theorem in The Geometer's Sketchpad®. It works.

This is interesting in itself. It gives the length of the angle bisector in terms of the triangle's parts:

Theorem *Using the notation in the second figure, the length of the angle bisector to side c is*

$$\frac{2ab\cos\theta}{a+b}, \text{ where } \theta = \tfrac{1}{2}m\angle C.$$

But what you *really* wanted was t_c as a function of the sidelengths. You can do that with a bit more work: Let $\alpha = m\angle C$ so that $\alpha = 2\theta$. Then you get two facts:

Fact 1

$$\cos\theta = \sqrt{\frac{1+\cos\alpha}{2}}$$

(This is a half-angle formula from trigonometry.)

Fact 2

$$\cos\alpha = \frac{a^2 + b^2 - c^2}{2ab}$$

(This is the Law of Cosines.)

Similarly,

$$t_b = \frac{\sqrt{ac[(a+c)^2 - b^2]}}{a+c}$$

and

$$t_a = \frac{\sqrt{bc[(b+c)^2 - a^2]}}{b+c}$$

Substituting in the theorem, you get (after a bit of simplification)

$$t_c = \frac{\sqrt{ab[(a+b)^2 - c^2]}}{a+b}.$$

This is what you were after. Squaring both sides, you have a nice result:

Theorem *Using the notation above,*

$$t_c^2 = \frac{ab[(a+b)^2 - c^2]}{(a+b)^2}.$$

A simplification Suppose that you want to compare t_c and t_b, the lengths of the angle bisectors to sides b and c. Scaling, you can assume that $a = 1$. Then, with this simplification, the above theorem says:

$$t_c^2 = \frac{b[(1+b)^2 - c^2]}{(1+b)^2}$$

$$t_b^2 = \frac{c[(1+c)^2 - b^2]}{(1+c)^2}.$$

The combining and factoring was done with a little help from a friend—the Mathematica® program.

To compare two things, subtract them:

$$t_c^2 - t_b^2 = \frac{b[(1+b)^2 - c^2]}{(1+b)^2} - \frac{c[(1+c)^2 - b^2]}{(1+c)^2}$$

$$= \frac{(c-b)(1+b+c)(1+b+c+3bc+b^2c+bc^2)}{(1+b)^2+(1+c)^2}.$$

This does it. $t_c = t_b \Leftrightarrow$ the numerator in this fraction is zero. But, since b and c are positive, the only way for the numerator to be zero is if the factor $(c - b)$ is 0; that is,

$$t_c = t_b \Leftrightarrow c = b.$$

Theorem *In a triangle, two angle bisectors are congruent if and only if the triangle is isosceles.*

LESSON

Investigations and Demonstrations

Lesson Objective

This lesson provides students with three activities which will help them refine their understanding of congruent triangles and proof.

Content Overview

The three "big" activities will challenge students to investigate, explain, prove, and present results to the class. The activities are rich in opportunities for computer exploration, writing, and making and testing conjectures. Each activity brings together ideas from more than one area of mathematics. All of the activities require students to demonstrate persistence, organization, and understanding of the main ideas in this unit.

Some ways these activities can be used successfully include the following:

- Have each student or group of students report results to the class with a presentation or poster. Use this as a culminating assessment activity.
- Form a computer lab unit that lasts one or two weeks. The unit should consist of those problems which are the most computer-related.

A brief summary of each activity is provided below.

Perpendicular bisectors Students prove the following theorem: "Any point on the perpendicular bisector of a line segment is equidistant from the endpoints of the line segment." Follow-up *On Your Own* problems involve paper folding, constructions, locating the center of a circle, and finding the intersection point of the perpendicular bisectors of sides of a triangle. Constructions work well with or without computers. This is an excellent extension of congruence ideas with connections to circle topics.

Angles and sides in triangles Students prove that the number of congruent angles in a triangle corresponds to the number of congruent sides. Then they investigate inequality relationships in triangles and the hypotenuse-leg congruence theorem.

Isosceles triangle proofs Students study four facts about isosceles triangles and prove that any two of them will prove all the rest. This activity extends understanding of medians, altitudes, and angle bisectors and provides lots of practice with proofs.

Planning Guide

Pacing	Activity	Materials	Homework Suggestions
Day 1	*Explore and Discuss* (SE p. 142)	cutouts of triangles	*On Your Own,* Problems 1 and 4
Day 2	Activity 1: Perpendicular Bisectors (SE p. 142)	• cups, glasses, or cans to trace • geometry software (optional)	*On Your Own,* Problems 2 and 3 *Take It Further,* Problem 15
Day 3	Activity 2: Angles and Sides in Triangles (SE p. 143)	No special materials needed.	*On Your Own,* Problems 6 and 7 *Take It Further,* Problems 16 and 17
Day 4	Activity 2: Angles and Sides in Triangles (SE p. 143)		*On Your Own,* Problems 8 and 9
Day 5	Activity 3: Isosceles Triangle Proofs (SE p. 143)	• compasses • protractors • rulers	*On Your Own,* Problems 5, 10, and 13
Day 6	Activity 3: Isosceles Triangle Proofs (SE p. 143)	• compasses • protractors • rulers	*On Your Own,* Problems 11, 12, and 14

Program Resources

- *Connected Geometry* CD-ROM, Module 2: Investigations 2.11 and 2.12
- *Solution and Problem Solving Resource,* pages 142–151
- *Assessment Resources,* Quiz 4 Lessons 5, 6, and 7, page 51

Preparation and Prerequisites

Students with some background in proving triangles congruent or in working with reflections will find the proofs reasonably easy.

Good hand-drawing tools are necessary for thorough investigations and presentations.

One proof in Activity 3 uses a theorem about angle bisectors that students may not know. (See the *Solution and Problem Solving Resource.*) Plan ahead for how you want to deal with this.

Students should be familiar with the congruence postulates, SSS, SAS, AAS, and ASA, and know the definitions of median, midline, and altitude for triangles. Knowledge of the Midline Theorem and area formulas will also be helpful but can be developed during this lesson.

Teaching the Lesson

Explore and Discuss *(Student page 142)*

Spend time discussing the three bulleted items in *Explore and Discuss* before beginning the activities. Students should be made aware that each activity will take some time to investigate, although each includes only one formal problem and one *Checkpoint* problem.

ACTIVITY 1

Perpendicular Bisectors *(Student page 142)*

Students begin by proving that the points on a perpendicular bisector are equidistant from the endpoints of the bisected segment. With this theorem and its converse proved, students move on to a series of construction problems involving triangles and circles in the *On Your Own* section.

The class session should be organized to include a balance of work time and presentation time.

The activity centers around two main questions:

- What is a perpendicular bisector?
- How do perpendicular bisectors of the sides of triangles behave?

ACTIVITY 2

Angles and Sides in Triangles *(Student page 143)*

This activity begins with a review of a familiar theorem: Triangles with two congruent sides have two congruent angles. The activity moves from this familiar ground into related, but probably new, territory. Students study the relationship between angle size and sidelength in scalene triangles. They may refine their ideas about triangle congruence and a modified SSA postulate in the *Take It Further* problems.

Students should work on this activity in small groups, discussing and sharing results as they work.

ACTIVITY 3

Isosceles Triangle Proofs *(Student page 143)*

In this activity, students study four statements about isosceles triangles and prove that any two of them will prove all the rest. A similar problem involving parallelograms is included in the *Take It Further* section.

This activity works very well as a group activity because the task at hand separates very neatly into manageable parts. The main investigation requires the completion of six proofs. Typically, each student in the group does one of the proofs, and all group members collaborate on the difficult ones.

The directions state, "Show that if any two of the statements are given, the other two statements can be proved." Obviously, the first thing students will have to do is figure out what all of the combinations are. Some students might not realize this and will jump in to do just one proof. Clarify that students must identify all of the combinations before they begin.

On Your Own *(Student pages 144–145)*

These problems provide students with the opportunity for individual practice. See the lesson Planning Guide for homework recommendations.

Take It Further (Student pages 146–147)

You may want to assign different *Take It Further* problems to different groups on the second day of this activity and have them share their results. For example, one group can work on HL congruence, one group on SSA, and one group on SSa.

Options and Extensions

Using Technology

Since the computer will speed up discovery of the major results, emphasize that students should find other new conjectures, explore when and why they are true, and explain all results.

The problems dealing with perpendicular bisectors of the sides of a triangle (Activity 1) are especially suitable for investigation in the computer lab using geometry software. The directions will need slight modification. Something like the following will suffice.

1. Draw a triangle using geometry software. Construct the perpendicular bisectors of all three sides.
2. Stretch your triangle into all different kinds of triangles. Notice that sometimes a perpendicular bisector seems to pass right through a vertex of the triangle. Sometimes more than one perpendicular bisector passes through a vertex. Describe the set of triangles which has exactly
   a. one perpendicular bisector passing through a vertex.
   b. two perpendicular bisectors passing through vertices.
   c. three perpendicular bisectors passing through vertices.
3. Notice that all three perpendicular bisectors meet at a point. Does this always happen? Change the triangle and study this intersection.
4. Depending on what you have found, either prove that the perpendicular bisectors *will* always meet at one point or provide a counterexample.
5. Describe anything else that you have discovered about the perpendicular bisectors of the sides of a triangle, where they meet, how they divide the triangle, and so on.

Alternate strategy: Make this more open. Don't give students the result. Simply ask them to talk about anything else they have discovered about the perpendicular bisectors, justifying their conjectures.

LESSON

Congruence in Quadrilaterals and Beyond

Lesson Objective

Students study the properties of quadrilaterals and the concept of congruence. Once the concept has been established, students extend it to 3-dimensional objects.

Content Overview

This lesson asks students to take their study of congruence one step further, considering questions about shapes that are not triangles, including 3-dimensional shapes. None of the tests developed here will be formalized or used later in the same way as the triangle congruence postulates.

Planning Guide

Pacing	Activity	Materials	Homework Suggestions
Day 1	*Explore and Discuss* (SE p. 148) Activity 1: Families of Quadrilaterals (SE pp. 148–149)	• BLM 20, p. 25 • protractors • rulers	*On Your Own,* Problems 1 and 2
Day 2	Activity 2: To Be Sure or Not to Be Sure . . . (SE pp. 149–150)	No special materials needed.	*On Your Own,* Problem 4
Day 3	Activity 3: Applications of Analysis and Proof (SE p. 150)	• BLM 18, p. 22 • geometry software (optional) • color pencils (optional)	Activity 3, Problem 20 *On Your Own,* Problem 3
Day 4	Activity 4: Proving Congruence for Quadrilaterals (SE pp. 151–152)	No special materials needed.	Activity 4, Problems 29 and 30 *Take It Further,* Problem 13
Day 5	Activity 5: Congruence in Three Dimensions (SE pp. 152–154)	BLM 19A and 19B, pp. 23–24	*On Your Own,* Problems 5–8
Day 6	Activity 5: Congruence in Three Dimensions (SE pp. 152–154)	BLM 19A and 19B, pp. 23–24	*On Your Own,* Problems 9–12

Program Resources

- *Connected Geometry* CD-ROM, Module 2: Investigations 2.13 and 2.14
- *Solution and Problem Solving Resource,* pages 152–168
- *Teacher Resources,* pp. 22–25
- *Assessment Resources,* Quiz 5 Lesson 8, page 52

Preparation and Prerequisites

Prior experience with compass and straightedge construction would be helpful. If a computer lab is available, plan to use it toward the end of this lesson.

Activity 5 assumes that students have a clear understanding of congruence and how we test for congruence in plane figures. Some questions also require a general knowledge of volume and surface area.

Teaching the Lesson

Explore and Discuss *(Student page 148)*

Begin with a short, class discussion and a "show and tell" session about quadrilaterals as they appear in the real world. This session should provide a low-key opportunity to review names and basic definitions.

ACTIVITY 1

Families of Quadrilaterals *(Student pages 148–149)*

Make sure students are doing constructions with exact measurements. Rough, freehand sketches simply won't force students to think about quadrilaterals' properties.

For some classes, providing a chart to check off properties will improve the output from this part of the activity. Place names of quadrilaterals across the top, and place the properties you want students to look for down the side.

Following the discussion, divide students into small groups or pairs to do the constructions. The constructions serve two purposes:

1. They provide a setting for reinforcing definitions. For example, to draw a rhombus you have to understand its main properties.
2. They provide information students will need in order to fully determine a quadrilateral. For example, some of the problems describe a unique figure, and others describe a whole set of possible figures. These problems will prepare students for a later discussion on congruence tests for quadrilaterals.

While students are working on the constructions, they should be keeping track of the properties of each quadrilateral. They will need this information to create the concept map suggested in the *Write and Reflect* problem.

To pull together the final results and encourage group productivity, have groups post their drawings on the bulletin board. Then there will be five or six drawings of each problem all together, ready to compare.

Conduct a discussion which leads to general agreement on which properties are true. Then students can begin working on Problem **11** (proving the properties). There is a huge amount of work here if all properties are proven. Divide the work in some reasonable manner, such as

- assigning each group a small set of proofs,
- proving only selected properties, or
- assigning each group one quadrilateral to work with.

Note that for Problems **1–11,** not everyone defines a trapezoid to be a quadrilateral with *exactly* two sides parallel; some say that a trapezoid should have *at* *least* two sides parallel. This definition lets you consider parallelograms as special cases of trapezoids.

Below are some ways to prove that a quadrilateral is a parallelogram:

- Show that both pairs of opposite sides are congruent.
- Show that one pair of opposite sides is congruent and parallel.
- Show that both pairs of opposite angles are congruent.
- Show that the diagonals bisect each other.

ACTIVITY 2

To Be Sure or Not To Be Sure . . . *(Student pages 149–150)*

The carpenter's door-frame problem and Problems **14–18** could be handled in a teacher-led discussion or by having each group write and present a convincing argument for one of the problems.

ACTIVITY 3

Applications of Analysis and Proof *(Student page 150)*

PROBLEMS 19–24 Work on these problems in the computer lab, if possible. They are challenging, so allow students plenty of time. Each problem might take a full class period. Explain to students that their investigation of the problems should have two phases: making conjectures and then proving the conjectures. After these investigations, students should do presentations (written and/or oral) explaining their conclusions and proofs.

PROBLEM 24 Distribute Blackline Master 18 to students. Encourage them to use color pencils to outline all the quadrilaterals that they find.

ACTIVITY 4

Proving Congruence for Quadrilaterals *(Student pages 151–152)*

Students look for congruence tests that will work for quadrilaterals. Since there are many correct answers to these questions, a major benefit of doing them will come in the debate over whether or not an answer is correct. After an initial full-class discussion, assign small groups to work on Problems **27–29,** which have students creating their own congruence tests. Invite students to present and debate their results.

PROBLEM 27 Note that there are no standard congruence tests for quadrilaterals, as there are for triangles. This problem provides students with an opportunity to explore and discover some results of their own, but there are no set answers that the authors are looking for.

ACTIVITY 5

Congruence in Three Dimensions *(Student pages 152–154)*

The concept of congruence will be well established by the time students reach this activity. Here students test congruence by extending it to 3-dimensional objects. The main themes are familiar:

- What information about two objects is necessary to prove that they are congruent?
- If you know that two objects are congruent, what do you know about the objects?

A set of thought-provoking questions about cubes, cylinders, and pyramids encourages students to exercise habits of mind. Students visualize objects as solids and as *nets* or *developments,* invent congruence tests, and observe what changes occur in a system when one restriction on the system is altered.

Begin this activity with some visualization exercises. Ask students to picture objects and then talk about congruence of the objects. You can use the first seven problems in the *Student Edition* for these visualization exercises, or try one of these:

- Imagine a right triangle. Picture the triangle rotating about one of its sides in such a way that a solid shape is created by the path of the rotation. What shape is formed? Will all of the solids made by rotating your triangle be congruent to each other?
- Picture a rectangular box. You want to pack a cylindrical can in the box so that it fits exactly (meeting the box at all sides). If you could find all of the cans that fit, would they be all congruent to each other?
- Jane has six pieces of cardboard, each of which is exactly the size of a regular sheet of notebook paper. Can she make a cardboard box out of them? *Follow up:* Since the answer is no, now imagine that Jane finds some scissors, but she can borrow them long enough to cut only *two* of the pieces of cardboard. Now she can make a box. But is there more than one shape box she can make?

Assume that Jane also has tape, but no scissors, and that the pieces have to be used whole without folding.

The visualizations should spark discussion about what determines congruence for solid objects. Then move to working on the remaining problems in the *Student Edition*. Students can work in small groups. At the conclusion of class or on the following day, provide presentations of the problems that have multiple solutions (for example, Problems **37** and **40**). You may want to ask: *Assuming that one solid figure has many possible nets, do all of its nets have anything in common? What restrictions are there on all nets for a given solid?*

In the supermarket dairy department, refrigerated pastry rolls are sold in a tube. Check out the way the cylinder unfolds when you open the tube!

PROBLEM 38 If students are having difficulty visualizing how to refold the nets into solid objects, provide them with Blackline Masters 19A and 19B. Encourage students to cut and refold the nets.

On Your Own *(Student pages 154–157)*

These problems provide students with the opportunity for individual practice. See the lesson Planning Guide for homework recommendations.

PROBLEM 2 Blackline Master 20 provides you with a copy of the flow chart.

Take It Further *(Student page 157)*

This problem will lead students in new directions or will challenge them to apply what they already know.

Options and Extensions

Without Technology

In this lesson, the authors suggested that the problems in Activity 3 be done on a computer. If the problems are done without a computer, students will move more directly to a theoretical solution, will probably make fewer conjectures, and will have to be encouraged to really look for counterexamples.

You may want to suggest that students make a number of sketches for each problem before making their final conjectures. For example, Problem **21** asks what type of quadrilateral is formed by connecting the midpoints of a rectangle's sides. On the computer, students can easily stretch a figure into many different-shaped rectangles and see that the inner figure remains a rhombus. Students working with paper drawings should sketch several different-shaped rectangles, trying to find any extreme that might change the apparent result.

Unit 2 Review

This unit review is intended to provide students with problems that will encourage them to look back at the unit as a whole. Students have one more opportunity to pull together, apply, and communicate the ideas they have developed by working on the activities throughout the unit.

It is especially important for students to have the opportunity to share their solutions with the class.

PROBLEM 1 This problem reviews the definition of *congruence.* Encourage students, if they can, to come up with their own definitions. If they cannot, remind them that they can use the one described in Activity 1 or the one the class decided on.

PROBLEM 2 Students may give an informal definition like "Two figures are congruent if one fits exactly on the other" or "Two figures are congruent if all of their parts match." Encourage students to describe tests they could perform like measuring corresponding lengths and angles.

PROBLEM 3 This problem reviews both the triangle congruence postulates and the notion of *included* sides and angles. Students may remember other tests as well, such as HL for right triangles and SSA (where the non-included angle is the largest in the triangle). Students should list ASA, AAS, SSS, and SAS. Included in their descriptions should be what is meant by an *included* side or angle and what the difference is between AAS and ASA. Drawings should show appropriate markings for corresponding sides and angles.

PROBLEM 4 This problem provides students with a refresher on using the congruence postulates in proofs.

You may want to ask different students to prove each of these using a different method—either Paragraph Style, Two Column Statement-Reason, or Outline Style.

a. These triangles can be proved congruent using SAS or SSS. In order to use SSS, you must show that opposite sides of a parallelogram are congruent and that the parallelogram's diagonal is congruent to itself. In order to use SAS, you must show that opposite sides of a parallelogram are congruent and opposite angles ($\angle B$ and $\angle D$) are congruent.

b. Students may jump to the conclusion that the triangles are congruent by AAA because $\angle A$ is congruent to itself. A gentle reminder should be given that AAA is not a congruence theorem but that students shouldn't forget about it because it will be coming up in another unit as a test for similarity.

c. The triangles are congruent by SAS. Students may want to "pull apart" the picture and work with the two triangles separately instead of overlapping. The fact that base angles of isosceles triangles are congruent should be used to show that $\angle A \cong \angle C$.

d. These triangles cannot be proved congruent because the midpoints given are not on congruent sides. In Problem **4c,** $\overline{AE}$, $\overline{EB}$, $\overline{CF}$, and $\overline{FB}$ were all congruent because E and F were midpoints of congruent sides. That is not the case in the figure in Problem **4d.**

e. The triangles are not congruent. In an isosceles triangle, nonbase sides are congruent, so $\overline{BA} \cong \overline{CD}$ and $\overline{BD}$ is congruent to itself. Nothing else, however, can be concluded about this figure.

PROBLEM 5

a. Students may choose to do a paper-and-pencil experiment, or, if you have use of the computer lab on the day you are completing this Unit Review, you may encourage students to investigate this problem with geometry software.

b. The altitudes of an equilateral triangle are congruent. This can be proved by showing that a series of three triangles is congruent by SAS (using the fact that equilateral triangles are equiangular).

c. If geometry software is available, this is a good problem to investigate on the computer.

d. Make a list of conjectures made by students and present them to the class. Ask individual students to explain their conjectures and proofs if possible.

PROBLEM 6 This problem reviews the fact that the sum of the measures of the angles in a triangle is 180°. Students must use the fact three times on three different triangles to solve the problem. Students will find that $x = 30$, $y = 90$, and $z = 60$.

PROBLEM 7 This problem reminds students that they can test figures besides triangles for congruence and asks them to recall one such test. SASAS is one possible congruence test for quadrilaterals—three consecutive sides along with the two included angles. ASASA is another congruence test for quadrilaterals.

UNIT 3

The Cutting Edge
Investigations in Dissections and Area

Unit Overview

This problem-based unit focuses on the mathematical topics of area and perimeter, dissection, and the Pythagorean Theorem. You will notice that the notes in this guide often refer to specific problems and the outcomes from students' investigations of them. The habits of mind focused on in this unit include algorithmic thinking, explaining and proving, and using formal and informal mathematical language to describe things.

Dissections and writing dissection algorithms provide a context for students to learn about area and perimeter and to get some more experience with proofs. Students who complete this unit will gain extensive experience in using the Pythagorean Theorem and will develop both an algebraic and a geometric understanding of the theorem. Several dissection and area proofs of the theorem are provided.

Learning Goals

1. Read, write, and *debug* algorithms.
2. Develop problem solving skills, especially mixing deduction with experimentation.
3. Understand the proof and application of the Pythagorean Theorem.

4. Improve visualization skills in both two and three dimensions.
5. Understand how area formulas are related properties of figures and develop a method to find the area of a polygon by using dissection.
6. Use geometric vocabulary correctly in proofs and explanations, including the following terms: bisect, perpendicular, altitude, median, midline, parallel, parallelogram, rectangle, square, rhombus, isosceles, equilateral, scalene, perpendicular bisector, tetrahedron, and cube.
7. Demonstrate knowledge of dissection, area, and polygonal figures.

Assessment Opportunities

Quizzes and Informal Assessment

- If this is your students' first exposure to the Pythagorean Theorem, assign more practice problems for homework.
- If the area formulas themselves are an important component in your curriculum, assign homework that requires using the formulas in calculation.
- Encourage students to use the script feature of the geometry software being used in class, and have them read and write dissection algorithms in the form of scripts.

Journal Ideas

This unit is unique in that students will be writing, revisiting, and refining algorithms. They will use these algorithms to discover area formulas. If your students keep a journal, they should write the algorithms in their journals and include refinements (and why they were necessary). These include:

- Lesson 1, Problems 1–5
- Lesson 2, Problems 2, 5, and 8
- Lesson 3, Problems 3, 7, and 10

In addition to these problems, there are numerous *Write and Reflect* and other problems throughout the unit that are appropriate for journal writing. Possible assignments:

- Lesson 1, *Write and Reflect,* Problems 7 and 12
- Lesson 1, *On Your Own,* Problem 11
- Lesson 1, *Take It Further,* Problem 14
- Lesson 2, Problems 10–12
- Lesson 3, *Write and Reflect,* Problems 12 and 19
- Lesson 4, Problem 5
- Lesson 5, Problems 4 and 6 and any proof from Activity 2
- Lesson 5, *Take It Further,* Problem 26
- Lesson 6, Problem 18

UNIT 3 Planning Guide

Lessons	Learning Goals	Assessment Opportunities	Suggested Pacing	Materials
LESSON 1 *Cut and Rearrange*	1, 2, 4, 7	*Checkpoint,* Problems 6 and 15	4 days	• BLM 21, p. 26 • BLM 22A–22E, pp. 27–31 • BLM 23, p. 32 • scissors • rulers • paper
LESSON 2 *Cutting Algorithms*	1, 2, 4, 6, 7	*Checkpoint,* Problems 5, 9, and 13 Quiz 1, *Assessment Resources,* p. 85	3 days	• scissors • rulers • paper
LESSON 3 *Area Formulas*	2, 5, 6, 7	*Checkpoint,* Problems 4, 8, 11, and 20 Quiz 2, *Assessment Resources,* p. 86 Mid-Unit Exam, *Assessment Resources,* pp. 88–96	4 days	• scissors • rulers • paper • compasses • tape
LESSON 4 *The Midline Theorem*	2, 4, 6	*Checkpoint,* Problem 6	2 days	• scissors • rulers • paper
LESSON 5 *The Pythagorean Theorem*	3, 4, 6, 7	*Checkpoint,* Problems 7 and 8	4 days	• BLM 24, p. 33 • prepared transparencies • scissors • rulers • paper
LESSON 6 *Analyzing Dissections*	2, 4, 5, 6, 7	*Checkpoint,* Problems 10 and 18 Quiz 3, *Assessment Resources,* p. 87	4 days	• BLM 25, p. 34 • paper • scissors • rulers • tape
UNIT 3 REVIEW		End-of-Unit Exam, *Assessment Resources,* pp. 97–102	2 days (including testing)	BLM 26, p. 35

LESSON

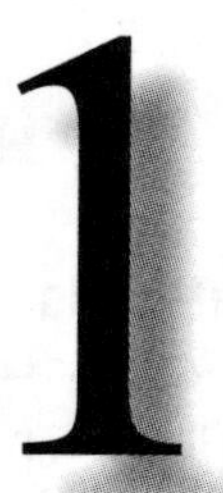

Cut and Rearrange

Lesson Objective

In this lesson, students solve dissection problems like the following: "Cut up a triangle and rearrange the pieces to form a rectangle."

Content Overview

To a casual visitor, the classroom might seem to be full of art students making collages. But, as the problems are solved and explained, the mathematics involved becomes clear and extensive.

To defend their solutions, students will need to understand properties of parallelograms, kites, trapezoids, rectangles, rhombi, and squares; and to develop general classifications for triangles and quadrilaterals. Ideas emerging will include the following: the concept of a relation, measure as a geometric invariant, dissection, and a relation called *scissors-congruent* which is equivalent to "has the same area as."

The novelty of the problems encourages students to develop new problem-solving strategies and habits of mind. These include using proof as a research technique and a method of persuasion, using algorithms as arguments, and using argument as a method for refining ideas.

Planning Guide

Pacing	Activity	Materials	Homework Suggestions
Day 1	*Explore and Discuss* (SE pp. 162–163) Activity 1: Some Cutting Problems (SE p. 164)	• BLM 21, p. 26 • BLM 22A–22E, pp. 27–31 • scissors • paper • rulers	Activity 1, Problem 3
Day 2	Activity 1: Some Cutting Problems (SE p. 164)	• BLM 22A–22E, pp. 27–31 • scissors • paper • rulers	*On Your Own,* Problems 1, 2, and 3
Day 3	Activity 2: Do the Cuts Really Work? (SE pp. 164–168)	• scissors • paper • rulers	*On Your Own,* Problems 4–7

Day 4	Activity 2: Do the Cuts Really Work? (SE pp. 164–168)	• BLM 23, p. 32 • scissors • paper • rulers	*On Your Own,* Problems 8–12

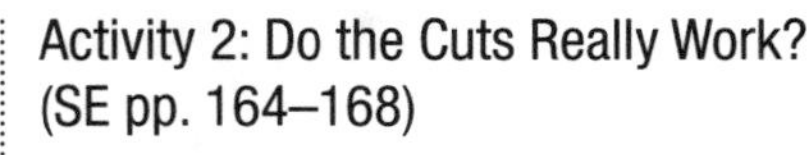

Program Resources

- *Connected Geometry* CD-ROM, Module 3: Investigations 3.1, 3.2, and 3.7
- *Solution and Problem Solving Resource,* pages 173–190
- *Teaching Resources,* pages 26–32

Preparation and Prerequisites

Hint: If the original copy of each figure is on colored paper and all of the cutting is done with figure on white paper, then students will never lose the original or accidentally cut it up.

Each student or group must have scissors, straightedges, and a supply of paper for cutting. Copies of the figures found on Blackline Masters 22A–22E can be made ahead or drawn by students but must be provided in some form that actually allows for cutting. You may want to make an overhead transparency of each figure to facilitate student explanations.

In the Student Edition, the term *scissors-congruent* is defined as follows:

> Figure *A* is *scissors-congruent* to figure *B* if *A* can be cut up and the pieces rearranged to form figure *B*.

One class chose to use *covers* instead of *scissors-congruent* because students felt that it better described the test they were performing. The authors chose not to use *covers* in the *Student Edition* because it has other mathematical meanings, but they encourage teachers to discuss with students possible names for this relation and to support their efforts at making definitions and inventing language to describe mathematical ideas.

The first day can be very frustrating to many students who don't know how to do these problems. But by day 2 or 3, there is usually plenty of success.

Below are some things to remember as you are teaching this lesson:

- Many students will have no idea how to do the problems, and they may begin by cutting almost randomly or with very awkward strategies. Don't give too many hints. The struggle pays off.
- Remind students that they must use all of the cut-up pieces in making the new shape so that the two figures are *scissors-congruent.*
- While students are working in groups, ask a lot of questions: "What do you think might work?" "How do you know that idea won't work?" "How do you know the shape you made is really a rectangle?" "Why did you make the cut right there?"
- At this point, if the solutions work for the particular figure in the problem, they should be considered correct. In the next lesson, students will be formalizing their solutions from this lesson into general methods that will work in all cases.

Teaching the Lesson

All of the problems in this lesson involve cutting and rearranging geometric shapes to produce other shapes that are equal in area. The relation "equal in area" is a theme that dominates the remainder of the unit, so it is important to have an initial discussion of what it means, as well as some agreement by the class about what term students will use to describe it.

Explore and Discuss (Student pages 162–163)

Distribute Blackline Master 21 to students. They can cut out the two right triangles and the square (make sure the sides of the right triangles are the same length as the sides of the square) or use the three pieces from a tangram set (see "Resources"). They can physically do the flips, slides, and rotations pictured in the demonstration and then use similar moves to solve the transformation problems presented. To preview some of the ideas coming later in the unit, you might ask students about the areas of the figures shown in the *Student Edition*. "Of the four figures (shown i–iv), which has the most area?" After some thinking, the class should conclude that shapes made of the same pieces have the same area, no matter how those pieces are arranged.

ACTIVITY 1

Some Cutting Problems (Student page 164)

Students are likely to come up with a variety of different and creative solutions for each of these problems. Be sure to ask, "Did anyone do the problem in a different way?"

Divide the class into groups to work on the first problem, the cutting of a parallelogram into a *scissors-congruent* rectangle. The groups are likely to produce several good solutions to this problem fairly quickly. Have a few students share their solutions with the class. Cutouts can be placed directly on the overhead projector. Once they are reassured that *these unusual problems* really do have solutions and that there can be more than one right answer, students should return to group work and try more problems.

The amount of time it takes to do the rest of the problems can vary greatly from class to class. It might take some classes a whole period to be successful with the first problem. One teacher spent a full day on each cutting problem, taking nearly two weeks to complete this activity. She reported that it was a highly successful activity, though, because her students felt a sense of accomplishment with their growing competence and because they learned so much mathematics as they were working.

ACTIVITY 2

Do the Cuts Really Work? (Student pages 164–168)

When students are presenting their solutions to the class, have them describe their method of solving each problem and explain *why* it works. Steer them away from vague statements, such as "It looked right."

Students may say, "I cut in the middle . . ." when explaining their solutions. You can ask clarifying questions like, "What do you mean by 'middle'? Do you mean at the midpoint?" Soon, the correct vocabulary will become a part of the classroom culture for explaining solutions. Students will learn to communicate more clearly in order for you to understand them and for them to understand each other.

On Your Own (Student pages 168–170)

These problems provide students with the opportunity for individual practice.

PROBLEM 1 This problem, the division of a trapezoid into a triangle of equal area, presents a good opportunity for discussing and reviewing the median, midline, altitude, and angle bisector. As students provide explanations, encourage correct use of terminology, and ask them to prove some of their results.

Take It Further (Student page 171)

These problems will lead students in new directions or will challenge them to apply what they already know.

Options and Extensions

The original article was Margaret Biggerstaff, Barb Halloran, and Carolyn Serrano, "Teacher to Teacher: Use Color to Assess Mathematics Problem Solving." Arithmetic Teacher *41 (February 1994), pp. 307–308.*

Teacher-to-Teacher

Carol Martignette-Boswell, a teacher from Arlington, MA, decided to adapt an assessment technique from NCTM's journal *Arithmetic Teacher* and incorporate peer assessment while working through this unit. After a group of students presented a solution to a cutting problem, the other groups rated the presentation using colored index cards, each of which had criteria written on the back:

WHITE CARD: 0 points. Incorrect solutions with no explanation.

- Unable to cut the pieces and complete a rearrangement.
- Unable to use mathematical language to give dimensions of the new shape in terms of the original shape.
- Unable to describe the process used to make the rearrangement.
- Unable to present an argument.

GREEN CARD: 1 point. Started on a solution but used an unsuitable strategy.

- Able to cut the pieces and make a rearrangement.
- Unable to use mathematical language to give dimensions of the new shape in terms of the original shape.
- Unable to describe the process used to make the rearrangement.
- Unable to present an argument.

YELLOW CARD: 2 points. Used a reasonable strategy but did not finish or reach a solution.

- Able to cut the pieces and complete the rearrangement.
- Used some mathematical language to give dimensions of the new shape in terms of the original shape.
- Unable to describe the process used to make the rearrangement.
- Unable to present an argument.

RED CARD: 3 points. Used a reasonable strategy to reach the correct solution but gave an unclear explanation.

- Able to cut the pieces and complete the rearrangement.
- Able to use mathematical language to give dimensions of the new shape in terms of the original shape.
- Able to describe the process used to make the rearrangement.
- Unable to present an argument.

BLUE CARD: 4 points. Used a reasonable strategy to reach a correct solution and gave a clear explanation.

- Able to cut the pieces and complete the rearrangement.
- Able to use mathematical language to give dimensions of the new shape in terms of the original shape.
- Able to describe the process used to make the rearrangement.
- Able to present an argument.

Of course there were discrepancies in the scoring, but not once did one group score a presentation "white" and another group score it "blue." The students found that they really *did* know what was needed to make a good explanation.

Resources

If tangrams are available, you may want to allow students to use them while exploring these transformations. Also refer to the Historical Perspective "A History of the Tangram" in the *Connected Geometry* CD-ROM, Module 3: Investigation 3.1.

LESSON

Cutting Algorithms

Lesson Objective

Students create reliable algorithms for dissecting any parallelogram into a rectangle, any triangle into a rectangle, and any trapezoid into a rectangle.

Content Overview

In the previous lesson, students were exploring, looking for solutions, and defending conjectures. The outcome was a reasonable explanation for a correct dissection of a particular figure. In this lesson, the emphasis shifts to algorithmic thinking, systematic testing, critical methods of analysis, and deductive reasoning. The outcome will be general algorithms which describe correct dissections for various types of problems.

Three main threads run through this lesson:

- understanding what algorithms are and learning to write them;
- understanding what is meant by a *standard* case and an *extreme* case and how these apply to the testing of algorithms; and
- continued exploration of area and of the determining properties of polygons.

This lesson aims to help students become more sophisticated in their understanding of the rigor involved in classifying shapes and in distinguishing between the general and the specific case.

Planning Guide

Pacing	Activity	Materials	Homework Suggestions
Day 1	*Explore and Discuss* (SE p. 172) Activity 1: Describing the Steps (SE pp. 172–173)	No special materials needed.	*On Your Own,* Problems 1, 2, and 3
Day 2	Activity 2: Checking an Algorithm (SE pp. 174–176)	• scissors • paper • rulers	*On Your Own,* Problems 8, 9, and 10 Perspective: Grace Murray Hopper
Day 3	Activity 3: Justifying the Cuts (SE p. 177)	No special materials needed.	*On Your Own,* Problems 4, 5, 6, 7, and 11

Program Resources

- *Connected Geometry* CD-ROM, Module 3: Investigation 3.3
- *Solution and Problem Solving Resource,* pages 191–198
- *Assessment Resources,* Quiz 1 Lessons 1 and 2, page 85

Preparation and Prerequisites

Students need to have completed the problems from Lesson 1. Be sure students bring to class their solution notes and the list of properties of rectangles that they developed in Lesson 1.

Teaching the Lesson

Students might be more familiar with other words for this idea, such as "recipe," "instructions," or "step-by-step plan."

Explore and Discuss *(Student page 172)*

Start the lesson by asking students the following question: "What is an algorithm?" Students have had a lot of experience with algorithms and can probably offer many good examples once they understand the meaning of the word.

ACTIVITY 1

Describing the Steps *(Student pages 172–173)*

Students are asked to write three algorithms, test them, rewrite them, discuss them, and then rewrite the algorithms one last time. To save time, consider switching from individual to group work after Problems **3** and **4,** and assign each group *one* of the algorithms to process through the next stages of discussion and writing.

Many students have had little experience with the sort of rigorous thinking required in this lesson. Such students may be content accepting a good solution for one case as a suitable solution for all cases that look vaguely similar in their eyes.

PROBLEM 5 You may want to assign each group or pair of students a different dissection and then have groups or pairs share their algorithms with the class.

ACTIVITY 2

Checking an Algorithm *(Student pages 174–176)*

There are at least two natural approaches to use when trying to find a special case or counterexample. One is to study the given algorithm and see if you can find places where it might break down. This approach works well for Problem **6;** you can see in the given picture that the altitude must bisect the opposite side, and you can ask yourself if that is, in fact, true.

Another approach is to study some extreme figures, not the standard ones you normally imagine. For example, in Problem **7,** you can begin by drawing many different types of parallelograms, being sure to include some oddly-shaped ones. It is these unusual figures that might cause an algorithm to fail. For this reason, it is important for students to keep these figures in mind as they write their own algorithms.

For Discussion (Student page 176)

By definition, a trapezoid is just a quadrilateral with exactly one pair of parallel sides. Most people imagine a trapezoid looking like this:

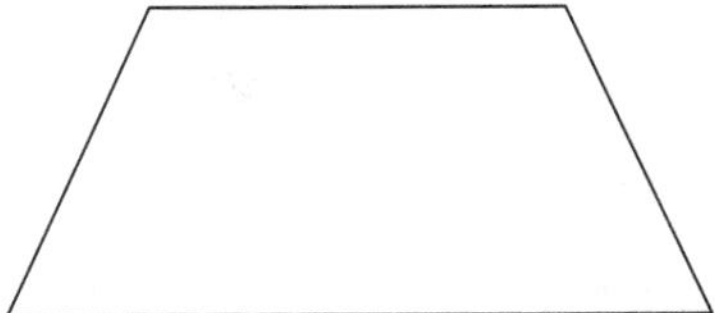

The following figures are also trapezoids, even though they are nonstandard:

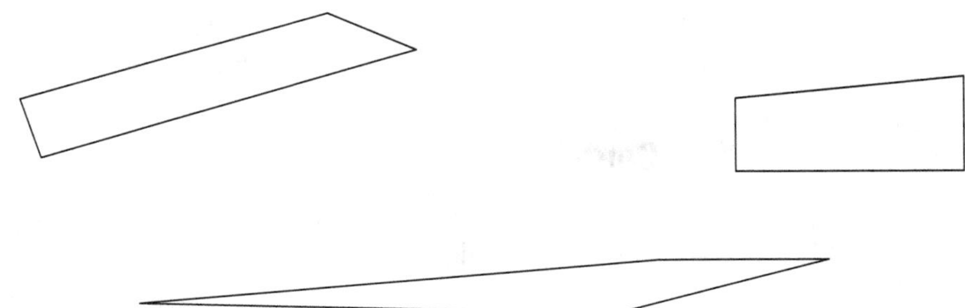

See the "Using Technology" section below for suggestions on extending this activity.

On Your Own (Student page 178)

These problems provide students with the opportunity for individual practice. See the lesson Planning Guide for homework recommendations.

Options and Extensions

Using Technology

The main focus of this lesson is on writing and checking algorithms, something computer programmers do all day long. To redirect this activity into the computer lab, use Lesson 2 as an opportunity to teach students how to use the *script* feature of the geometry software being used in class. Then have students read and write dissection algorithms in the form of scripts. For example, you can assign students the following:

- Write and test a script that will dissect a given parallelogram and rearrange the parts into a rectangle.
- Study a script that is already written; then imagine and draw the construction you think it will make. Compare your drawing to what the script actually does on the computer.

A script or macro is a list of instructions saved on the computer. If you "play the script" or "run the macro," the computer will carry out the full list of instructions.

Writing algorithms (programs) in Logo also makes sense. For example:

- Write a Logo program that will construct a trapezoid or parallelogram. Explain why it produces a figure with all of the correct properties.
- Write a Logo program that will draw a parallelogram that is marked with the cutting lines needed to dissect it into a *scissors-congruent* rectangle. Explain why the Logo commands produce the correct dissection marks.

LESSON

Area Formulas

Lesson Objective

This lesson is designed to help students develop their own area formulas for parallelograms, triangles, trapezoids, and circles from their cutting algorithms.

Content Overview

If students' past experience with formulas has been memorization and application, this lesson could be a real "Aha!" experience. One student exclaimed, "So *that's* where the formula came from!"

In Lesson 2, students found ways to take a triangle and make it into a rectangle. They formalized the cuts and rearranged them into algorithms and then explained why the algorithms worked. In this lesson, students will compare the dimensions of the triangle to its *scissors-congruent* rectangle, expressing the dimensions of the rectangle in terms of the base and height of the triangle. The area formula for the triangle emerges as students express the area of the *scissors-congruent* rectangle: If the triangle's base is b and height is h, then the rectangle's base is b and its height is $\frac{1}{2}h$, giving both figures the area $\frac{1}{2}bh$.

Planning Guide

Pacing	Activity	Materials	Homework Suggestions
Day 1	*Explore and Discuss* (SE p. 180) Activity 1: Parallelograms (SE pp. 180–181)	• scissors • paper • rulers	*On Your Own,* Problems 5 and 6 *Take It Further,* Problems 13, 20, and 21
Day 2	Activity 2: Triangles (SE pp. 181–182)	• scissors • paper • rulers	*On Your Own,* Problems 1–4 *Take It Further,* Problems 12, 14, and 19
Day 3	Activity 3: Trapezoids (SE pp. 183–184)	• scissors • paper • rulers	*On Your Own,* Problems 8–11 *Take It Further,* Problems 15, 16, and 17
Day 4	Activity 4: Circles (SE pp. 184–186)	• scissors • paper • rulers • compasses • tape	*On Your Own,* Problem 7 *Take It Further,* Problem 18

Program Resources

- *Connected Geometry* CD-ROM, Module 3: Investigation 3.4
- *Solution and Problem Solving Resource,* pages 199–209
- *Assessment Resources,* Quiz 2 Lesson 3, page 86

Preparation and Prerequisites

Completion of Lesson 2 is necessary for understanding this lesson because students will use the algorithms they have developed to create their own area formulas.

The area formulas developed here all depend on students' knowledge of the fact that the area of a rectangle is base × height or length × width.

Teaching the Lesson

In this lesson, students are asked to assign variables to represent the base(s) and height of an uncut figure (a triangle, parallelogram, or trapezoid), to cut and rearrange the figure into a rectangle, and then to express the base and height of the rectangle in terms of the dimensions of the original uncut figure. These tasks require a degree of abstraction that may be confusing and difficult for some students. Plan your teaching accordingly.

Explore and Discuss *(Student page 180)*

Students should explore the idea of an array of 1 × 1 units. They should also understand that a 3 × 4 rectangle is the same as a 4 × 3 rectangle because one is just a rotation of the other.

ACTIVITY 1

Parallelograms *(Student pages 180–181)*

The first of four area formulas developed from dissections is introduced in this activity. It might be a good idea to work on this first one as a class so that the thinking process is modeled for students who might find various steps—like assigning variables to the appropriate quantities—confusing on their own. First, as a class, work through the development of a formula for the area of a parallelogram using one of the cutting algorithms that your class developed. Then ask students to work, alone or in groups, to reconstruct the argument on their own, perhaps in a journal.

ACTIVITY 2

Triangles *(Student pages 181–182)*

This lesson contains a mathematically shaky definition of *altitude,* both for triangles and trapezoids. The fact that most triangles have three different altitudes makes wording a definition awkward, so the student materials are written to be more clear but less precise. You can decide if this imprecision is a problem for your class. If so, you can develop a more precise definition if you wish.

ACTIVITY 3 Trapezoids *(Student pages 183–184)*

There are many trapezoid dissections, some of which make for easier area formulas than others. The following dissection, while elegant, makes the area formula difficult because you are not sure about the length of the base of the rectangle.

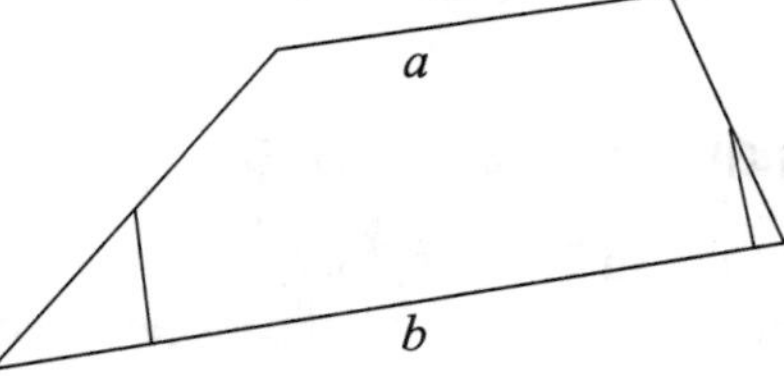

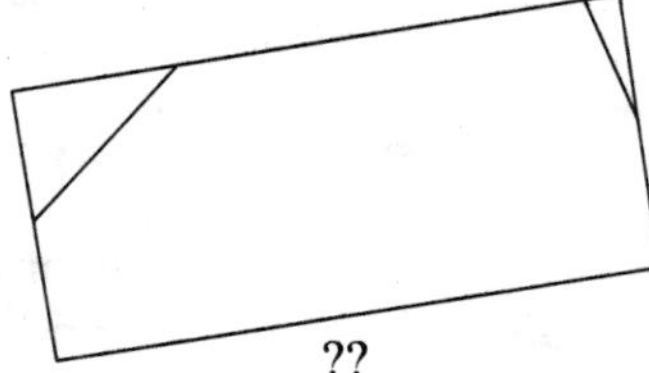

However, turning the trapezoid into either a triangle with base $a + b$ and height h or a parallelogram with base $a + b$ and height $\frac{1}{2}h$ will lead students more quickly to a formula.

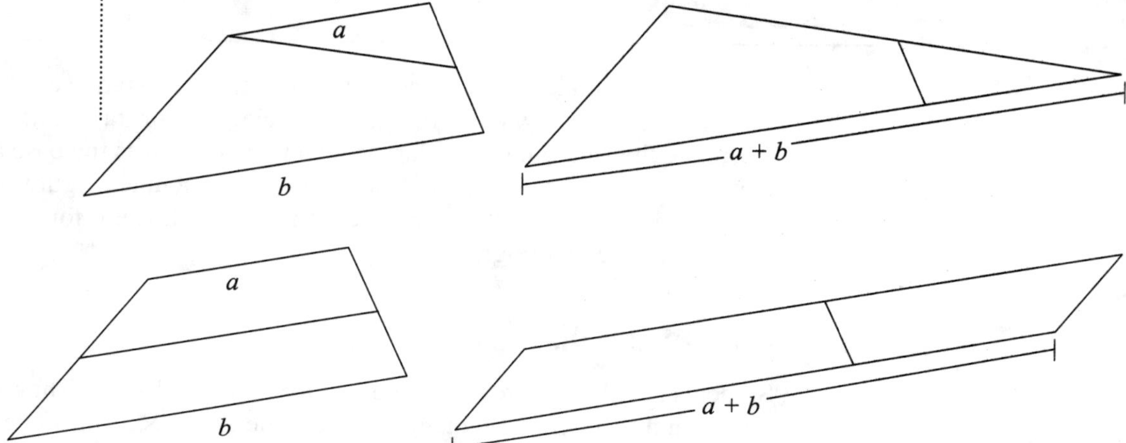

ACTIVITY 4 Circles *(Student pages 184–186)*

The area formula for a circle is formalized in Unit 4. For now, have students participate in the discussion about their "almost" rectangles, and encourage them to develop a formula from there.

For Discussion *(Student page 184)*

It is not possible to dissect a circle into a rectangle in a finite number of cuts because circles are not made up of line segments. You will see below that you can dissect a circle into figures that are *almost* rectangles, but they will always have some edges that consist of arcs, not line segments.

For Discussion *(Student page 186)*

The lengths of the sides of the various shapes are precisely $\frac{1}{2}C$ and r. Moreover, the number π is defined precisely; it is the ratio of C to r. This argument is weak when one makes the jump from the scalloped shapes to the rectangle. This step requires a bit of justification.

The problem doesn't have to end here. You can come back later to try to improve your argument, perhaps after learning more mathematics.

On the other hand, the argument is convincing, and it provides you with some insight. Even if you are not completely convinced of its validity, you at least have some knowledge of where the area formula for a circle comes from.

On Your Own (*Student pages 187–189*)

These problems provide students with the opportunity for individual practice. See the lesson Planning Guide for homework recommendations.

Take It Further (*Student pages 189–192*)

Problem **15** requires students to realize that the equal distances mentioned represent the altitudes of the two triangles. These altitudes are not shown in the drawing. Note that point P is arbitrary, and BP and SP are not necessarily equal. The triangles share base $\overline{DP}$.

Options and Extensions

Using Technology

Problem **7** from *On Your Own* can be done on the computer. The directions printed in the *Student Edition* are still suitable for computer work. Students will simply use geometry software to experiment, to verify which statements *appear* to be true, and to construct counterexamples for the false statements. If this problem is done in the computer lab, you might want students to present their solutions on the computer rather than in writing.

Problem **19** from *Take It Further* can also be done with computer software. Students can create a triangle and then find a way to move one vertex without changing the area. Ask students to describe what shape the vertex traces out and how that connects to their area formula.

LESSON

The Midline Theorem

Lesson Objective

The purpose of this lesson is to build a formal proof of the Midline Theorem. In doing so, students will have the opportunity to use the skills they have developed while studying congruence and proof.

Content Overview

Cutting along midlines is one of the most popular techniques for solving the dissection problems in the previous lesson. Students quickly discover the simplicity of solutions that use these cuts. They have probably become familiar with the Midline Theorem even if they haven't named it or proved it yet.

Planning Guide

Pacing	Activity	Materials	Homework Suggestions
Day 1	*Explore and Discuss* (SE p. 193) Activity: Proving the Midline Theorem (SE p. 194)	• scissors • paper • rulers	*On Your Own,* Problems 4–7
Day 2	Activity: Proving the Midline Theorem (SE p. 194)	• scissors • paper • rulers	*On Your Own,* Problems 1, 2, 3, and 8 *Take It Further,* Problem 9

Program Resources

- *Connected Geometry* CD-ROM, Module 3: Investigation 3.5
- *Solution and Problem Solving Resource,* pages 210–212

Preparation and Prerequisites

Students may need to be reminded of the ways to prove that a quadrilateral is a parallelogram.

Students should have some experience creating congruent triangle proofs and have knowledge of the basic properties of parallelograms and parallel lines.

Teaching the Lesson

Explore and Discuss (Student page 193)

Begin this lesson with a review of the dissection pictured in the *Explore and Discuss* and a clarification of the following student statement: "The midline is half as long as the base."

ACTIVITY

Proving the Midline Theorem (Student page 194)

PROBLEM 1 Students, working in small groups, should explore midlines, as indicated in the *Write and Reflect* question, and explain to the class how they investigated the problem. The class can then move to the development of the formal proof as outlined in the text. For many classes, this is best done as a full class discussion, with the proof emerging on the chalkboard or overhead projector.

An interesting discussion should ensue if you say, "The midline is half as long as the third side of the triangle. What if we created 'tri-lines' by connecting trisection points on the sides of a triangle? What is the relationship of the tri-line length to the length of the base of a triangle?"

On Your Own (Student pages 195–196)

These problems provide students with the opportunity for individual practice. See the lesson Planning Guide for homework recommendations.

Take It Further (Student page 196)

These problems will lead students in new directions or will challenge them to apply what they already know.

Options and Extensions

Using Technology

If your class has access to computers, allow students to explore triangle midlines on the computer using geometry software. Use directions, such as the following:

1. Draw a triangle. Draw a midline segment by connecting the midpoints of two sides of the triangle.
2. Measure the length of the midline, the length of the third side of the triangle, and all the angles.
3. Stretch the triangle into all different sizes and shapes. Observe what happens to the measurements you made. Does the midline *always* measure half the base?
4. What other invariants can you find in this situation?

Problem **9** from *Take It Further* makes for an even more exciting computer lab exploration. In fact, the investigation of midlines in quadrilaterals should be done on the computer, if at all possible. The constructions are not difficult; there are a lot of possible conjectures students can make, and their knowledge of triangle midlines should give them some intuition about what to look for in the quadrilateral situations.

LESSON

The Pythagorean Theorem

Lesson Objective

Students explore and explain dissection proofs of the Pythagorean Theorem.

Content Overview

This varied problem set includes numerous examples involving calculation, searching for patterns, Pythagorean triples, and the distance formula. After this lesson, a short historical essay describes the secret society of Pythagoreans.

Planning Guide

Pacing	Activity	Materials	Homework Suggestions
Day 1	*Explore and Discuss* (SE p. 198)	transparencies of proof	*On Your Own,* Problems 3–9,
Day 2	Activity 1: A Dissection Proof (SE pp. 198–201)	• scissors • paper • rulers • transparencies	*On Your Own,* Problems 10–14
Day 3	Activity 1: A Dissection Proof (SE pp. 198–201)	• scissors • paper • rulers	*On Your Own,* Problems 1, 2, 15, 16, 17, and 18
Day 4	Activity 2: Pick-a-Proof (SE pp. 201–203)	BLM 24, p. 33	*On Your Own,* Problems 19–24 *Take It Further,* Problem 25

Program Resources

- *Connected Geometry* CD-ROM, Module 3: Investigations 3.6 and 3.12
- *Solution and Problem Solving Resource,* pages 213–230
- *Teaching Resources,* page 33

Preparation and Prerequisites

To perform calculations using the Pythagorean Theorem, students will need to have some experience with square roots. The distance formula problems assume basic knowledge of the x-y coordinate plane, but these problems can be skipped if your students have no experience yet with coordinates.

This lesson centers around a dissection proof of the Pythagorean Theorem. Prepare in advance an overhead transparency of this proof and the Bhāskara proof in order to facilitate class discussion and explanation. Study the problem set in advance to decide which topics are important and how much time you want to devote to each.

Teaching the Lesson

The Pythagorean Theorem is certainly one of the major concepts in high school mathematics. It is presented here because it is demonstrated so beautifully by dissection proof. One such proof is explained in detail in the text, and others are presented later in this unit in Activity 2.

Explore and Discuss *(Student page 198)*

Lead a discussion about how the Bhāskara proof proves the Pythagorean Theorem.

ACTIVITY 1

A Dissection Proof *(Student pages 198–201)*

Use an overhead transparency that shows the shaded squares. Ask a student to identify and label those segments which are length *a,* length *b,* and length *c.*

Focus the class discussion on reading and explaining the dissection proof. Students can work with a partner or in small groups to read and understand the proof. When you think they have figured it out, allow one or more students to explain the proof to the class.

ACTIVITY 2

Pick-a-Proof *(Student pages 201–203)*

Assign one of the proofs to each student or group. Give students ample time to work through and write up the proof. Class presentations of the proofs are appropriate as informal assessments.

Blackline Master 24 can be used with Problem 8.

On Your Own *(Student pages 203–207)*

These problems provide students with the opportunity for individual practice.

PROBLEMS 8, 13, AND 14 These problems ask students to look for patterns. The patterns are obvious only if students express the lengths in radical form. If students are not familiar with simplified radicals, suggest that they look for patterns in the squared sidelengths.

Take It Further *(Student pages 208–209)*

These problems will lead students in new directions or will challenge them to apply what they already know.

Options and Extensions

Using Technology

PROBLEM 27 This problem is quite successful as a computer exercise. The constructions are not difficult if students have had some previous experience with geometry software. Below are some sample questions to ask (directions follow):

In this lesson, there is a picture proof of the Pythagorean Theorem showing a right triangle with a square constructed on each side. Have you ever wondered whether those absolutely *had* to be squares? If they were semicircles or some other polygon, would the areas of the two smaller ones still add up to the area of the biggest one? Use geometry software to investigate.

1. Construct a right triangle using geometry software.
2. On each side of the right triangle, construct a semicircle. Make sure that the diameter of the semicircle is the same as the length of the side of the right triangle.
3. Now calculate the areas of the three semicircles. What is their relationship?
4. Investigate what happens if you construct equilateral triangles on all three sides of the right triangle. How about rectangles? Unusually shaped polygons?
5. Can the Pythagorean Theorem be "unsquared"? Prepare a written summary of what you have found, with drawings to illustrate your work.
6. For an extra challenge, include an algebraic explanation of your findings.

Tell students: "You may have to leave the whole circle showing in the sketch." Some software won't hide half the circle.

Be sure to explain any rules that determine which shapes work.

Resources

The following sources were consulted in researching the Perspective essay on the Pythagorean Theorem and the Pythagorean Society. Students who want to learn more about these topics may wish to do some reading from these sources.

- Calinger, Ronald. *Vita Mathematica: Historical Research and Integration with Teaching.* (MAA Notes) The Mathematical Association of America, 1997.
- Eves, Howard. *An Introduction to the History of Mathematics,* 4th ed. Holt, Rinehart & Winston, 1990.
- Kline, Morris. *Mathematics in Western Culture.* Oxford University Press, 1964.
- "Past Present (we)—Present Future (you)." Association for Women in Mathematics Newsletter 9(6), Nov/Dec 1979, 11–17.
- Russell, Bertrand. *History of Western Philosophy.* Simon and Schuster, 1975.

Mathematics Connections

The search for *Pythagorean triples,* integers that can be lengths of the three sides of a right triangle, leads to surprising applications of both the algebra of Gaussian integers and the algebra of points on the plane with rational coordinates.

But this is just the beginning. The general question, "Can you find a geometric figure that has some collection of specified parts whose measures are in a particular algebraic system?" leads to some fascinating algebraic questions. This "Diophantine geometry" is concerned with questions like the ones below.

1. Can you find points A, B, and C on the plane with integer coordinates so that $\triangle ABC$ has integer sidelengths?

What if you insist that the triangle has no horizontal or vertical sides and is not a right triangle?

2. Which integers are areas of right triangles whose sidelengths are rational numbers?
3. Are there any scalene triangles with integer sidelengths and a 60° angle?
4. Are there any scalene triangles with integer sidelengths and integer area?

Are there any scalene triangles with rational side lengths and rational area?

These questions all sound alike, but, as is typical in algebra, some are quite simple to solve and some are amazingly difficult. Question 2 remains an open problem, although significant progress has been made in the last two decades.

Not surprisingly, there are some coherent methods from algebra that can be used to investigate problems like these; in this section, you will look at two such methods, "norm equations" and "secants and conics."

Finding Pythagorean triples amounts to finding triples of integers (a, b, c) so that $a^2 + b^2 = c^2$. If you are thinking "Gaussian integers," the form $a^2 + b^2$ should look familiar. It is the *norm* of the Gaussian integer $a + bi$. Just to refresh your memory, here are the relevant definitions and properties:

. . . but were afraid to ask.

All you ever wanted to know about conjugation and Norm.

1. If $z = a + bi$ is a Gaussian integer, the "complex conjugate" of z, written $\bar{z}$, is defined by $\bar{z} = a - bi$.
2. Using this definition, the following properties of conjugation hold:
   a. $\overline{z + w} = \bar{z} + \bar{w}$ for all Gaussian integers z and w.
   b. $\overline{zw} = \bar{z}\,\bar{w}$ for all Gaussian integers z and w.
   c. $z = \bar{z} \Leftrightarrow z \in \mathbb{R}$
   d. $z\bar{z} = a^2 + b^2$, a nonnegative integer.
3. The norm of z, written $N(z)$ is defined as the product of z and its complex conjugate $N(z) = z\bar{z}$.
4. Using this definition, the following properties of norm hold:
   a. $N(zw) = N(z)\,N(w)$ for all Gaussian integers z and w.
   b. $N(z) = a^2 + b^2$, a nonnegative integer.

Exercise Show that if z is a Gaussian integer, then

$$N(z^2) = (N(z))^2.$$

Notice that the right side of this equation is a *perfect square.* It is the square of an integer.

This exercise is a key to one of the nicest ways around for generating Pythagorean triples. The idea goes like this:

- The equation $a^2 + b^2 = c^2$ can be written $N(z) = c^2$, where $z = a + bi$. So you are looking for Gaussian integers whose norms are perfect squares.
- The exercise above says that the norm of a Gaussian integer will be a perfect square if the Gaussian integer is itself a perfect square.
- So, to generate Pythagorean triples, pick a Gaussian integer at random, and square it. The square will be a Gaussian integer $a + bi$ whose norm, $a^2 + b^2$, will be a perfect square. That is, $a^2 + b^2$ will equal c^2 for some integer c, and (a, b, c) will be a Pythagorean triple.

1. State this method precisely, and prove that it works.
2. Implement this method in your computer algebra system, and use it to generate a few hundred Pythagorean triples.

3. This method produces duplicates and sometimes produces negative “legs.” Refine the algorithm so that it produces only positive triples and produces no duplicates.
4. Even after you eliminate duplicates, there are annoying triples like (6, 8, 10) that show up and are simply multiples of a “primitive” triple (this one is twice (3, 4, 5)). Characterize those values of z so that z^2 will generate a *primitive* Pythagorean triple.

Well, there are equilateral triangles, but how about scalene ones?

Finding Pythagorean triples requires integer sided triangles with a right angle. A natural generalization is to ask for integer sided triangles with some *other* kind of angle. For example, are there any triangles with integer side lengths and a 60° angle?

Suppose there are.

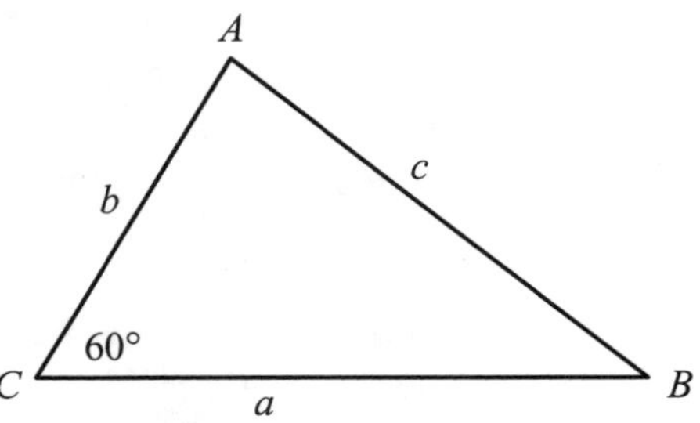

Figure 1: Integer sidelengths, $m\angle C = 60°$

In the case of a right triangle, the Pythagorean Theorem gives a relationship among the three sides, $a^2 + b^2 = c^2$. In a triangle where $\angle C$ is not a right angle, $a^2 + b^2$ is *not* the same as c^2, but there is a theorem that generalizes Pythagoras and tells how the sides are related:

Theorem The Law of Cosines *If the sides of a triangle are labeled as in Figure 2,*

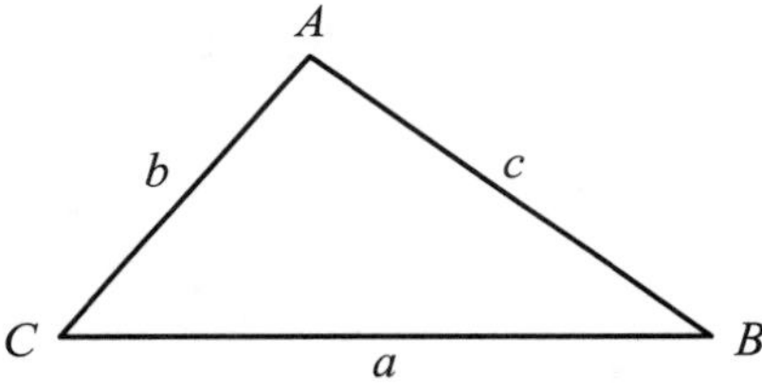

Figure 2

Here, “C means the measure of ∠BCA.

then $c^2 = a^2 + b^2 - 2ab \cos C$.

So, you have Figure 1 as shown below.

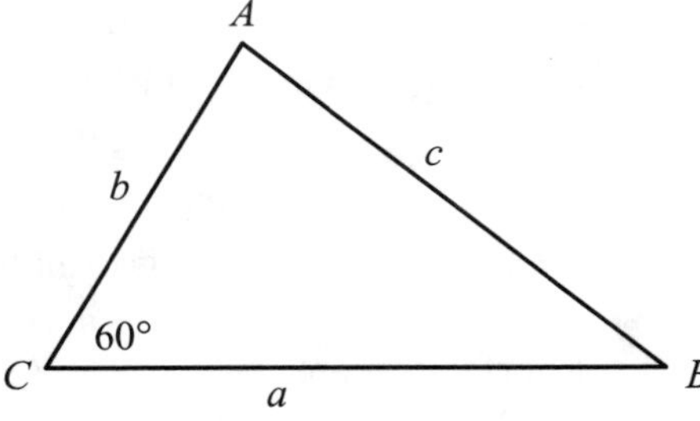

Figure 1: Integer sidelengths, $m\angle C = 60°$

By the Law of Cosines,

$$\begin{aligned} c^2 &= a^2 + b^2 - 2ab \cos 60° \\ &= a^2 + b^2 - 2ab \cdot \tfrac{1}{2} \\ &= a^2 + b^2 - ab. \end{aligned}$$

So finding the kind of triangles we want amounts to finding triples of integers (a, b, c) so that $a^2 - ab + b^2 = c^2$. Just as before, you are looking for $a, b \in \mathbb{Z}$ so that $a^2 - ab + b^2$ is a perfect square. Some wishful thinking is in order.

If $a^2 - ab + b^2$ were the *norm* of something, and if that norm function behaved like the ordinary norm from the Gaussian integers (in particular, if the norm of a product were the product of the norms), then you would be able to use the same method: Take a thing, square it, and then its norm will

- have the right form $(a^2 - ab + b^2)$, and
- be a perfect square.

But, you say, this is only wishful thinking. The norm function is what it is. If $z = a + bi$, then $N(z) = a^2 + b^2$, *not* $a^2 - ab + b^2$. Norm is norm, and you cannot change it.

Well, the norm function is not the norm of $a + bi$, but suppose it were the norm of $a + b\omega$ for some complex number ω. Work backwards and see if you can figure out what ω has to be. Remember, the norm is the product of the number and its conjugate, so, if a and b are integers,

$$\begin{aligned} N(a + b\omega) &= (a + b\omega)\,(\overline{a + b\omega}) \\ &= (a + b\omega)\,(\overline{a} + \overline{b\omega}) \\ &= (a + b\omega)\,(\overline{a} + \overline{b}\,\overline{\omega}) \\ &= (a + b\omega)\,(a + b\overline{\omega}) \\ &= a^2 + ab(\omega + \overline{\omega}) + b^2(\omega\overline{\omega}), \end{aligned}$$

As usual, justify each step in the calculation sequence.

and if you want this to be $a^2 - ab + b^2$, then you want

$$\begin{aligned} \omega + \overline{\omega} &= -1 \text{ and} \\ \omega\overline{\omega} &= 1. \end{aligned}$$

Well, that pretty much nails ω down: You know the sum of ω and its complex conjugate (it is -1), and you know the product $\omega\overline{\omega}$ (it is 1). So, ω is a root of the quadratic equation

$$x^2 + x + 1 = 0,$$

because

$$x^2 - (\text{the sum of the roots})x + (\text{the product of the roots}) = 0.$$

The other root is then $\omega = \dfrac{-1 - i\sqrt{3}}{2}$. That will work, too.

Using the quadratic formula, you get

$$\omega = \frac{-1 + i\sqrt{3}}{2},$$

and you can now generate as many triples of integers (a, b, c) so that $c^2 = a^2 - ab + b^2$ as you like.

For example, start with $z = 3 + 2\omega$. Then square both sides of the equation.

$$\begin{aligned} z^2 &= (3 + 2\omega)^2 \\ &= 9 + 12\omega + 4\omega^2 \\ &= 9 + 12\omega + 4(-1 - \omega) \quad \text{(Don't forget: } \omega^2 + \omega + 1 = 0.) \\ &= 5 + 8\omega \end{aligned}$$

and voilá:

$$5^2 - 5 \cdot 8 + 8^2 = 49, \text{ a perfect square!}$$

So, the triangle whose sides have lengths 5, 8, and 7 has a 60° angle.

Or a triangle with sides of lengths 5 and 8 and an included angle of 60° has a third side of length 7.

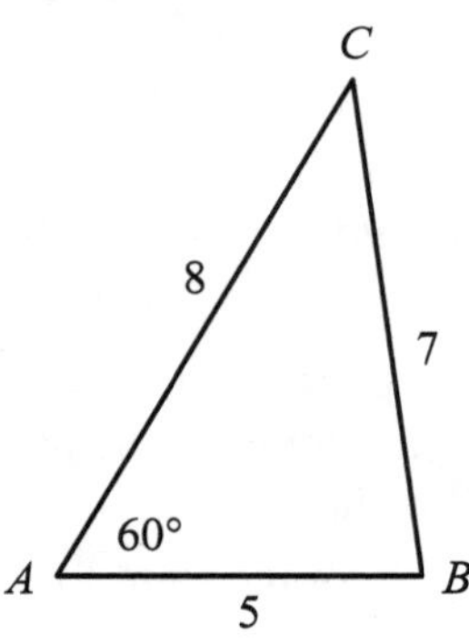

A (5, 8, 7) triangle has a 60° angle.

Notice that when you were looking for a triangle with integer sidelengths and a 60° angle, you were led to search for a complex number ω such that

$$\omega + \overline{\omega} = -1 \text{ and}$$
$$\omega\overline{\omega} = 1.$$

This meant that $\omega^2 + \omega + 1 = 0$, producing two choices for ω. In fact, what you really needed was this defining behavior ($\omega^2 + \omega + 1 = 0$) and *not* the precise value ($\frac{-1 + i\sqrt{3}}{2}$). You needed to know just that when you calculate with "expressions" in ω, powers higher than 2 can be "folded back" using the equation $\omega^2 = -\omega - 1$. This idea of using the behavior of something instead of its value is an important one in algebra. It is also very close to the way many high school students deal with complex numbers: They treat "i" as a formal symbol whose square can be replaced by -1 anytime it shows up. Many teachers think this is mindless mechanical behavior; maybe we're too hard on students.

"Good mathematics is not how many answers you know but how you behave when you don't know the answer."
— anonymous

Exercise The problem of finding a triangle with integer sides and one angle θ comes down to finding a complex number α such that the norm of $a + b\alpha$ has the form that comes from applying the Law of Cosines to a generic triangle of the desired type. Express α in terms of θ, and give a condition that θ has to meet in order for this problem to have a solution.

A geometric approach There is another way to generate Pythagorean triples, using the unit circle and coordinate geometry.

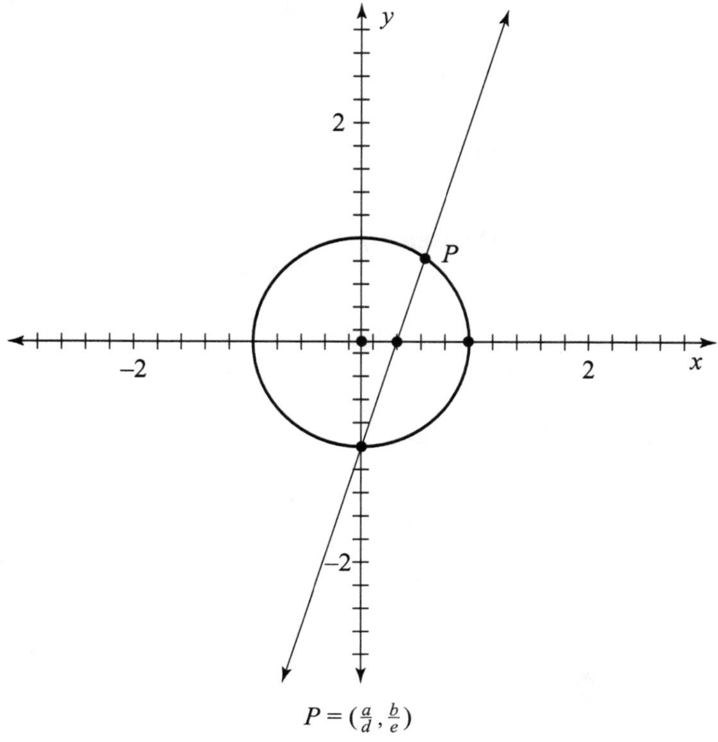

$P = (\frac{a}{d}, \frac{b}{e})$

The equation of the unit circle is $x^2 + y^2 = 1$. So if we can find "rational points" on the circle, such as $(\frac{a}{d}, \frac{b}{e})$, then

$$\left(\frac{a}{d}\right)^2 + \left(\frac{b}{e}\right)^2 = 1$$

$$a^2e^2 + b^2d^2 = d^2e^2$$

$$(ae)^2 + (bd)^2 = (de)^2,$$

and the numbers *ae, bd,* and *de* are a Pythagorean triple. But how do you find these points?

Theorem *If a line passes through the point* $(0, -1)$ *and has rational slope, then its other intersection with the unit circle will be a rational point.*

Proof: The equation of the line is $y = \frac{a}{b}x - 1$, where a and b are integers. Substitute for y in the equation of the circle to get

$$x^2 + \left(\frac{a}{b}x - 1\right)^2 = 1$$

$$x^2 + \left(\frac{a^2}{b^2}\right)x^2 - \frac{2a}{b}x + 1 = 1$$

$$\left(\frac{a^2 + b^2}{b^2}\right)x^2 - \frac{2a}{b}x = 0$$

$$(a^2 + b^2)x^2 - 2abx = 0$$

$$x = \frac{2ab}{a^2 + b^2}.$$

Since a and b are integers, $\frac{2ab}{a^2 + b^2}$ is a rational number, so x is rational. A similar argument shows that y is rational as well.

Now look back at the problem of finding triangles with integer sides and one 60° angle. You want triples so that $a^2 - ab + b^2 = c^2$. Can you use a similar geometric approach to generate them?

- Graph $x^2 - xy + y^2 = 1$. What kind of object is it?
- If you have a rational point on the graph of $x^2 - xy + y^2 = 1$, can you use it to find the integer-sided triangle you are looking for?

Theorem *If a line passes through the point* $(0, -1)$ *and has rational slope, then its other intersection with the graph of* $x^2 - xy + y^2 = 1$ *will be a rational point.*

Exercise Can you prove this theorem?

LESSON

Analyzing Dissections

Lesson Objective

In this lesson, students study what happens to the perimeter of a figure when it is dissected.

Content Overview

Studying some of their previous cutting algorithms, students first establish that perimeter does *not* remain invariant. Then, working with an iterative cutting algorithm on a square, they investigate whether perimeter ever changes in a predictable manner. Students explore the following question: *If the dissection of the figure follows a repeated pattern, is there a pattern to the increase in the perimeter?*

Planning Guide

Pacing	Activity	Materials	Homework Suggestions
Day 1	*Explore and Discuss* (SE p. 211) Activity 1: A Parallelogram Cut to a Rectangle (SE pp. 211–215)	No special materials needed.	*On Your Own,* Problem 4
Day 2	Activity 1: A Parallelogram Cut to a Rectangle (SE pp. 211–215)		*On Your Own,* Problems 1, 2, and 3
Day 3	Activity 2: Area and Perimeter (SE pp. 215–219)	• BLM 25, p. 34 • scissors • paper • rulers	*On Your Own,* Problems 5, 6, and 7
Day 4	Activity 2: Area and Perimeter (SE pp. 215–219)	• BLM 25, p. 34 • scissors • paper • rulers • tape	*On Your Own,* Problems 8 and 9 *Take It Further,* Problem 10

Program Resources

- *Connected Geometry* CD-ROM, Module 3: Investigations 3.8, 3.9, 3.10, and 3.11
- *Solution and Problem Solving Resource,* pages 231–240
- *Teaching Resources,* page 34
- *Assessment Resources,* Quiz 3 Lessons 4, 5, and 6, page 87

Preparation and Prerequisites

In preparation, students must have accomplished the basic dissections of a parallelogram, a triangle, and a trapezoid into a rectangle. The major decision you will need to make in preparation for this lesson is whether you wish to do the activity on the computer.

In the square dissection, Problems **13–18,** students must repeatedly construct isosceles right triangles from a given hypotenuse. They will need some kind of construction tool to assist them. If no special drawing tools are available, students can mark off two sides of a 3" × 5" card in $\frac{1}{8}$- or $\frac{1}{4}$-inch units. If the card is placed correctly, tracing along its edges will result in an almost perfect isosceles right triangle.

Teaching the Lesson

Explore and Discuss *(Student page 211)*

Students should be *completely* convinced by now that area is invariant under dissection. But what about perimeter? Give students time to read and understand Jeremy's argument. Allow them to discuss the validity of his approach with classmates.

ACTIVITY 1

A Parallelogram Cut to a Rectangle *(Student pages 211–215)*

You may want to read the dialogue aloud. The questions that follow the dialogue call for students to analyze the suggested solution to dissection problems. Both problems are fairly easy and assess students' understanding of basic dissection.

ACTIVITY 2

Area and Perimeter *(Student pages 215–219)*

Group work is advantageous here because each student can dissect a different-shaped parallelogram or use a different algorithm for dissection. Hence, the group ends up with a lot of evidence to use in drawing conclusions.

PROBLEMS 11–12 These are really warm-up problems to start students thinking about how dissection does (or doesn't) change perimeter. Students can work through them quickly and then move on to the more interesting (and time-consuming) dissection of the square. Blackline Master 25 can be used with Problem **11.**

PROBLEMS 14–18 In the square dissection, students must repeatedly construct isosceles right triangles from a given hypotenuse. They will need some kind of construction tool to assist them in doing these constructions.

Introduce the square dissection, starting on page 216, with the following question: "Imagine a dissection that gets repeated many times. Do you think you can predict a pattern for the repeated changes in perimeter?" The rules for dissecting a square are clearly outlined in the Student Edition. Again, set students right to work to see what they can come up with.

PROBLEMS 15 AND 17 After students have completed the dissection algorithm, they are asked to determine the perimeter of the new figure. Measurement is possible but tedious and inaccurate. Encourage students to compute the perimeter by studying the way the figure has been formed. They can use the Pythagorean Theorem or the ratio of side to hypotenuse in a 45–45–90 right triangle if they know it. Analysis of the emerging pattern will also be much easier using these calculations rather than by measuring.

On Your Own *(Student pages 219–221)*

These problems provide students with the opportunity for individual practice.

PROBLEM 4 This problem can be done on the computer. The directions printed in the *Student Edition* are suitable for computer work. Students can use geometry software to experiment, to verify which statements *appear* to be true, and to construct counterexamples for the false statements. If this problem is done in the computer lab, you might want students to present their solutions on the computer rather than in writing.

Take It Further *(Student page 221)*

This problem will lead students in new directions or will challenge them to apply what they already know.

Options and Extensions

Optional warm-up problem for Activity 2 Start with an 8 × 8 square (perimeter = 32). Cut it in half vertically and horizontally. Now you have four 4 × 4 squares. Line them up end-to-end to make a long rectangle (4 × 16). Cut twice again, and line these rectangles up end-to-end to make an even longer rectangle (2 × 32); cut and line up again and again. What do you know about these rectangles? Their areas? Will there be a predictable pattern for the perimeters?

The square dissection can be done by drawing instead of cutting. Start with a 16 × 16 (or 32 × 32) square drawn on a large sheet of graph paper. For each full application of the algorithm, sketch the changes in pencil. Then draw the completed new form with a different color pen. With graph paper, the isosceles triangles are easy to draw.

The square problem gives rise to the topics of recursion and fractals. Adding a few more activities on those topics will delight many students.

The figure that is formed after one full application of the square dissection algorithm *will* tile the plane. Algorithms like this can be used to make tessellation drawings. Ask students if the second or third stage figures also tile the plane.

Unit 3 Review

This unit review is intended to provide students with problems that will encourage them to look back at the unit as a whole. Students have one more opportunity to pull together, apply, and communicate the ideas they have developed by working on the activities throughout the unit.

It is especially important for students to have the opportunity to share their solutions with the class.

PROBLEM 1 Students have algorithms for dissecting scalene triangles, right triangles, and trapezoids into rectangles from Lesson 1. Copies of the figures are on Blackline Master 26.

PROBLEM 2 The following distinction should be made: If two figures are *scissors-congruent* they have the same area, but if two figures have the same area they are not necessarily *scissors-congruent*.

PROBLEM 3 Students should have created a general algorithm in Lesson 2 for this dissection. They should be able to clearly justify each step.

PROBLEM 4 Students should rely on the definition of *scissors-congruent* to come to the conclusion that the area formula for the parallelogram is also bh.

PROBLEM 5 Students should be aware that you can change perimeter without changing area and vice versa.

PROBLEM 6 Have students check their algorithm. Ask: "Does it work for obtuse triangles, or do you have to position them in a certain way? Does it work for long, skinny rectangles, or do you have to position them in a certain way?"

PROBLEM 7 Students should be able to state the Pythagorean Theorem. They should also know that, while the Pythagorean Theorem is a statement about areas, it is also useful for finding lengths of sides of right triangles.

PROBLEM 8 Students will need to use the Pythagorean Theorem to find some missing lengths in these figures.

PROBLEM 9 Students should use their knowledge of the Midline Theorem to solve this problem.

UNIT 4

A Matter of Scale

Pathways to Similarity and Trigonometry

Unit Overview

A Matter of Scale focuses on three related, overarching themes: scale drawing, similarity, and trigonometry.

Students read maps and blueprints, using the provided scales to calculate distances and lengths. They examine enlargements and reductions to formulate their own tests for deciding what makes a well-scaled copy. They then apply this knowledge to pairs of triangles and polygons, again developing methods to recognize scaled copies.

Students use two different techniques for creating scale drawings, both related to the notion of *dilation.* They use these methods to draw their own scaled copies and then prove that the methods do indeed work. The proofs establish two important triangle similarity results: the Side-Splitting Theorem and the Parallel Theorem.

Students prove some classic triangle similarity tests, including AA, SAS, and SSS, and use these tests to explore a variety of simple, yet accurate, methods for determining unknown distances and heights.

Another similarity application challenges students to use geometry software to build a rectangle that maintains its area and that stays a rectangle even when any of its parts are moved. A follow-up activity connects this work to the concept of the geometric mean.

The next group of lessons, Lessons 11–13, focuses on how the area and perimeter of objects are affected by scaling. The lessons discuss how one might determine the area and perimeter of objects with curves and develops proofs for the area and circumference formulas of a circle. An historical overview of π is also included. Throughout this section, students get an intuitive introduction to the notion of limits.

"An Introduction to Trigonometry" encourages students to develop their own methods for finding unknown sidelengths of triangles well before it introduces the names of the trigonometric ratios. Students ultimately decide for themselves what information is the most useful to have when looking for the lengths of unknown triangle sides.

The trigonometry lesson concludes with an activity that relates to the Pythagorean Theorem work that students did in Unit 3.

Learning Goals

1. Understand that *scale factor* measures change in linear dimension when a picture is scaled.
2. Approximate the scale factor between two pictures by measuring.
3. Use a given scale factor to interpret a map or blueprint.
4. Decide if two figures are well-scaled copies of each other.
5. Describe and use two methods for constructing enlargements or reductions of shapes.
6. Apply and explain the ratio and parallel methods and the Parallel and Side-Splitting Theorems.
7. Define similarity in terms of scaling or dilation.
8. Draw conclusions about angles and sides of similar triangles.
9. Articulate and use tests for triangle similarity: AA, SAS, SSS.
10. State and apply the fact that the area of a scaled figure is related by the square of the scale factor.
11. Explain the ideas of "inner and outer sums" and making finer grids to approximate the areas of curved figures.
12. Explain and use the method of linear approximation to find perimeters of curved figures.
13. Find the area and circumference of circles, given their radii.
14. Describe what π is and give an approximation of its value.
15. Describe the method of approximating circles with inscribed and circumscribed regular polygons.
16. Explain sine, cosine, and tangent in terms of invariant ratios in right triangles.
17. Use ideas from triangle similarity to show that ratios are invariant.
18. Given two sidelengths of a right triangle, find the third length, as well as the sine, cosine, and tangent of each angle.
19. Express the height, and therefore the area, of triangles and parallelograms in terms of a side and an angle.
20. See the Pythagorean Theorem as a special case of a more general rule about the sides of triangles.

Assessment Opportunities

Quizzes and Informal Assessment

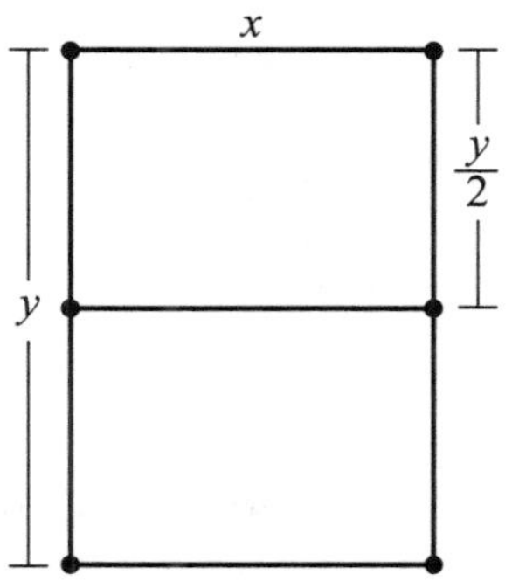

You can start with half a sheet of paper, so you can keep the other half as the "original" for comparison.

- After Lesson 12, *On Your Own,* Problem **12** in Lesson 12, ask students: "Is there some rectangle you can start with for which you can do the ripping activity and end up with one set of similar rectangles?" This is a good problem for integrating algebra. It amounts to finding x and y so that

$$\frac{x}{y} = \frac{\frac{x}{2}}{y} \qquad 2x^2 = y^2 \qquad x = \sqrt{2}y$$

- Here's another ripping activity you can have your students do. Start with any right triangle. Construct the altitude from the right angle to the hypotenuse. Then tear, creating two new triangles. Ask: "Are these two triangles scaled copies of the original?" Encourage students to explain their answers. This activity requires at least the conjecture of AA similarity for triangles from Lesson 9. You are creating two triangles, each with a right angle and with one other angle shared with the original, so they are both similar to the original and to each other.

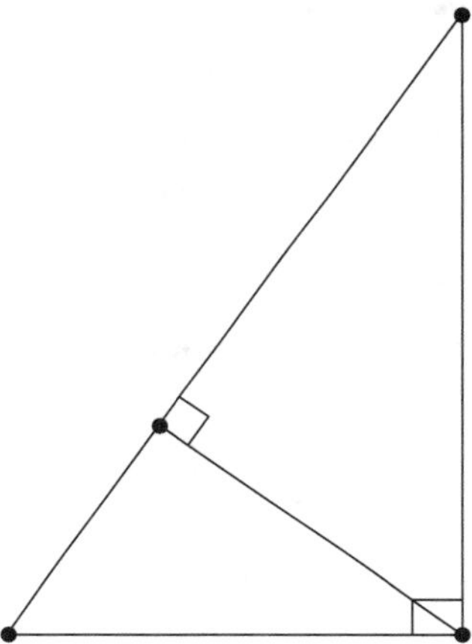

- *Checkpoint* Problem **7** in Lesson 1 suggests a short project in which students create a floor plan of a given space. It requires a lot of measurement of the space, as well as measurement of the furnishings, windows, doors, and so on.
- A careful write-up of Lesson 14. Students should include such points as:

1. When is

$$a^2 + b^2 = c^2?$$
$$a^2 + b^2 < c^2?$$
$$a^2 + b^2 > c^2?$$

2. Did you use trigonometry and the results from Lesson 14 to justify the answers to the questions in Problem 1?
3. How did you find the areas of the two parallelograms?
4. What is the generalized Pythagorean Theorem?
5. Does one formula work for all triangles, or do we need separate formulas?

Journal Ideas

Students keep writing assignments in a journal. Possible assignments:

- Lesson 4, Problems 9 and 10. Explain why two triangles must be scaled copies of each other.
- Lesson 6. Explain how a triangle can be scaled.
- Lesson 7, Problems 12 and 17. Write a proof for the Parallel Theorem.
- Lesson 7, Problem 13. Write a proof for the Side-Splitting Theorem.
- Lesson 7, *On Your Own,* Problem 1. Write the Parallel Theorem and the Side-Splitting Theorem using segment names.
- Lesson 8, Problem 1. Prove that the conjecture about midpoints of quadrilaterals is correct.
- Lesson 8, Problems 5 and 6. Use the Side-Splitting Theorem to prove generalizations about midpoints in quadrilaterals.
- Lesson 9, Problems 2 and 3. Explain whether similar figures are congruent, if they are similar to the same figure, and/or if they are similar to each other.
- Lesson 9, Problem 11. Draw and list attributes of a pair of triangles to see if there are tests for triangle similarity.
- Lesson 9, Problem 16. Prove the AAA Similarity Theorem.
- Lesson 9, Problem 21. Prove the SAS Similarity Theorem.
- Lesson 9, Problem 30. Prove the SSS Similarity Theorem.
- Lesson 10, Problem 26. Provide a written explanation of how to build a collection of equal-area rectangles out of long wooden sticks.
- Lesson 10, *On Your Own,* Problem 5. Write a proof of a power-of-a-point conjecture.
- Lesson 11, Problem 1. Complete and prove a theorem.
- Lesson 12. Argue that as the mesh of graph paper gets finer, the difference between outer and inner sums gets smaller.
- Lesson 12, Problem 19. Explain why the difference between the outer and inner perimeters gets smaller as the number of sides gets larger.
- Lesson 13, Problem 2. Argue the claim that if the area of a circle with radius 1 is K, then the area of a circle with radius r is Kr^2.
- Lesson 13, *Write and Reflect,* Problem 4. Write an answer to a question regarding the area of a circle.
- Lesson 15, *Write and Reflect,* Problem 7. Explain how a theorem is applied to a triangle.

UNIT 4 Planning Guide

Lessons	Learning Goals	Assessment Opportunities	Suggested Pacing	Materials
LESSON 1 *Introduction to Maps and Blueprints*	1	*Checkpoint,* Problems 3 and 7 Quiz 1, *Assessment Resources,* p. 115	2 days	• rulers • calculators
LESSON 2 *What Is a Scale Factor?*	1, 2	*Checkpoint,* Problems 4, 9, and 13 Quiz 2, *Assessment Resources,* p. 116	3 days	• rulers • calculators
LESSON 3 *What Is a Well-Scaled Drawing?*	1, 4	*Checkpoint,* Problem 3	1 day	• BLM 27, p. 36 • graph paper
LESSON 4 *Testing for Scale*	3	*Checkpoint,* Problems 4, 11, and 15 Quiz 3, *Assessment Resources,* p. 117	4 days	• BLM 28, p. 37 • BLM 29, p. 38 • BLM 30, p. 39 • BLM 31, p. 40 • BLM 32, p. 41 • rulers • scissors • calculators • protractors
LESSON 5 *Curved or Straight? Just Dilate!*	5	*Checkpoint,* Problem 5	1 day	• paper • rulers
LESSON 6 *Ratio and Parallel Methods*	5, 6	*Checkpoint,* Problems 6 and 10 Quiz 4, *Assessment Resources,* p. 118	3 days	• paper • rulers • geometry software (optional)
LESSON 7 *The Side-Splitting and Parallel Theorems*	6, 8	*Checkpoint,* Problems 7, 14, and 18	5 days	• BLM 33, p. 42 • geometry software
LESSON 8 *Midpoints in Quadrilaterals*	6	*Checkpoint,* Problem 7 Quiz 5, *Assessment Resources,* pp. 119–120 Mid-Unit Exam, Assessment Resources, pp. 129–138	2 days	geometry software
LESSON 9 *Defining Similarity*	7, 8, 9	*Checkpoint,* Problems 5, 10, and 31 Quiz 6, *Assessment Resources,* pp. 121–122	4 days	No special materials needed.

LESSON 10 *Using Similarity*	8, 9	*Checkpoint,* Problems 11, 20, 27, and 36 Quiz 7, *Assessment Resources,* p. 123	7 days	• BLM 34, p. 43 • tape measures • calculators • straightedges • lined notebook paper • geometry software
LESSON 11 *Areas of Similar Polygons*	10	*Checkpoint,* Problems 10 and 13 Quiz 8, *Assessment Resources,* p. 124	2 days	• rulers • scissors • geometry software (optional)
LESSON 12 *Areas and Perimeters of Blobs and Circles*	11, 12, 13, 14, 15	*Checkpoint,* Problems 7, 11, 19, and 22 Quiz 9, *Assessment Resources,* p. 125	5 days	• graph paper • large paper • rulers
LESSON 13 *Circles and 3.14159265358979323 . . .*	13, 14	*Checkpoint,* Problems 6 and 10 Quiz 10, *Assessment Resources,* p. 126	2 days	calculators
LESSON 14 *An Introduction to Trigonometry*	16, 17, 18, 19	*Checkpoint,* Problems 7 and 11 Quiz 11, *Assessment Resources,* p. 127	3 days	calculators
LESSON 15 *Extending the Pythagorean Theorem*	20	*Checkpoint,* Problem 11 Quiz 12, *Assessment Resources,* p. 128	3 days	geometry software
UNIT 4 REVIEW		End-of-Unit Exam, *Assessment Resources,* p. 139–145	2 days (including testing)	graph paper

L E S S O N

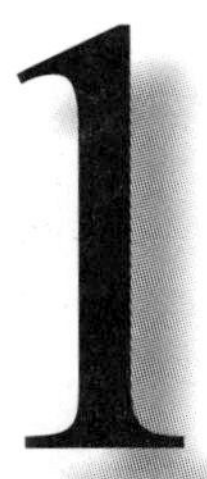

Introduction to Maps and Blueprints

Lesson Objective

This lesson introduces students to the concept of scaling.

Content Overview

Students use a map of downtown Seattle to compute distances between various locations. Students also work with blueprints of a house to determine such measurements as the height of a chimney and the dimensions of the house's entire second floor.

Planning Guide

Pacing	Activity	Materials	Homework Suggestions
Day 1	*Explore and Discuss* (SE p. 226) Activity 1: Maps (SE pp. 226–227)	• rulers • calculators	*On Your Own,* Problems 1, 2, and 3
Day 2	Activity 2: Reading a Blueprint (SE pp. 228–229)	• rulers • calculators	*On Your Own,* Problems 4 and 5

Program Resources

- *Connected Geometry* CD-ROM, Module 4: Investigation 4.1
- *Solution and Problem Solving Resource,* pages 245–246
- *Assessment Resources,* Quiz 1 Lesson 1, page 115

Preparation and Prerequisites

Before starting this lesson, you might ask students how they estimate distances when using a map. Many maps include a segment that represents some number of actual miles. In a case like this, people often put two of their fingertips at the endpoints of the segment and count how many segments fit between the two locations they care about. Then this number is converted into miles by using the given scale factor. Students should have a general familiarity with ratios and proportions.

Teaching the Lesson

Explore and Discuss *(Student page 226)*

You may want to have other maps available for students to examine and to enable them to use other scales.

ACTIVITY 1

Maps *(Student pages 226–227)*

This activity provides a good opportunity to review some of the basic properties of ratios and proportions. For instance, if 1 inch on the map represents 600 feet, then how many feet do 5 inches represent?

Maps are just one of several places on which students might have encountered scaling.

ACTIVITY 2

Reading a Blueprint *(Student pages 228–229)*

PROBLEM 4 Students can use one of several strategies to solve this problem. They can use the edge of a sheet of paper to mark off a length that represents 3 feet, the distance from the top of the roof to the top of the chimney, and then count how many of these lengths fit into the desired measurement. Or they can measure the actual length of the distance representing 3 feet and then set up a proportion to solve for the desired measurement. Both methods are worth mentioning if students do not suggest them.

The answers your students obtain in the blueprint activity will probably vary since their measurements may not be entirely precise.

While finding the blueprints for this activity, the authors noticed that the lengths indicated on a drawing are not always consistent with each other. For instance, one length might be labeled "3 feet," while another length twice as long might be labeled "7 feet." It might be interesting for students to look at other blueprints and check the consistency of the measurements on them.

On Your Own *(Student pages 229–230)*

These problems provide students with the opportunity for individual practice. See the lesson Planning Guide for homework recommendations.

LESSON

What Is a Scale Factor?

Lesson Objective

This lesson develops a more precise definition of scale factor and explains how to calculate it.

Content Overview

The lesson begins with a student discussion on the meaning of the term *scale factor.* The remaining problems come in two varieties:

- Given a figure and a scale factor, compute the lengths of the parts of the figure after it has been scaled.
- Given two figures, compute the factor by which one has been scaled to obtain the other.

The lesson concludes by examining how scaling affects the areas of squares and triangles and the volumes of cubes.

Planning Guide

Pacing	Activity	Materials	Homework Suggestions
Day 1	*Explore and Discuss* (SE p. 231) Activity 1: A Matter of Interpretation (SE pp. 231–233)	• rulers • calculators	*On Your Own,* Problems 1 and 2
Day 2	Activity 2: Calculating Scale Factors (SE pp. 233–234)	• rulers • calculators	*On Your Own,* Problem 3 *Take It Further,* Problem 6
Day 3	Activity 3: Area and Volume (SE pp. 234–235)	• rulers • calculators	*On Your Own,* Problems 4 and 5

Program Resources

- *Connected Geometry* CD-ROM, Module 4: Investigations 4.2 and 4.3
- *Solution and Problem Solving Resource,* pages 247–251
- *Assessment Resources,* Quiz 2 Lesson 2, page 116

Preparation and Prerequisites

Students should have a basic understanding of fractions and decimals.

Teaching the Lesson

Explore and Discuss *(Student page 231)*

Students discuss what it means to "scale a square by a factor of $\frac{1}{2}$." There is more than one way to interpret this statement. Students might assume that scaling by $\frac{1}{2}$ means that the sidelengths of a square will be half as long, or they might think the area of the square will be halved. Both ideas are certainly valid, but the former meaning is the standard one.

ACTIVITY 1

A Matter of Interpretation *(Student pages 231–233)*

PROBLEM 1 This problem reminds students that not all features of an object change when it is scaled—the square, for instance, maintains its 90° angles.

The remaining problems give students practice in calculating with both fractional and decimal scaling factors.

ACTIVITY 2

Calculating Scale Factors *(Student pages 233–234)*

PROBLEM 5 This problem presents pairs of scaled pictures and asks students to determine the scale factor needed to transform one into the other. Students will need rulers to measure distances and (if desired) calculators to convert the fractional answers into decimals. The problems provide a good opportunity to discuss how to calculate scale factor. In part **b,** for example, there are numerous measurements one might take to determine the scale factor of the five-pointed stars. In each star, students might pick two of the tips (making sure to pick the same tips in both stars), measure the distance between both sets of tips, and then calculate the ratios of the distances. Or students might measure the length of a side of each star (making sure to pick corresponding sides) and then compute the ratios of the side lengths. All methods should produce the same answer, with slight variations due to measuring inaccuracies.

ACTIVITY 3

Area and Volume *(Student pages 234–235)*

The problems in this section provide a preview of a more detailed study of area and volume to come in Lesson 11.

On Your Own *(Student pages 235–236)*

These problems provide students with the opportunity for individual practice. See the lesson Planning Guide for homework recommendations.

Take It Further *(Student page 236)*

This problem will lead students in new directions or will challenge them to apply what they already know.

LESSON

What Is a Well-Scaled Drawing?

Lesson Objective

Students use their prior knowledge to describe what well-scaled drawings are.

In this lesson, the term "well-scaled" is used to describe copies that are drawn in proportion to the original. After this lesson, the term "scaled" is used for the same concept.

Content Overview

Students compare a picture of a horse skeleton to four copies—some well-scaled and some poorly scaled—to determine which features are required for a well-scaled drawing. They then are introduced to some of the numerical attributes of scaled copies—equal ratios of corresponding parts.

Planning Guide

Pacing	Activity	Materials	Homework Suggestions
Day 1	*Explore and Discuss* (SE pp. 237–238) Activity: How Can You Tell? (SE pp. 238–239)	• BLM 27, p. 36 • graph paper	*On Your Own,* Problems 1, 2, and 3

Program Resources

- *Connected Geometry* CD-ROM, Module 4: Investigation 4.4
- *Solution and Problem Solving Resource,* pages 252–253
- *Teaching Resources,* page 36

Teaching the Lesson

Explore and Discuss *(Student pages 237–238)*

Distribute Blackline Master 27 to students.

When students explain how they decided which horse skeletons were well-scaled copies of the original picture, you might hear answers like, "Picture **i** isn't a well-scaled copy because it's been stretched horizontally." Such answers are fine, but you might challenge your students a bit more by asking, "What if I'm not convinced the picture has been stretched? If I gave you a ruler and a protractor, what measurements could you take that would help convince me that picture **i** is not a well-scaled copy?"

The purpose of asking this question is to get students thinking about the angle and ratio requirements necessary in order for two figures to be scaled copies of each other. Students might, for example, say that the angle of the horse's neck relative to the body is not the same in each picture.

ACTIVITY

How Can You Tell? *(Student pages 238–239)*

The problems in this activity focus on the numerical aspects of testing for scaled copies.

On Your Own *(Student pages 239–240)*

These problems provide students with the opportunity for individual practice. See the lesson Planning Guide for homework recommendations.

Students will need graph paper to complete these problems for homework.

LESSON

Testing for Scale

Lesson Objective

In this lesson, students develop tests for checking whether pairs of rectangles, triangles, and polygons are scaled copies of each other.

Content Overview

The lesson begins by asking students to check to see if two rectangles or two triangles are scaled copies of each other. Later, students check other polygons. Some tests involve measurement and calculation, while others rely strictly on visual checks.

Planning Guide

Pacing	Activity	Materials	Homework Suggestions
Day 1	*Explore and Discuss* (SE p. 241) Activity 1: Scaled Rectangles and Triangles (SE pp. 241–242)	• BLM 28, p. 37 • rulers • scissors • calculators	*On Your Own,* Problems 1, 2, and 3
Day 2	Activity 2: Checking for Scale Without Measuring (SE pp. 242–245)	• BLM 29, p. 38 • BLM 30, p. 39 • BLM 32, p. 41 • rulers • scissors • calculators	*On Your Own,* Problems 4 and 5
Day 3	Activity 2: Checking for Scale Without Measuring (SE pp. 242–245)	• BLM 29, p. 38 • BLM 30, p. 39 • rulers • scissors • calculators • protractors	*On Your Own,* Problems 6 and 7
Day 4	Activity 3: Scaled Polygons (SE pp. 246–247)	• BLM 31, p. 40 • rulers • scissors • calculators	*On Your Own,* Problems 8 and 9

Program Resources

- *Connected Geometry* CD-ROM, Module 4: Investigations 4.5, 4.6, and 4.7
- *Solution and Problem Solving Resource,* pages 254–260
- *Teaching Resources,* pages 37–41
- *Assessment Resources,* Quiz 3 Lessons 3 and 4, page 117

Preparation and Prerequisites

Students should be familiar with the characteristics of scaled copies introduced in Lesson 3.

Teaching the Lesson

One of the best ways to begin learning about scaled polygons is to cut out, measure, and play with actual polygons. The lesson starts with simple polygons like rectangles and then asks students to develop scaling tests for arbitrary polygons.

Explore and Discuss *(Student page 241)*

It is important to be able to properly use the terms "corresponding sides" and "proportional," as they make talking about scaled copies much simpler. In the rectangles provided, the shorter sides of lengths 2 and 3 are corresponding sides, as are the sides of lengths 6 and 9. You can say either that the ratios of these *corresponding* sides are equal or say the corresponding sides are *proportional.*

ACTIVITY 1

Scaled Rectangles and Triangles *(Student pages 241–242)*

Ask students whether it is necessary to check angles to determine whether two rectangles are scaled copies of each other.

PROBLEM 3 Blackline Master 28 can be provided to students.

PROBLEM 4 This problem points out that if you compute the inappropriate ratios, you might be misled into believing that two triangles are not scaled copies of each other.

ACTIVITY 2

Checking for Scale Without Measuring *(Student pages 242–245)*

PROBLEM 5 Provide Blackline Master 29 to students. The rectangles in this problem may look like scaled copies, but some measuring shows that they are not.

PROBLEM 6 This problem shows three pairs of rectangles and asks which pairs are scaled copies of each other. You will notice that there are some dotted lines included on these pictures with no explanation provided. The lines are a preview of things to come in Lesson 7. For now, if students ask you why the lines are there, ask them whether these lines can help them check if the rectangles are scaled copies of each other. One possible conjecture is the following: "If the dotted lines that join the corresponding vertices all meet at a single point (as they do in parts **b** and **c**), then the rectangles are scaled copies of each other."

It's possible, too, that if your students' measurements are a little off, they will say that *none* of the rectangle pairs are scaled copies of each other. In this case, mention that because of measuring inaccuracies, even well-scaled figures might not have the numbers work out perfectly.

PROBLEM 7 Distribute Blackline Master 30 to students. Encourage them to explain what makes a good test for recognizing scaled triangles.

PROBLEMS 7–8 These problems encourage students to find ways to check for scaled triangles without taking any measurements. When students cut out and play with the scaled triangles in Problem **7,** they might overlap the triangles so that they meet at a common vertex *A,* as shown in the picture below.

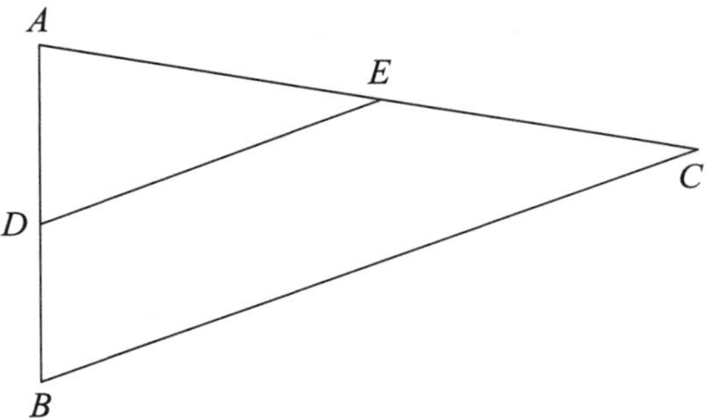

When the triangles are aligned this way, notice that

- a pair of corresponding angles overlap perfectly at $\angle A$.
- $\overline{AD}$ and $\overline{AB}$, as well as $\overline{AE}$ and $\overline{AC}$, line up.
- $\overline{DE}$ is parallel to $\overline{BC}$.

For Discussion *(Student page 244)*

This discussion is important since it introduces the terms *corresponding sides* and *proportional.*

ACTIVITY 3

Scaled Polygons *(Student pages 246–247)*

In this activity, students develop tests to determine when two polygons are scaled copies.

PROBLEM 13 Blackline Master 31 provides a copy of the trapezoid.

On Your Own *(Student pages 247–248)*

These problems provide students with the opportunity for individual practice.

PROBLEM 4 You may want to provide Blackline Master 32 to students.

PROBLEMS 8–9 You may want to review some of the terms used in these problems before assigning them for homework.

LESSON

Curved or Straight? Just Dilate!

Lesson Objective

This lesson introduces students to the act of scaling a figure.

Content Overview

Scaling figures that have only straight lines is fine, but how does one scale figures with curves? This lesson introduces a useful way to scale both polygons and curved figures—the *dilation* method.

Planning Guide

Pacing	Activity	Materials	Homework Suggestions
Day 1	*Explore and Discuss* (SE p. 249) Activity: Making Scaled Copies (SE pp. 249–250)	• paper • rulers	*On Your Own,* Problems 1, 2, 3, and 4

Program Resources

- *Connected Geometry* CD-ROM, Module 4: Investigations 4.8 and 4.9
- *Solution and Problem Solving Resource,* pages 261–262

Preparation and Prerequisites

Students should understand the meaning of the term *scale factor.*

Teaching the Lesson

It's important that your students get lots of practice with the dilation method since they will use it extensively in the following activity.

Explore and Discuss *(Student page 249)*

Students may come up with several ideas about how to scale the curve. Ask them to demonstrate their ideas, if possible.

ACTIVITY

Making Scaled Copies *(Student pages 249–250)*

As your students work through this activity, here are some points to keep in mind:

- Emphasize that when the Student Edition asks your students to "dilate a figure by a factor of *r*," it is asking them to scale the figure by *r*, using the dilation method. Later in the unit, students will prove that dilation really does produce scaled copies.
- Remind students that they can pick the "center of dilation" point to be anywhere they want. Its location affects only where the scaled image gets drawn. You can stress this idea by asking each student to pick a different center of dilation and then have students compare their work (see part **b** of Problem **1**).
- One key insight to emphasize is that a dilated copy is always in the same orientation as the original (see part **b** of Problem **2**).
- Spend some time dilating figures by only a factor of 2 so that students get a feel for how the method works. Then ask them to dilate by other factors (see Problem **3**).
- If students draw too few rays when dilating a figure, they won't get a very detailed scaled copy. Encourage students to draw more rays if they're not happy with their results. At the same time, point out how drawing more rays can be a potential limitation of scaling curved figures by hand.

On Your Own *(Student page 251)*

These problems provide students with the opportunity for individual practice.

PROBLEM 1 The mirror activity produces surprising results. When students stand in front of a mirror and trace the image of their face onto it, the mirror picture is half the size of their face. The reason this works (explained in the *Solution and Problem Solving Resource*) depends on dilation.

Take It Further *(Student page 251)*

These problems will lead students in new directions or will challenge them to apply what they already know.

Options and Extensions

Using Technology

After students have practiced dilating with a pencil and a ruler, they can move on to the section "Using Geometry Software to Dilate More Points" found on the *Connected Geometry* CD-ROM, Investigation 4.9. This section explains how to create a simple construction that simultaneously draws a figure, along with its half-size copy. The result is similar to a pantograph. This is an excellent way for students to view a continuous, rather than a discrete, version of the dilation method.

LESSON

Ratio and Parallel Methods

Lesson Objective

This lesson introduces two related methods for dilating a picture—the ratio and parallel methods.

Content Overview

Students explore both techniques for dilating and then model the parallel method with geometry software.

Planning Guide

Pacing	Activity	Materials	Homework Suggestions
Day 1	*Explore and Discuss* (SE pp. 252–253)	• rulers • paper • geometry software (optional)	*On Your Own,* Problem 1
Day 2	Activity 1: The Ratio Method for Dilating a Polygon (SE pp. 253–255)	• rulers • paper • geometry software (optional)	*On Your Own,* Problems 2 and 3
Day 3	Activity 2: The Parallel Method for Dilating a Polygon (SE pp. 255–256)	• rulers • paper • geometry software (optional)	*On Your Own,* Problem 4 *Take It Further,* Problem 6

Program Resources

- *Connected Geometry* CD-ROM, Module 4: Investigation 4.10
- *Solution and Problem Solving Resource,* pages 263–268
- *Assessment Resources,* Quiz 4 Lessons 5 and 6, page 118

Preparation and Prerequisites

Students should be familiar with the dilation material introduced in the previous lesson. It's possible to work on this lesson by drawing the figures on standard notebook-size paper, but the measuring and drawing will be easier if you provide slightly larger sheets.

Teaching the Lesson

Start by reviewing the dilation material in the previous lesson. How did students make scale drawings that were twice as large as the original pictures? Half as large? The technique that students used is called the ratio method and is the first one described in this lesson.

Explore and Discuss *(Student pages 252–253)*

Students are given an example of how to scale a polygon $ABCDE$ by $\frac{1}{2}$. Encourage students to draw their own polygons and then scale them by $\frac{1}{2}$ using the ratio method. Depending on where students place their center of dilation, they might end up with a scaled polygon that overlaps the original. You might want to give all of your students the same polygon to scale, but allow each of them to choose their own center of dilation. If they then compare results, they will see that they have all obtained scaled polygons but that each polygon is in a different location. As mentioned in Problem **6,** these scaled polygons have sides that are parallel to the original polygon, an important fact that is used to introduce the "parallel" method.

ACTIVITY 1

The Ratio Method for Dilating a Polygon *(Student pages 253–255)*

PROBLEM 3 This problem is important because it shows what happens when you pick a center of dilation that coincides with a vertex of the polygon you want to scale.

PROBLEM 4 This problem is also worth spending some time on because it illustrates a common mistake that students make when using dilation.

ACTIVITY 2

The Parallel Method for Dilating a Polygon *(Student pages 255–256)*

The second method for dilating polygons, the parallel method, requires students to draw segments parallel to the sides of their original polygon. It's probably best to ask students to simply draw, rather than construct, the segments as best they can, judging by eye what looks parallel.

On Your Own *(Student page 256)*

These problems provide students with the opportunity for individual practice. See the lesson Planning Guide for homework recommendations.

Take It Further *(Student page 257)*

These problems will lead students in new directions or will challenge them to apply what they already know.

Options and Extensions

Using Technology

If you have geometry software available, you do not have to worry about students drawing parallel lines "by eye," because the software can automatically create parallel lines. You will find a complete description of the geometry software method in the *Take It Further* section. Modeling the parallel method with geometry software also has another benefit: Students can *slide* their dilated polygon back and forth and watch as it grows and shrinks, always remaining a scaled copy of the original polygon.

LESSON

The Side-Splitting and Parallel Theorems

Lesson Objective

In this lesson, students construct proofs for the Side-Splitting and Parallel Theorems.

Content Overview

Students perform experiments that lead to two important results about triangles: the Parallel and Side-Splitting Theorems. Students prove these theorems by exploring a proof attributed to Euclid.

Planning Guide

Pacing	Activity	Materials	Homework Suggestions
Day 1	*Explore and Discuss* (SE pp. 258–259)	geometry software	*Take It Further,* Problems 10, 11, and 12
Day 2	Activity 1: Nested Triangles (SE pp. 259–262)	• BLM 33, p. 42 • geometry software	*On Your Own,* Problems 3, 4, and 5
Day 3	Activity 1: Nested Triangles (SE pp. 259–262)	geometry software	*On Your Own,* Problems 1 and 2 *Take It Further,* Problems 14 and 15
Day 4	Activity 2: Proving the Parallel and Side-Splitting Theorems (SE pp. 262–264)	geometry software	*On Your Own,* Problem 6 *Take It Further,* Problem 13
Day 5	Activity 3: Proving the Parallel Theorem Continued (SE pp. 264–266)	geometry software	*On Your Own,* Problems 7, 8, and 9

Program Resources

- *Connected Geometry* CD-ROM, Module 4: Investigations 4.11 and 4.12
- *Solution and Problem Solving Resource,* pages 269–281
- *Teaching Resources,* page 42

Preparation and Prerequisites

Students should be familiar with the dilation methods for creating scaled drawings.

Teaching the Lesson

Explore and Discuss *(Student pages 258–259)*

The problems in the *Explore and Discuss* prepare students to investigate and prove the Side-Splitting and Parallel Theorems.

ACTIVITY 1

Nested Triangles *(Student pages 259–262)*

The ratio and parallel methods both produce scale drawings, but why do they work? This activity begins to answer that question by noting that each dilation picture is composed of *nested triangles.* Nested triangles look like those below.

$\overline{DE}$ is parallel to $\overline{BC}$.

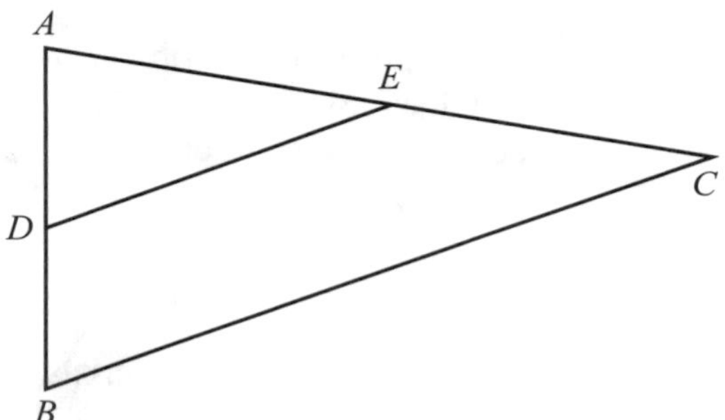

Students should recognize the Side-Splitting and Parallel Theorems as generalizations of the Midline Theorem, which was already proved.

Students are provided with three experiments to help them think about the properties of these special sets of triangles. All three experiments lead to the important Parallel and Side-Splitting Theorems.

ACTIVITY 2

Proving the Parallel and Side-Splitting Theorems *(Student pages 262–264)*

In order for students to understand Euclid's proof, they need to be comfortable with the result from part **b** of the *Explore and Discuss:* If two triangles have the same height, the ratio of their areas is the same as the ratio of their bases. The first three problems of the activity give students practice in proving and applying this theorem and reinforce the idea that any two triangles with the same base and height lengths will have the same area.

Euclid's proof of the Parallel Theorem is provided three times. The first time, all of the details are slowly given; the second time, the steps are consolidated to highlight the theorem's key aspects; and the third time, some indication is given of how one might discover the proof. Students who understand the proof well should then be able to follow the same basic setup to prove the Side-Splitting Theorem in Problem **6.**

ACTIVITY 3

Proving the Parallel Theorem Continued *(Student pages 264–266)*

Students use what they have learned to prove part b of the Parallel Theorem: The ratio of the length of the parallel side to a given segment is equal to the common ratio.

On Your Own *(Student pages 266–269)*

These problems provide students with the opportunity for individual practice.

PROBLEM 4 Copies of the picture are provided on Blackline Master 33.

PROBLEM 5 This problem relates back to Problem **6** in Lesson 4. In that problem, students were asked whether various pairs of rectangles were scaled copies of each other. Dashed lines were provided in the pictures, but students didn't know why they were there. One conjecture that students might have made was, "If the dashed lines that join the corresponding vertices all meet at a single point, then the rectangles are scaled copies of each other." Now students can prove that this is indeed true.

Take It Further *(Student pages 270–271)*

These problems will lead students in new directions or will challenge them to apply what they already know.

Options and Extensions

Without Technology

Experiments One and Three in Activity 1 are designed to be used with geometry software. If you decide not to use software, you can give your students pictures of nested triangles, like the one on page 146 of this guide. Ask students to take measurements using a ruler.

LESSON

Midpoints in Quadrilaterals

Lesson Objective

Students use the Side-Splitting Theorem to prove that the geometric figure formed by connecting the midpoints of an aribtrary quadrilateral is a parallelogram.

Content Overview

- With or without geometry software, students discover properties of an arbitrary quadrilateral, as well as its "midpoint quadrilateral."
- Students test their conjecture about the "midpoint quadrilateral" and prove that it is true.

Planning Guide

Pacing	Activity	Materials	Homework Suggestions
Day 1	*Explore and Discuss* (SE p. 272) Activity: Why Does It Happen? (SE pp. 272–273)	geometry software	*On Your Own,* Problems 1, 2, and 3
Day 2	Activity: Why Does It Happen? (SE pp. 272–273)	geometry software	*On Your Own,* Problems 4, 5, and 6

Program Resources

- *Connected Geometry* CD-ROM, Module 4: Investigation 4.12
- *Solution and Problem Solving Resource,* pages 282–288
- *Assessment Resources,* Quiz 5 Lessons 7 and 8, pages 119–120

Preparation and Prerequisites

Students should be familiar with the statement of the Side-Splitting Theorem.

Teaching the Lesson

Although geometry software is not necessary for this lesson, it fits nicely with many of its problems.

Explore and Discuss *(Student page 272)*

If students draw an arbitrary quadrilateral with their geometry software and then connect its midpoints, they will see that the inner quadrilateral is a parallelogram regardless of how they drag the vertices of the outer quadrilateral. Problem **1** asks them to prove this result.

ACTIVITY

Why Does It Happen? *(Student pages 272–273)*

PROBLEM 1 You might give your students a hint by suggesting that they draw the segment connecting points A and C in their outer quadrilateral. Notice that the illustration accompanying this problem shows three different configurations of quadrilateral $ABCD$, two of which look a bit out of the ordinary. It's interesting to ask students whether they consider all three figures to be quadrilaterals and if they can prove the midpoint result for all of them.

On Your Own *(Student pages 274–275)*

These problems provide students with the opportunity for individual practice. See the lesson Planning Guide for homework recommendations.

Take It Further *(Student pages 275–276)*

These problems will lead students in new directions or will challenge them to apply what they already know.

Options and Extensions

Resources

For more extensions of midpoints in quadrilaterals, check out the article, "The Sidesplitting Story of a Midpoint Polygon," published in *The Mathematics Teacher* 87 (April 1994): 249–256.

L E S S O N

Defining Similarity

Lesson Objective

Students are introduced to two definitions of *similarity* and learn about the similarity notation, ~, as well as prove triangle similarity theorems.

Content Overview

Students examine scaled copies of a horse and are introduced to the notion of similar figures. Notation and vocabulary are introduced and compared to notation and vocabulary used with congruent figures. Students then formulate similarity tests for triangles.

Planning Guide

Pacing	Activity	Materials	Homework Suggestions
Day 1	*Explore and Discuss* (SE pp. 279–280) Activity 1: Similarity (SE pp. 280–282)	No special materials needed.	*On Your Own,* Problem 1
Day 2	Activity 2: Similar Triangles (SE pp. 282–283)		*On Your Own,* Problems 2, 3, 4, 5, and 6
Day 3	Activity 3: Tests for Similar Triangles (SE pp. 283–286)		*On Your Own,* Problems 7, 8, 9, and 10
Day 4	Activity 3: Tests for Similar Triangles (SE pp. 283–286)		*On Your Own,* Problems 11, 12, 13, 14, and 15

Program Resources

- *Connected Geometry* CD-ROM, Module 4: Investigations 4.14 and 4.15
- *Solution and Problem Solving Resource,* pages 289–301
- *Assessment Resources,* Quiz 6 Lesson 9, pages 121–122

Preparation and Prerequisites

Students should be familiar with the term *dilation.*

Teaching the Lesson

Explore and Discuss *(Student pages 279–280)*

Two possible definitions of similarity are given—one involving scaling and the other dilation. The dilation definition isn't quite complete. It says that two figures are similar if one is a dilation of the other. While this is true, it limits similar figures to those pictures that are both oriented in the same way. (Recall that dilation does not change the orientation of a figure.) To help students see that this definition does not encompass all similar figures, the problems show a horse and a scaled copy of it that are pointing in opposite directions. Ask students if they can modify the definition to include this case.

ACTIVITY 1

Similarity *(Student pages 280–282)*

Students are familiar with the notation and vocabulary of congruence. It should therefore be an easy transition to using the notation and vocabulary of similarity.

ACTIVITY 2

Similar Triangles *(Student pages 282–283)*

PROBLEM 9 Students are asked to prove that two triangles—one with sides twice as long as the other—are similar. This is an important proof to understand, as it is the basis of the SSS Triangle Similarity Theorem introduced in the next activity.

ACTIVITY 3

Tests for Similar Triangles *(Student pages 283–286)*

The proofs of the AA, SAS, and SSS theorems often receive minimal attention in geometry texts. Since the theorems form the basis for so many problems that students will solve in the future, including trigonometry, you should find time to cover them.

After students have developed their own Triangle Similarity Theorems (Problem **11**), you can start with the AA theorem. Notice that the *Student Edition* refers to this theorem as "AAA" rather than "AA." That's because students need to figure out for themselves that it's not necessary to write "AAA," since just two angles will automatically determine the measure of the third angle (see Problem **17**).

If you carefully review the provided written proof of the AA theorem with your class, your students can then do the SAS proof themselves, as the proofs are nearly identical. The proof of the SSS theorem is slightly more complicated and uses the dilation definition of similarity.

On Your Own *(Student pages 287–290)*

These problems provide students with the opportunity for individual practice. See the lesson Planning Guide for homework recommendations.

Take It Further *(Student page 291)*

PROBLEM 16 One of the authors' favorite problems to pose to everyone (not just students) is the napkin problem. This problem can be assigned as an informal assessment.

LESSON

Using Similarity

Lesson Objective

Students use their knowledge of similarity and properties of similar figures to calculate distances, split segments into congruent parts and create constant-area rectangles.

Content Overview

Students explore three different "real-world" applications of similarity. Several experiments are provided that allow students to split a segment into any number of congruent pieces without taking a single measurement. Students prove a surprising result about chords of a circle that all pass through a common point—the *power-of-a-point* theorem. They then apply the theorem to create a *constant-area rectangle* with geometry software. A constant-area rectangle is one whose dimensions can change but whose area remains fixed as a vertex is dragged. Students are also introduced to the concept of *geometric mean.* Given two segments of lengths a and b, students construct their geometric mean—a segment of length $\sqrt{ab}$.

Planning Guide

Pacing	Activity	Materials	Homework Suggestions
Day 1	*Explore and Discuss* (SE p. 292) Activity 1: Calculating Distances and Heights (SE pp. 292–295)	• tape measures • calculators	*On Your Own,* Problems 1 and 2
Day 2	Activity 1: Calculating Distances and Heights (SE pp. 292–295)	• tape measures • calculators	*On Your Own,* Problem 3
Day 3	Activity 2: Segment Splitters (SE pp. 295–297)	• BLM 34, p. 43 • straightedge • lined notebook paper	*On Your Own,* Problem 4 Perspective: Segment-Splitting Devices
Day 4	Activity 3: A Constant-Area Rectangle (SE pp. 297–299)	geometry software	*On Your Own,* Problems 5 and 6
Day 5	Activity 3: A Constant-Area Rectangle (SE pp. 297–299)	geometry software	*On Your Own,* Problem 7

Day 6	Activity 4: The Geometric Mean (SE pp. 299–303)	geometry software	*On Your Own,* Problem 8
Day 7	Activity 4: The Geometric Mean (SE pp. 299–303)	geometry software	*Take It Further,* Problem 9

Program Resources

- *Connected Geometry* CD-ROM, Module 4: Investigation 4.16
- *Solution and Problem Solving Resource,* pages 302–324
- *Teaching Resources,* page 43
- *Assessment Resources,* Quiz 7 Lesson 10, page 123

Preparation and Prerequisites

Students should be familiar with the AA Triangle Similarity Theorem, scientific notation, the Parallel Theorem, and the fact that inscribed angles in a circle that intercept the same arc are equal in measure. They should also have facility in calculating with numbers written in scientific notation (by hand or with a calculator).

Teaching the Lesson

Explore and Discuss *(Student page 292)*

It should be clear to students that the person with the larger shadow (Nancy) is taller. It may be less clear how to find one height given the other. Encourage students to draw a picture. When they get the two right triangles set up, you might want to talk about what the hypotenuse represents (rays of the sun) and why the hypotenuses of the two triangles are parallel. You might want to ask: "Why does the length of a person's shadow change during the day, and when does it disappear?"

ACTIVITY 1

Calculating Distances and Heights *(Student pages 292–295)*

There are three different applications of similarity in this activity that allow students to find unknown distances and heights:

- *A Sea Story* By comparing the length of an outstretched thumb to the height of an object it covers (in this case, a mountain), students are able to compute the distance to the mountain. Problem **2** encourages students to try this technique with an actual object to see how well it works.
- *A "Shady" Method* This is the classic application of similarity, using the length of a shadow to figure out the height of a tree. Students can try this method for themselves, by finding, for example, the height of their school flagpole.
- *Tiny Planets* This very timely question asks students to figure out how big the planet of our nearest star would appear to the naked eye, supposing that we found such a planet.

For all of these applications, students will find that their calculations are only approximate. You might discuss with them what factors contribute to the inaccuracies.

ACTIVITY 2

Segment Splitters *(Student pages 295–297)*

The two experiments described in this activity are really surprising: Imagine being able to divide a segment into any number of congruent pieces without taking a single measurement! To give your students the excitement of this discovery, it might be a good idea to jump right into these experiments *without* giving an introduction, such as "Today you will be dividing a segment into congruent pieces . . . ."

These experiments work well when done by pairs of students, with half the class working on Experiment One and the other half Experiment Two. Both groups can then report their findings to the rest of the class when everyone has finished.

Blackline Master 34 for Experiment One is provided.

ACTIVITY 3

A Constant-Area Rectangle *(Student pages 297–299)*

Typically, the power-of-a-point theorem appears in geometry books as a mere curiosity. Students learn the theorem, prove it, use it in some numerical problems, and then move on. It probably leaves no lasting impression. This activity attempts to remedy that situation by showing how the theorem can be used to create an interesting animated object with geometry software—a constant-area rectangle.

Specifically, the geometry that lies behind the power-of-a-point theorem becomes the "engine" that drives the movement of the constant-area rectangle. By setting the theorem in motion, students are able to uncover relationships that the theorem's static counterpart in a textbook cannot reveal.

The first, and probably most important, thing to say about this activity is that you should definitely work it through yourself before trying it with your students. The authors have adopted a novel approach to teaching the power-of-a-point theorem (as described above), but it does require some preparation.

ACTIVITY 4

The Geometric Mean *(Student pages 299–303)*

This activity begins with several rectangle challenges. Students are asked to construct the missing side of a rectangle so that the completed rectangle has an area equal to that of a given rectangle. The "Ways to Think About It" section shows how this construction can be done, and, as you will see, the method involves applying the results from the power-of-a-point material.

The activity concludes with a return to the challenge from Activity 3: How can you construct a constant-area rectangle using geometry software? This time, however, students are asked to build the rectangle using the geometric mean results developed in this activity. You'll find a downloadable sketch of this construction created with The Geometer's Sketchpad®, as well as a Java animation, at the *Connected Geometry* Web site: http://www.edc.org/LTT/ConnGeo.

On Your Own *(Student pages 303–305)*

These problems provide students with the opportunity for individual practice. See the lesson Planning Guide for homework recommendations.

Take It Further *(Student page 306)*

These problems will lead students in new directions or will challenge them to apply what they already know.

Options and Extensions

Resources

Just as the authors were putting the finishing touches on this unit, there came news that two students from Greens Farms Academy in Connecticut devised their own method for splitting a segment into any number of congruent parts using geometry software. For a complete account of their method, see the article "Euclid, Fibonacci, Sketchpad" by Daniel C. Litchfield and David A. Goldenheim, *The Mathematics Teacher* (January 1997): 8–12.

Activity 3 begins with a brief review of the distinction between drawing a rectangle with geometry software and constructing one. The activity assumes a fair degree of familiarity with the construction tools of dynamic geometry, so students should be comfortable with the idea of making geometric constructions with the software. If your class is not at this level or you do not have sufficient lab time, you can instead show them pre-made sketches of constant-area rectangles. You will find a downloadable sketch created with *The Geometer's Sketchpad* at the *Connected Geometry* Web site: http://www.edc.org/LTT/ConnGeo. You will also find Java animations of the sketch at this site.

For more background information on this activity, see the article "Theorems in Motion: Using Dynamic Geometry to Gain Fresh Insights" by Daniel P. Scher, *The Mathematics Teacher* 89 (April 1996): 330–332.

In *Take It Further,* Problem **13,** a collection of similar triangles is used to create lengths that form a geometric sequence. This construction dates back to Descartes and can be extended with geometry software to create logarithmic curves. For a wonderful discussion of the construction and its potential uses in the classroom see the article "Drawing Logarithmic Curves with Geometer's Sketchpad: A Method Inspired by Historical Sources" by David Dennis, *Geometry Turned On* (MAA Notes #41, 1977): 147–156.

LESSON

11 Areas of Similar Polygons

Lesson Objective

This lesson is designed to encourage students to discover the affect of scaling on the area of polygons.

Content Overview

In this lesson, students begin by discovering how the areas of rectangles and triangles are affected by scaling. They then use these results to answer the same question for general polygons. The apothem of a regular polygon is introduced, along with a way to use it to calculate the areas of regular polygons.

This lesson includes the following topics:

- When a rectangle or triangle is scaled by a factor of r, the ratio of the area of the scaled copy to the original is r^2.
- When an arbitrary polygon is scaled by a factor of r, the ratio of the area of the scaled copy to the original is r^2. This is shown by dividing the polygon into triangles.
- To find the area of a regular polygon, one can use the following formula: area $= \frac{1}{2}$(perimeter)(apothem).

Planning Guide

Pacing	Activity	Materials	Homework Suggestions
Day 1	*Explore and Discuss* (SE p. 310) Activity 1: Comparing Areas (SE pp. 310–312)	• rulers • scissors • geometry software (optional)	*On Your Own,* Problems 1, 2, and 3
Day 2	Activity 1: Comparing Areas (SE pp. 310–312) Activity 2: Introducing the Apothem (SE p. 312)	No special materials needed.	*On Your Own,* Problems 4 and 5

Program Resources

- *Connected Geometry* CD-ROM, Module 4: Investigation 4.17
- *Solution and Problem Solving Resource,* pages 325–332
- *Assessment Resources,* Quiz 8 Lesson 11, page 124

Preparation and Prerequisites

Students should be able to scale rectangles and triangles and have some knowledge of elementary algebra.

Teaching the Lesson

Explore and Discuss *(Student page 310)*

One of the most effective ways for students to see how a change in scale affects the area of a rectangle or triangle is to actually draw the figure, scale it, and see how many copies of the scaled copy fit inside the original. Students either draw and scale the figures by hand or use geometry software to do the scaling for them.

ACTIVITY 1

Comparing Areas *(Student pages 310–312)*

PROBLEM 6 The area of Polygon 1 is $a + b + c + d$, while the area of Polygon 2 is $ar^2 + br^2 + cr^2 + dr^2$. In order for students to see that the ratio of the areas is r^2, you might need to point out that the area of Polygon 2 can be rewritten as $r^2(a + b + c + d)$.

ACTIVITY 2

Introducing the Apothem *(Student page 312)*

The apothem and the area formula for regular polygons are introduced here because they will be used in Lesson 12 to derive a relationship between the area and circumference of a circle.

On Your Own *(Student page 313)*

These problems provide students with the opportunity for individual practice. See the lesson Planning Guide for homework recommendations.

Take It Further *(Student pages 313–314)*

PROBLEMS 6–7 These problems provide students with another practical application of area and scaling—constructing scale drawings of two plots of land to determine which has the larger area. Making the scale drawings and calculating their areas involve a fair amount of work and can serve as an excellent project. Students can use either a pencil, ruler, and protractor or geometry software to create the scale drawings.

LESSON

12 Areas and Perimeters of Blobs and Circles

Lesson Objective

This lesson introduces students to techniques for finding the perimeters of curves and approximating the circumference of circles and develops a formula that relates the area of a circle to its circumference.

Content Overview

In Lesson 11, students examined how much the areas of polygons change when they are scaled. This lesson extends the process to closed curves and circles and asks how their areas change when they are scaled. Fundamental concepts from calculus, such as sequences, approximations, and limits, are introduced in an intuitive way to allow students to answer the questions.

- How can we find the areas of figures that have curves? We can obtain better and better approximations for the area of a curved figure by laying finer and finer ruled graph paper on top of it and counting how many squares cover the figure.
- In particular, graph paper can be used to estimate the area of a unit circle.
- When a curved figure is scaled by r, the ratio of the scaled copy to the original is r^2.
- To find the perimeter of a closed curve (affectionately called a "blob" in the Student Edition), you can approximate it using a series of straight lines.
- To find the circumference of a circle, you can inscribe and circumscribe polygons with more and more sides on the circle. The perimeters of these polygons serve as upper and lower bounds for the circumference and approach a common value as the number of polygon sides grows.
- The formula "area of circle $= \frac{1}{2}$(circumference)(radius)" is developed as an extension of the polygon area formula from Lesson 11.

Planning Guide

Pacing	Activity	Materials	Homework Suggestions
Day 1	*Explore and Discuss* (SE p. 315) Activity 1: Inner and Outer Sums (SE pp. 316–318)	graph paper	*On Your Own,* Problems 1 and 2
Day 2	Activity 1: Inner and Outer Sums (SE pp. 316–318)	• graph paper • large paper	*On Your Own,* Problem 3

Day 3	Activity 2: Comparing the Areas of Blobs (SE pp. 318–320)	graph paper	*On Your Own,* Problems 4, 5, 6, and 7
Day 4	Activity 3: Perimeters of Blobs and Circles (SE pp. 320–322)	rulers	*On Your Own,* Problems 8, 9, and 10
Day 5	Activity 4: Connecting Area and Circumference (SE pp. 323–324)	No special materials needed.	*On Your Own,* Problems 11 and 12 *Take It Further,* Problem 14

Program Resources

- *Connected Geometry* CD-ROM, Module 4: Investigations 4.18 and 4.19
- *Solution and Problem Solving Resource,* pages 333–341
- *Assessment Resources,* Quiz 9 Lesson 12, page 125

Preparation and Prerequisites

Students should be familiar and comfortable with topics from Lesson 11.

Teaching the Lesson

This lesson serves as groundwork for many of the ideas that your students will eventually encounter if they study calculus. It's intended to be an informal, intuitive introduction to concepts like sequences and limits, and no previous knowledge of these ideas is assumed.

Explore and Discuss *(Student page 315)*

Before introducing the grid method described in the *Student Edition,* be sure to ask students to come up with their own ideas about how to estimate the area of the "blob." Once you begin the grid method, students should be able to suggest ways to make it give better and better approximations. When students reach calculus, they do not always get the chance to actually take measurements and try out this grid method for approximating area. By giving them the chance to do so here, you will help them build their intuition so that they will be ready for a more formal approach in calculus.

ACTIVITY 1

Inner and Outer Sums *(Student pages 316–318)*

Rather than just tell students that the area formula for a circle is πr^2, the *Student Edition* develops the formula from scratch. If students have derived this formula in Unit 3, *The Cutting Edge,* you may want to point out the similarities between the two derivations.

PROBLEM 6 This problem begins the development of the area formula for circles. It asks students to draw a circle with a 1-foot radius and estimate its area. Once students know the area of a circle with radius 1 foot, they will be able to use this value to figure out the area of any circle in Activity 4.

ACTIVITY 2 Comparing the Areas of Blobs *(Student pages 318–320)*

PROBLEM 8 This problem is an informal proof that when a closed curve is scaled by r, its area changes by r^2. The basic thinking behind this proof is that a curve can be approximated by a grid of squares and that each individual square grows by a factor of r^2 when the curve itself is scaled.

ACTIVITY 3 Perimeters of Blobs and Circles *(Student pages 320–322)*

This activity is an informal introduction to perimeter concepts that your students will eventually encounter if they study calculus. The basic question here is the following: *How can you estimate the perimeter of a curve and then improve your estimate?* The approach—estimating the perimeter with a series of straight lines—is one that your students should be able to suggest. Make sure to give students a chance to try this method with either the "blob" provided in the *Student Edition* or another curve that you supply (perhaps a larger one).

A similar, but not identical, approach to perimeter and area for circles is given in the module The Cutting Edge.

The section "Perimeters of Circles" extends the perimeter estimation technique to circles and introduces the important idea of circumscribing polygons about a circle and inscribing polygons into a circle. Again, being able to actually try this idea is important. For convenience sake, pictures of 4-sided, 8-sided, and 16-sided polygons inscribed in and circumscribed about a circle are provided so that students have only to take measurements. They can also use the polygon scripts provided with geometry software to draw the polygons.

ACTIVITY 4 Connecting Area and Circumference *(Student pages 323–324)*

Perhaps the most challenging part of this lesson is Activity 4. Here's a capsule summary of its main ideas:

1. The area formula for a regular polygon is $A = \frac{1}{2}Pa$, where P is the perimeter and a is the apothem.
2. Since you can estimate the area of a circle by inscribing a polygon in it, you should be able to use the polygon area formula to estimate the area of a circle. This approximation will get better and better as the number of polygon sides increases.
3. When the inscribed polygon has many sides, its perimeter is essentially the circumference of the circle, and its apothem approaches the circle's radius. Thus, you can replace P by C (circumference) and a by r (radius) to obtain the circle area formula $A = \frac{1}{2}Cr$.

On Your Own *(Student pages 324–326)*

These problems provide students with the opportunity for individual practice. See the lesson Planning Guide for homework recommendations.

Take It Further *(Student pages 326–327)*

These problems will lead students in new directions or will challenge them to apply what they already know.

LESSON

13 Circles and 3.14159265358979323846...

Lesson Objective

This lesson derives the area and circumference formulas for circles and provides an historical introduction to π.

Content Overview

- If a circle is scaled by r, then the ratio of the area of the scaled copy to the original is r^2. This results in a general formula for the area of a circle: If the radius of a circle with radius 1 is K, then the area of a circle with radius r is Kr^2.
- The value of K is approximately 3.14 and is known as π.
- The formula for the area of a circle is substituted into the following equation: "area of circle $= \frac{1}{2}$(circumference)(radius)." Thus, a general formula for the circumference of a circle has been derived.

Planning Guide

Pacing	Activity	Materials	Homework Suggestions
Day 1	*Explore and Discuss* (SE p. 328) Activity 1: An Area Formula for Circles (SE pp. 328–330)	calculators	*On Your Own,* Problems 1, 2, and 3 Perspective: All About π
Day 2	Activity 2: Circumference (SE p. 330)	calculators	*On Your Own,* Problems 4, 5, and 6

Program Resources

- *Connected Geometry* CD-ROM, Module 4: Investigation 4.20
- *Solution and Problem Solving Resource,* pages 342–347
- *Assessment Resources,* Quiz 10 Lesson 13, page 126

Preparation and Prerequisites

Students should be familiar and comfortable with topics from Lessons 11 and 12.

Teaching the Lesson

Explore and Discuss *(Student page 328)*

Encourage students to test Theorem 4.9 on several circles and attempt to formulate an argument that it is true for all circles.

ACTIVITY 1

An Area Formula for Circles *(Student pages 328–330)*

In order to derive the area formula for a circle, students first need to know the area of a circle with radius 1 foot (Problem **6** from Lesson 12). Now is a good time to review this problem. This activity builds up to the area formula of a circle in increments.

PROBLEM 1 This problem uses the area of a circle with radius 1 foot to find the area of any circle. This is an important problem, and you will probably want to go through it carefully. Some of its key points are:

- The area of a circle with radius 1 foot is approximately 3.1 square feet.
- When a curved figure, in particular, a circle, is scaled by a factor of r, its area changes by r^2. Thus, a circle with a radius of 5 feet, for example, has an area of approximately $3.1(5)^2$ square feet.

Students are then asked to prove Theorem 4.10, which says that the area of a circle with radius r is Kr^2, where K is the area of a circle with radius 1. Notice that the authors do not immediately call the area of a unit circle π. They prefer to stress the idea that π is a constant, and, aside from its fancy appearance, there is nothing particularly magical about it.

ACTIVITY 2

Circumference *(Student page 330)*

After Problem **10,** invite students to read the Perspective "All About π."

On Your Own *(Student pages 331–332)*

These problems provide students with the opportunity for individual practice. See the lesson Planning Guide for homework recommendations.

Take It Further *(Student pages 332–333)*

These problems will lead students in new directions or will challenge them to apply what they already know.

Options and Extensions

Perspective: All About π

The historical overview on π can lead to some student projects. A side note in the text makes reference to an excellent article on π in *The New Yorker.* It's a substantial, humorous piece that students can read and then report on to the class. The book *A History of Pi* (also mentioned in the Perspective) is another good source for a project report.

You can also direct your students to the World Wide Website http://www.go2net.com/internet/useless/useless/pi.html, which contains some fun information about pi.

Another book about π is *The Joy of Pi* by David Blatner, published by Walker and Company. A related Web site, http://www.joyofpi.com, contains information about pi and links to many other pi-related sites on the World Wide Web.

LESSON

An Introduction to Trigonometry

Lesson Objective

Students use their knowledge of similarity to work with trigonometric ratios and find lengths of sides and angle measures of right triangles, as well as areas of triangles.

Content Overview

Students are introduced to the trigonometric words *sine, cosine,* and *tangent.* They then solve right triangle problems using this new terminology. Students use trigonometry to derive the triangle area formula $A = \frac{1}{2}ab \sin \theta$.

Planning Guide

Pacing	Activity	Materials	Homework Suggestions
Day 1	*Explore and Discuss* (SE pp. 336–337) Activity 1: What Is Trigonometry? (SE pp. 337–339)	calculators	*On Your Own,* Problems 1 and 2
Day 2	Activity 1: What Is Trigonometry? (SE pp. 337–339)	calculators	*On Your Own,* Problems 3, 4, 5, and 6
Day 3	Activity 2: An Area Formula for Triangles (SE pp. 340–341)	calculators	*Take It Further,* Problem 9

Program Resources

- *Connected Geometry* CD-ROM, Module 4: Investigations 4.21, 4.22, and 4.23
- *Solution and Problem Solving Resource,* pages 348–360
- *Assessment Resources,* Quiz 11 Lesson 14, page 127

Preparation and Prerequisites

In order to understand the ideas behind trigonometry, students should be familiar with the basic properties of similar triangles, such as equal ratios of corresponding sides, covered earlier in this unit. Students should also know the standard area formula for triangles, area $= \frac{1}{2}$(base)(height).

Teaching the Lesson

Explore and Discuss *(Student pages 336–337)*

The problems in this section look at two right triangles, both of which have one acute angle of 27°. These problems stress that even though the triangles have different sizes, the ratios of their sides are the same.

ACTIVITY 1

What Is Trigonometry? *(Student pages 337–339)*

This activity introduces students to the trigonometric names given to the ratios mentioned above. You should make sure that students are able to find trigonometric values using their calculators. Be on the lookout for students whose calculators are set in radian rather than degree mode.

PROBLEM 6 This problem introduces students to the "special" angles (30°, 45°, and 60°) for which they can find the exact values of sine, cosine, and tangent.

ACTIVITY 2

An Area Formula for Triangles *(Student pages 340–341)*

PROBLEM 8 This problem asks students how to find the area of a triangle when they are given the lengths of two sides and the measure of the included angle. The problem gives specific numbers so that students do not have to generalize the procedure all at once. Before moving on to Problem **9,** which does ask students to find a general formula, you might give them a few more problems with specific numbers so that they start to see the pattern.

On Your Own *(Student pages 341–342)*

These problems provide students with the opportunity for individual practice. See the lesson Planning Guide for homework recommendations.

Take It Further *(Student pages 342–343)*

These problems will lead students in new directions or will challenge them to apply what they already know.

LESSON

15 Extending the Pythagorean Theorem

Lesson Objective

Students extend their knowledge of the Pythagorean Theorem to work with nonright triangles and arrive at the Law of Cosines formula.

Content Overview

Unit 1 contains another intriguing derivation of the Law of Cosines.

Students' typical introduction to the Law of Cosines is a highly algebraic one—after lots of symbol manipulation, they arrive at the formula $c^2 = a^2 + b^2 - 2ab \cos C$. There's something not entirely satisfying about this method. The Law of Cosines formula is very close to the Pythagorean Theorem, but the Pythagorean Theorem can be proved with very nice geometric dissection arguments (see Unit 3). Given the similarity of the Pythagorean Theorem and the Law of Cosines, the authors wondered whether there was also a geometric dissection to prove the Law of Cosines. Well, they found one!

Planning Guide

Pacing	Activity	Materials	Homework Suggestions
Day 1	*Explore and Discuss* (SE pp. 344–345)	geometry software	*Explore and Discuss,* part b
Day 2	Activity: A Recipe for Extending the Pythagorean Theorem (SE pp. 345–348)	geometry software	*On Your Own,* Problems 2 and 3
Day 3	Activity: A Recipe for Extending the Pythagorean Theorem (SE pp. 345–348)	geometry software	*On Your Own,* Problem 1 *Take It Further,* Problem 6

Program Resources

- *Connected Geometry* CD-ROM, Module 4: Investigation 4.24
- *Solution and Problem Solving Resource,* pages 361–367
- *Assessment Resources,* Quiz 12 Lesson 15, page 128

Preparation and Prerequisites

For this lesson, students should be familiar with the Pythagorean Theorem.

Teaching the Lesson

Explore and Discuss *(Student pages 344–345)*

The problems in this section ask students to experiment with nonright triangles to see if the Pythagorean relationship still holds.

ACTIVITY

A Recipe for Extending the Pythagorean Theorem *(Student pages 345–348)*

This "recipe" is a dynamic geometry construction that requires students to be able to construct squares and parallelograms. Encourage students to keep referring to the illustration that accompanies this construction so that they don't construct a square or parallelogram facing the wrong direction. If students find the construction too difficult, you might provide them with a pre-made one.

PROBLEM 2 By experimenting with the construction, students should be able to conjecture that the area of square *ADEB* is equal to the sum of the areas of the two smaller squares and two parallelograms. This is the main conjecture that students will develop in this activity.

PROBLEMS 5–6 Now that students know the relationship among these areas, all that remains is to algebraically determine their values. Finding the areas of the squares is straightforward, but calculating the parallelograms' area requires using the result from Problem **10** in Lesson 14.

PROBLEM 7 Theorem 4.11 brings this information all together in one formula.

PROBLEM 9 This problem asks students to apply Theorem 4.11 to two triangles, finding the lengths of unknown sides. You will notice that this activity never mentions the Law of Cosines by name. Rather than immediately ask students to remember the algebraic formula $c^2 = a^2 + b^2 - 2ab \cos C$, it makes sense to stick with geometric dissections, at least for a little while. In this way, students will view right triangles as a case in which two squares are added together to form a larger square and general triangles as a case in which two squares and *two parallelograms* are combined to form a larger square. These facts help to emphasize that the Pythagorean Theorem needs only slight modifications in order for it to work for all triangles.

On Your Own *(Student page 348)*

These problems provide students with the opportunity for individual practice. See the lesson Planning Guide for homework recommendations.

Take It Further *(Student pages 348–349)*

PROBLEM 5 This problem provides a nice tie-in to the Pythagorean Theorem. By making $\triangle ABC$ a right triangle in the software construction, the two parallelograms disappear, and you are left with a picture that nicely illustrates a dissection proof of the Pythagorean Theorem (see the *Solution and Problem Solving Resource* for details).

Options and Extensions

Without Technology

This lesson can be done without geometry software, but it loses much of its impact because students are not able to experiment with different triangles. Even if you do not have enough computers for your whole class, it is still effective if you use just one computer in front of the classroom to demonstrate the construction.

Mathematics Connections

Why Is This Dissection Equivalent to the Law of Cosines? The authors chose not to equate this dynamic geometry construction with the Law of Cosines, but if you are using this book with a more advanced group, you can easily make the connection. Theorem 4.11 says that $c^2 = a^2 + b^2$ plus the area of two parallelograms. The area of these parallelograms combined is $2ab \sin(\theta - 90°)$. From trigonometry, you know that $\sin(\theta - 90°)$ is equal to $\sin\theta \cos 90° - \cos\theta \sin 90° = -\cos\theta$. Thus $c^2 = a^2 + b^2 + 2ab(-\cos\theta)$, or equivalently, $c^2 = a^2 + b^2 - 2ab(\cos\theta)$.

Unit 4 Review

This unit review is intended to provide students with problems that will encourage them to look back at the unit as a whole. Students have one more opportunity to pull together, apply, and communicate the ideas they have developed by working on the activities throughout the unit.

It is especially important for students to have the opportunity to share their solutions with the class.

PROBLEM 1 Students should be able to set up the appropriate ratios $\frac{1 \text{ in.}}{5 \text{ mi}}$, $\frac{1 \text{ in.}}{10 \text{ min}}$, and so on and use them to interpret the map.

PROBLEM 2 Students should be able to take appropriate measurements of lengths and angles to determine if the figures are similar or not. If they are, students should calculate ratios, side of small:side of large, or the reciprocal. Things to watch for:

- Students assume that the figures are similar and just measure for scale factor.
- In looking for a scale factor, students take the ratio of two lengths on the same figure.
- In reporting the scale factor, students simply say a number without describing which direction that factor applies (from first to second or from second to first).

PROBLEM 3 Students should know that the area of a scaled figure changes as the square of the scale factor. If students answer $\frac{3}{5}$, they are not clear on this point. Also, when reporting the ratio of areas as $\frac{9}{25}$, it should be clear that the ratio is copy:original.

PROBLEM 4 This problem gets at the same understanding as Problem **3,** but this problem requires at least two steps. Students must find the ratio of the areas and then recognize that the squares of the scale factor, or they must realize that they want the ratios of sidelengths, and they can find those from the areas. If students simply take the ratio of the areas (80:5 or a scale factor of 16), then they do not understand the relationship between scale factor and area.

PROBLEM 5 The idea here is that students articulate some important properties of similarity. If they are thinking about polygons, they might say "…their sides are in proportion and their corresponding angles are congruent." This is fine, but you might encourage students to expand upon it a little by asking: "What about circles? What about cylinders?" A clearer response might be, "…their corresponding lengths are in proportion and their corresponding angles are congruent." The definitions provided in the book build on ideas of congruence and dilation: "Two figures are similar if one is congruent to a dilation of the other."

PROBLEM 6 This is simply a review of triangle similarity tests, but encourage students not just to list letters (AA, SSS, SAS), but to explain what the letters mean. For similarity, SSS means three sides *in proportion,* not three sides congruent, for example. Also, watch for students who confuse similarity with congruence and list ASA and/or don't include AA.

PROBLEM 7 The idea here is to think about shapes that are completely determined by a single dimension: regular polygons, cubes, circles, spheres, and so on. Irregular figures will not work here.

PROBLEM 8 Students should be comfortable using either the ratio or parallel method to create a dilation.

PROBLEM 9 This problem asks students to review the method of inner and outer sums for approximating areas. The answer given should be a range, such as $2.5 \text{ in}^2 < A < 4 \text{ in}^2$. If students come up with a single number, they may have averaged the two values (a logical thing to do when thinking about approximation). The notion of "trapping" a number between upper and lower bounds that converge is an important one and should be emphasized.

PROBLEM 10 These problems simply ask students to recall and apply the area formula for circles.

PROBLEM 11 This problem asks students to be a bit creative in finding areas. First, they must recognize that the height of the triangle allows them to find the area of both the circle and the triangle. Then, they must recognize the shaded region as the area of $\frac{1}{2}$ the circle plus the triangle. Finally, students must realize that the white region is the area of the circle minus the shaded region. (Alternately, they may see the white region as half the circle minus the triangle.) It is not important for students to report areas exactly (in terms of π) or approximately, but rather that they understand these relationships.

PROBLEM 12 This problem provides a review of the definitions of sine, cosine, and tangent in terms of the sides of a right triangle. If students write numbers rather than ratios of sides, they may not understand the meaning and use of these functions.

PROBLEM 13 This problem asks students to plug numbers into the ratios from Problem **12.** Given the legs of a right triangle, students must find the hypotenuse with the Pythagorean Theorem (or by recognizing the 3, 4, 5 triple) and plug 3, 4, and 5 into the ratios.

PROBLEM 14 This problem requires students to connect the Law of Cosines (Theorem 4.11 in the Student Edition) to the Pythagorean Theorem by thinking about what happens when $m\angle C$ is 90°. Seeing connections between theorems, especially recognizing when one theorem is a special (but important) case of another, is an important habit of mind.

UNIT 5

The Language of Coordinates and Vectors

Connecting Geometry and Algebra

Unit Overview

This unit provides an introduction to analytical geometry—from the notion of what a coordinate system is to standard Cartesian coordinates in two and three dimensions and continuing on to vectors. Habits of mind include picturing the visible and the invisible, proving, and using different systems.

The first lesson of this unit provides an introduction to coordinates in one, two, and three dimensions. Lesson 1 is ideal for a high school class not yet familiar with coordinates (an algebra, geometry, or integrated mathematics course). Topics include plotting points and lines, deriving the midpoint and distance formulas, working with points in 3-dimensional space, thinking about collinearity, and numerical properties of the coordinates of basic shapes.

As the unit progresses, students explore how algebraic manipulations on coordinates transform points and objects in a Cartesian coordinate system. Students learn about translations, dilations, and reflections of shapes by operating (arithmetically) on the coordinates of the points that make them up. New notation is introduced—$(x, y) \mapsto (2x + 3, 2y - 4)$—to describe transformations on points.

The unit begins to introduce vectors informally as *arrows* with length and direction, a notion which is developed further in the unit. Mathematicians point out that vectors are not arrows: They are equivalence classes or translations. The authors believe students can see vectors in that way. In the activities in this unit, students build up to those views—first using vectors as translations and later in the unit thinking about

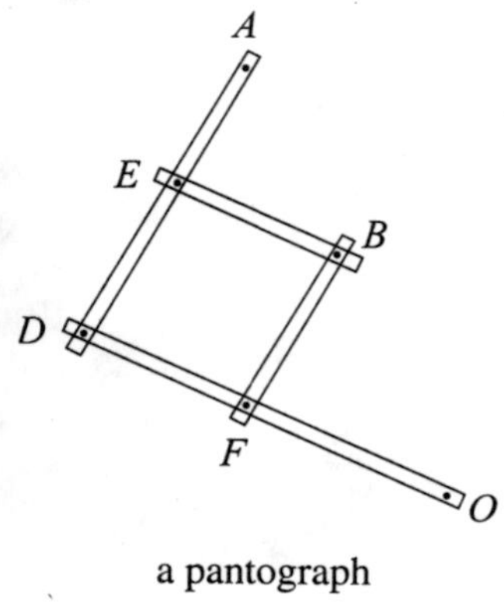

a pantograph

equivalent vectors as those with the same length and direction, no matter where their *start point* is. The authors assume that this is the first time your students have seen vectors, so the treatment remains informal. Students can focus on the big ideas so that when they encounter vectors again—in calculus, physics, or linear algebra, for example—they are ready to think about them in more formal ways.

Toward the end of this unit, the notion of vectors and the operations of adding and scaling points are formalized. This unit also develops the proofs of two theorems that focus on the algebra of points and ends with students using vectors to prove some standard Euclidean geometric results and to analyze how a pantograph works. The unit is an ideal exploration for more advanced classes and for classes working seriously with the notion of proof. The last lesson of this unit is a review of slope and equations of lines that is presented by using what students know about vectors.

Learning Goals

1. Use the Cartesian coordinate system in one, two, and three dimensions.
2. Plot points given coordinates and read coordinates from points on a coordinate grid.
3. Find the midpoint and the distance between two points.
4. Relate the midpoint formula to similar triangles and the distance formula to the Pythagorean Theorem.
5. Scale figures by operating on the coordinates of points.
6. Translate figures by operating on coordinates.
7. Interpret and write rules using " $\mapsto$ ", for example, $(x, y) \mapsto (2x + 1, 2y)$.
8. Describe which operations on coordinates produce congruent figures, which produce similar figures, and which produce distortions.
9. Give examples of equivalent rules—rules that show a different process with the same result.
10. Operate on points: Scale a point by a number, add two points, add a point to every point on a figure, and so on.
11. Explain that all multiples of a point lie along a line through that point and the origin.
12. Describe where cA is located, relative to A and O, for different values of c, including $c > 1$, $0 \le c \le 1$, $c < 0$, $c = 0$, and $c = 1$.
13. Describe and implement two ways to add points: adding the coordinates and using the "parallelogram method."
14. Determine if two vectors are parallel and if two vectors are equivalent (parallel and the same length).
15. Read, complete, and create proofs using coordinates, vectors, and the algebra of points.
16. Use vector algebra to write equations for and establish properties of lines.

Assessment Opportunities

Quizzes and Informal Assessment

- If you want to conduct a short assessment on the coordinate system and the plotting of points, you might create a quiz with problems like these:
  1. Why is the location of points important?
  2. Describe the characteristics of x- and y-coordinates in each of the four quadrants in the Cartesian coordinate system.
  3. Create any graph and label the points with letters. Identify each point.
- For informal assessment, create a short quiz with problems that use the midpoint and distance formulas.

Journal Ideas

Students keep writing assignments in a journal. Possible assignments:

- Lesson 2, *Write and Reflect,* Problem 42. Explain how two triangles are congruent and how two triangles are similar.
- Lesson 2, *Write and Reflect,* Problem 51. Give a set of instructions for finding points that are collinear to a given point.
- Lesson 2. Start with the Pythagorean Theorem and turn it into the distance formula.
- Lesson 6, *Write and Reflect,* Problem 3. Describe how a scaled point is related to the original point.
- Lesson 6, *Write and Reflect,* Problem 4. Explain the "scaling" operation.
- Lesson 7, *Write and Reflect,* Problem 8. Go through a proof and give reasons for each step.

UNIT 5 Planning Guide

Lessons	Learning Goals	Assessment Opportunities	Suggested Pacing	Materials
LESSON 1 *Introduction to Coordinates*	1, 2	*Checkpoint,* Problems 8 and 18 Quiz 1, *Assessment Resources,* p. 158	2 days	graph paper
LESSON 2 *Lines, Midpoints, and Distance*	1, 2, 3, 4	*Checkpoint,* Problems 12, 43, and 52 Quiz 2, *Assessment Resources,* p. 159	3 days	graph paper

LESSON 3 *Coordinates in Three Dimensions*	1, 2, 3, 4	*Checkpoint,* Problems 8, 11, and 18 Quiz 3, *Assessment Resource,* p. 160	3 days	• graph paper • pencils • tape • clay • toothpicks • stiff paper • scissors
LESSON 4 *Stretching and Shrinking Things*	5, 7, 8	*Checkpoint,* Problem 9 Quiz 4, *Assessment Resources,* p. 161	2 days	• BLM 35, p. 44 • BLM 36, p. 45 • BLM 37, p. 46 • graph paper
LESSON 5 *Changing the Location of Things*	6, 7, 8, 9	*Checkpoint,* Problem 10 Quiz 5 *Assessment Resources,* p. 162 Mid-Unit Exam, *Assessment Resources,* pp. 169–175	2 days	graph paper
LESSON 6 *Adding Points and Scaling Points*	10	*Checkpoint,* Problems 18, 31, and 36 Quiz 6, *Assessment Resources,* pp. 163–164	3 days	• BLM 38, p. 47 • BLM 39, p. 48 • BLM 40, p. 49 • BLM 41, p. 50 • graph paper
LESSON 7 *The Algebra of Points*	11, 12	*Checkpoint,* Problems 12, 20, 24, 32, and 36 Quiz 7, *Assessment Resources,* p. 165	5 days	• BLM 42, p. 51 • BLM 43, p. 52 • graph paper
LESSON 8 *Vectors and Geometry*	13, 14, 15	*Checkpoint,* Problems 17 and 24 Quiz 8, *Assessment Resources,* p. 166	3 days	• BLM 44, p. 53 • BLM 45, p. 54 • BLM 46, p. 55 • BLM 47, p. 56 • BLM 48, p. 57 • graph paper
LESSON 9 *Slope and Equations of Lines*	16	*Checkpoint,* Problems 5, 14, and 19 Quiz 9, *Assessment Resources,* pp. 167–168	3 days	graph paper
UNIT 5 REVIEW		End-of-Unit Exam, *Assessment Resources,* pp. 176–181	2 days (including testing)	• BLM 49, p. 58 • graph paper

LESSON

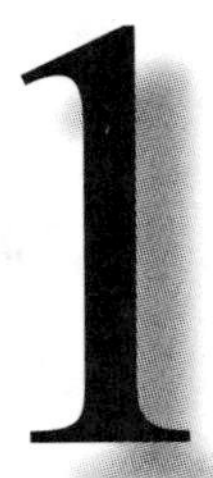

Introduction to Coordinates

Lesson Objective

Students learn the basics of Cartesian coordinates and how to plot points.

Content Overview

- Coordinates on a number line
- Coordinates on a Cartesian plane
- Points on horizontal and vertical lines
- Polar coordinates on a 2-dimensional coordinate system

Planning Guide

Pacing	Activity	Materials	Homework Suggestions
Day 1	*Explore and Discuss* (SE p. 354) Activity 1: One of Two Common Systems (SE pp. 355–357)	graph paper	*On Your Own,* Problems 1–5
Day 2	Activity 2: Coordinate Practice (SE pp. 358–359)	graph paper	*On Your Own,* Problems 6–11

Program Resources

- *Connected Geometry* CD-ROM, Module 5: Investigations 5.1 and 5.2
- *Solution and Problem Solving Resource,* pages 371–380
- *Assessment Resources,* Quiz 1 Lesson 1, page 158

Preparation and Prerequisites

This introductory lesson requires no prior knowledge of coordinates.

Teaching the Lesson

If students already have a good deal of knowledge of the coordinate system you should be able to move fairly quickly through this lesson.

Explore and Discuss *(Student page 354)*

These problems introduce students to the need for locating and labeling points on various systems.

ACTIVITY 1

One of Two Common Systems *(Student pages 355–357)*

For Discussion *(Student page 357)*

Encourage some early conjectures about operations on coordinates. Follow with the discussion about changing signs. Relate the discussion on changing signs back to Problem **5.** If you start with two positive coordinates, what happens when you make the first one negative instead? What happens when you make the second one negative? What happens when both signs are negative? You may want to introduce the following notation and definition of reflection:

Note that these statements don't depend on whether x and y are positive or negative.

- If $A = (x, y)$, then $B = (-x, y)$ is the reflection of A over the y-axis.
- If $A = (x, y)$, then $C = (x, -y)$ is the reflection of A over the x-axis.
- If $A = (x, y)$, then $D = (-x, -y)$ is the reflection of A over first one axis and then the other. (Some teachers refer to this as reflecting A over the origin.)

ACTIVITY 2

Coordinate Practice *(Student pages 358–359)*

Students explore the properties of points that are on horizontal and vertical lines and learn how to tell if points lie on horizontal or vertical lines.

On Your Own *(Student pages 359–362)*

These problems provide students with the opportunity for individual practice. See the lesson Planning Guide for homework recommendations.

Take It Further *(Student pages 362–363)*

These problems will lead students in new directions or will challenge them to apply what they already know.

Options and Extensions

Supplementary Activities

To start developing an informal notion of function on the plane, you might try the following short activity:

For example, have students stand at (−5, 0), (−4, 0), . . ., (0, 0), . . . , (4, 0), (5, 0), *and so on. Ask students to identify their starting and ending coordinates.*

This grid will quickly get too big to be in the classroom. It's a fun activity to do outside if you can. Or students can estimate how far away the person at (5, 0) *will be. Will he or she still be on the school grounds?*

Logo also features `pos`, `xcor`, *and* `ycor` *commands that return the value of the current position, the current x-coordinate or the current y-coordinate. You can use these commands to save your current position and return to it later.*

Create a coordinate grid for your classroom. Have students stand along the x-axis of your classroom grid. Then ask them to follow and act out rules like the following:

- Make your second coordinate the same as your first.
- Make your second coordinate the negative of your first.
- Make your second coordinate twice as much as your first, half as much, or any other multiple.
- Make your second coordinate the square of your first.
- For the person at the origin, make your second coordinate 1. For everyone to his or her right, make your second coordinate twice as much as the person before you. Where should the people to the left of the person at (0, 1) stand? Will anyone have a second coordinate of zero? A negative second coordinate?

Afterwards, ask students to sketch (freehand) the various shapes in which they were standing.

Using Technology

Pieces of paper, the floor or wall of a room, or a planar space in your mind's eye can be divided into the four quadrants of a Cartesian plane. Then the 2-dimensional drawing or image of any object can be examined on that plane. Logo does the same thing with the screen of a computer, and you can take advantage of it if you program in Logo. The "home" position of the turtle is at the origin, with coordinates (0, 0). Picture a horizontal line running across your screen and a vertical line running down the screen, each passing through "home." Those are your coordinate axes.

1. Write a program in Logo that will draw the x- and y-axes on your screen.
2. You can use Logo's `setpos`, `setx`, and `sety` commands to tell the turtle exactly where to go on the screen.
   a. Try the following commands. For each command, start from "home" and from other locations on the screen.
      - `setpos` [−20, 50]
      - `setx` 100
      - `sety` −60

   b. Try a few more examples of `setpos`, `setx`, and `sety`.

   c. Explain what each command does to the turtle—both to its location on the screen and to the direction in which it points.
3. You can use `setpos`, `setx`, and `sety` to draw shapes exactly where you want them on the screen. Draw a quadrilateral with vertices at (90, 50), (−80, 30), (−120, −60), and (50, 10).
4. Use `setpos`, `setx`, and `sety` to draw a square with sidelength 95 and one vertex at (45, 10).
5. Write a procedure that will draw a square with a sidelength that you input and one vertex at a point that you input.

LESSON

Lines, Midpoints, and Distance

Lesson Objective

Students develop the midpoint and distance formulas.

Content Overview

This lesson contains a brief review of point plotting and then moves on to developing what the authors call "coordinate sense." Students will learn about:

- horizontal and vertical lines;
- collinearity;
- midpoints; and
- distance.

Students also explore the equivalence of two different methods for finding midpoints.

Planning Guide

Pacing	Activity	Materials	Homework Suggestions
Day 1	*Explore and Discuss* (SE p. 366) Activity 1: Midpoints and Distance between Points (SE pp. 366–369)	graph paper	*On Your Own,* Problems 1, 2, 3, 4, 5, and 6
Day 2	Activity 2: Midpoint and Distance Formulas (SE pp. 369–373)	graph paper	*On Your Own,* Problems 7, 8, 9, 10, 11, 12, and 13
Day 3	Activity 3: Lines (SE pp. 373–374)	graph paper	*On Your Own,* Problems 14, 15, 16, and 17

Program Resources

- *Connected Geometry* CD-ROM, Module 5: Investigations 5.3 and 5.4
- *Solution and Problem Solving Resource,* pages 381–395
- *Assessment Resources,* Quiz 2 Lesson 2, page 159

Preparation and Prerequisites

Students should have familiarity with the coordinate plane and plotting points, with the Pythagorean Theorem since it is used to find distances, and with the term *congruent* since it is used in some problems.

Teaching the Lesson

Explore and Discuss *(Student page 366)*

You will want to hold a class discussion to summarize some important ideas:

- On a horizontal line, all points have the same y-coordinate.
- On a vertical line, all points have the same x-coordinate.

ACTIVITY 1

Midpoints and Distance between Points *(Student pages 366–369)*

End the activity with another summarizing discussion. Ask:

- How do you find the distance between two points on a vertical or horizontal line?
- How do you find the midpoint of a horizontal or vertical segment?
- How do you find the distance if two points are not on a vertical or horizontal line?

PROBLEM 7 Ask: *Why do you get a circle?* Students should realize (or you should point out) that this is exactly the definition of a circle: the set of points a fixed distance from a center point. As a follow-up, ask students to name six points that are five units from the point (1, 1). Can they find a rule to generate points on a circle? (Example: $(\sqrt{x}, \sqrt{25 - x^2})$ for $x \leq 25$)

PROBLEM 8 Conclude with a discussion about distance, and use the Pythagorean Theorem to find distance.

PROBLEMS 9–10 Follow up with a class discussion on how different students or groups solved these problems. Ask them to describe their methods for finding the midpoint of a nonvertical, nonhorizontal segment. Students can then *individually* write up Problems **11** and **12.**

ACTIVITY 2

Midpoint and Distance Formulas *(Student pages 369–373)*

If students are unfamiliar with subscripts, read from that section aloud in class, answering questions and clarifying as necessary.

A more traditional proof of the midpoint formula than the one provided in the *Student Edition* uses the distance formula and slope rather than the intermediate steps of finding two other midpoints. If your students already know about slope, you may want to present this proof after it is clear that they know the distance formula.

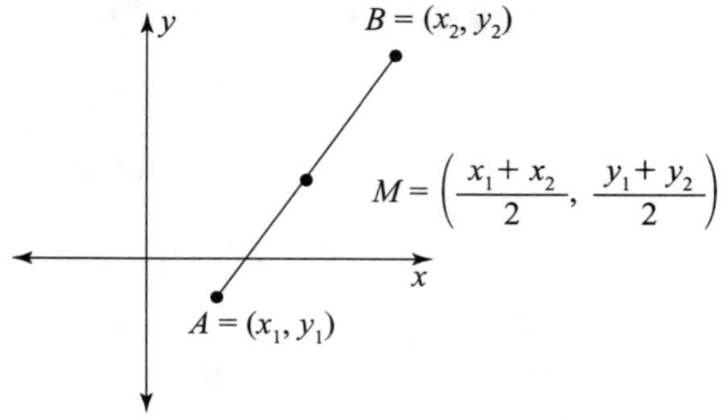

$$\text{slope of } \overline{AB} = \frac{y_2 - y_1}{x_2 - x_1}$$

$$\text{slope of } \overline{MB} = \frac{y_2 - \frac{y_1 + y_2}{2}}{x_2 - \frac{x_1 + x_2}{2}} = \frac{y_2 - y_1}{x_2 - x_1}$$

So, M is on the line containing $\overline{AB}$.

$$AM = \sqrt{\left(x_1 - \frac{x_1 + x_2}{2}\right)^2 + \left(y_1 - \frac{y_1 + y_2}{2}\right)^2}$$

$$= \frac{1}{2}\sqrt{(x_1 - x_2)^2 + (y_1 - y_2)^2}$$

$$BM = \sqrt{\left(x_2 - \frac{x_1 + x_2}{2}\right)^2 + \left(y_2 - \frac{y_1 + y_2}{2}\right)^2}$$

$$= \frac{1}{2}\sqrt{(x_2 - x_1)^2 + (y_2 - y_1)^2}$$

So, $AM = BM$. Therefore, M is the midpoint of $\overline{AB}$.

After you show students the proof, ask the following question: *Why is $(x_1 - x_2)^2$ the same as $(x_2 - x_1)^2$?* As part of the discussion on the distance formula, present different possible arrangements of two points such as those present below. Ask the class, "Given the formula in the Student Edition, does it matter which is x_1 and which is x_2?"

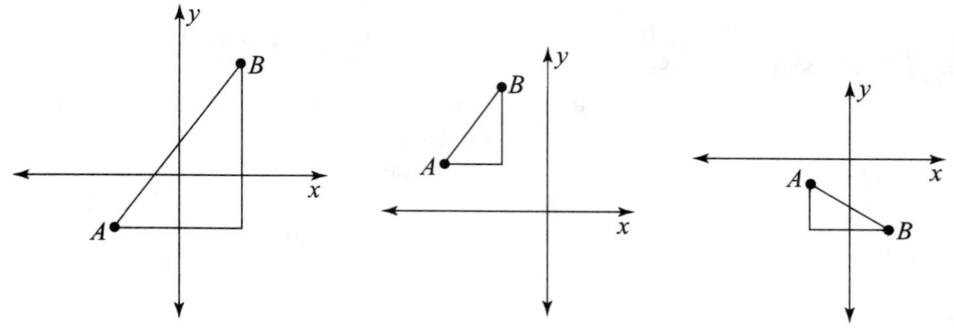

ACTIVITY 3

Lines (Student pages 373–374)

PROBLEM 51 Spend some time discussing students' responses to this problem and applying their methods to the *Checkpoint* problem for this activity.

On Your Own (Student pages 374–376)

These problems provide students with the opportunity for individual practice.

PROBLEM 9 This problem asks students to prove half of the Midline Theorem:

If students know about slope, it is not hard to prove the other half of the theorem as well.

THEOREM (Midline Theorem) *A segment connecting the midpoints of two sides of a triangle is parallel to the third side and half as long.*

In Unit 3, *The Cutting Edge,* students proved this theorem using congruent triangles. If students have seen both proofs, it might be interesting to compare them. Ask: "Which proof was easier to understand? Does one proof give you more insight into *why* than the other?"

Take It Further (Student pages 376–377)

These problems will lead students in new directions or will challenge them to apply what they already know.

LESSON

Coordinates in Three Dimensions

Lesson Objective

Students extend their coordinate sense to three dimensions.

Content Overview

In this lesson, students will

- build models of $\mathbb{R}^3$;
- think about shapes in space in terms of coordinate descriptions; and
- extend the midpoint and distance formulas to three dimensions.

Planning Guide

Pacing	Activity	Materials	Homework Suggestions
Day 1	*Explore and Discuss* (SE pp. 378–379) Activity 1: Points in Three-Dimensional Space (SE pp. 380–381)	• pencils • tape • clay • toothpicks • stiff paper • scissors • graph paper	*On Your Own,* Problems 1, 2, and 3
Day 2	Activity 2: Midpoints and Distance in Three Dimensions (SE pp. 381–382)	graph paper	*On Your Own,* Problems 4, 5, and 6
Day 3	Activity 3: Shapes in the Plane and in Space (SE pp. 382–384)	graph paper	*On Your Own,* Problems 7, 8, and 9

Program Resources

- *Connected Geometry* CD-ROM, Module 5: Investigations 5.5 and 5.6
- *Solution and Problem Solving Resource,* pages 396–402
- *Assessment Resources,* Quiz 3 Lesson 3, page 160

Preparation and Prerequisites

Students should have had some work with the Cartesian coordinate plane before doing this lesson.

Teaching the Lesson

You may want to set up your classroom as a 3-dimensional coordinate system for the introduction of this lesson, using a corner of the room and the intersection of the walls and floor as the axes.

Explore and Discuss *(Student pages 378–379)*

One of the most useful things you can do to help students visualize 3-dimensional coordinate systems is to start out with them building their own models of a 3-dimensional coordinate system.

You may choose to have individual students or groups create each of the 3-dimensional models.

For the model of planes using stiff paper, you may want to add a "grid" by gluing graph paper onto each side of the three sheets of stiff paper. This requires a little care to ensure that the slits are made along axes, but the graph paper helps some students with picturing points in space.

ACTIVITY 1

Points in Three-Dimensional Space *(Student pages 380–381)*

Students should refer to their models for help with the visualization problems. For homework, students may benefit from a model to use at home. The three-pencils model is sturdy, portable, and easy to recreate at home.

ACTIVITY 2

Midpoints and Distance in Three Dimensions *(Student pages 381–382)*

Students will extend their knowledge of finding midpoints and distance in two dimensions to the 3-dimensional coordinate system.

ACTIVITY 3

Shapes in the Plane and in Space *(Student pages 382–384)*

PROBLEMS 12–14 As students complete these problems, ask the following:

- What is the same about all of the coordinates of points on a circle centered at the origin? Centered at some other point?
- How does this idea extend to spheres?

PROBLEM 17 Ask the following:

- If $x + y = 12$ and $x - y = 12$ are both lines, how do they differ? What about things that look like them (for example, $4x + 3y = 12$)? This is a good time to review the equation of a line if your students have seen it before or to preview it if they have not.
- Why do the product and ratio produce such different shapes? How does the line for $\frac{y}{x} = 12$ relate to and differ from the line $y - x = 12$?
- What shapes do you get with $xy = 12$? Can you explain what happens near the axes?

On Your Own *(Student pages 384–386)*

These problems provide students with the opportunity for individual practice. See the lesson Planning Guide for homework recommendations.

Take It Further *(Student page 386)*

These problems will lead students in new directions or will challenge them to apply what they already know.

LESSON

Stretching and Shrinking Things

Lesson Objective

In this lesson, students learn two methods for scaling objects in the plane.

Content Overview

In this lesson, students scale objects

- by operating on the coordinates of the points on the figures and
- by stretching and shrinking vectors.

Planning Guide

Pacing	Activity	Materials	Homework Suggestions
Day 1	*Explore and Discuss* (SE p. 387) Activity: Stretching and Shrinking with Coordinates (SE pp. 387–390)	• BLM 35, p. 44 • BLM 36, p. 45 • graph paper	*On Your Own,* Problems 1, 2, 3, and 4
Day 2	Activity: Stretching and Shrinking with Coordinates (SE pp. 387–390)	• BLM 35, p. 44 • BLM 36, p. 45 • BLM 37, p. 46 • graph paper	*On Your Own,* Problems 5, 6, and 7

Program Resources

- *Connected Geometry* CD-ROM, Module 5: Investigations 5.7 and 5.8
- *Solution and Problem Solving Resource,* pages 403–410
- *Teaching Resources,* pages 44–46
- *Assessment Resources,* Quiz 4 Lesson 4, page 161

Preparation and Prerequisites

This lesson assumes familiarity with coordinates and point plotting.

Explore and Discuss *(Student page 387)*

If you have large pieces of graph paper or a graph board, you can have students demonstrate these problems and discuss the process as a class.

ACTIVITY

Stretching and Shrinking with Coordinates *(Student pages 387–390)*

PROBLEMS 1–6 After working on these problems, students should discuss their rules for what happens to figures when the coordinates of their points are multiplied by some number.

As a class, read about and discuss the "vector method" for scaling pictures.

The big idea in all of these problems is that multiplying the x- and y-coordinates of each point on a figure by some positive number scales the figure by that number, so you end up with a similar figure. There are some subtleties involved, however, and it is up to you how much you want to focus on these points:

- This is actually a dilation of the figure, not just a scaling of it. The figure will move closer to the origin if the scale factor is less than 1 and farther from the origin if the scale factor is greater than 1.
- For some positive number a, if you multiply the x-coordinate by a and the y-coordinate by $-a$, you get a scaled and flipped (reflected over the x-axis) copy of the figure. If you multiply the x-coordinate by $-a$ and the y-coordinate by a, the figure is scaled and reflected over the y-axis. If both the x- and y-coordinates are multiplied by $-a$, the figure is scaled by a and reflected over both axes.
- If you multiply the x- and y-coordinates by different numbers, you get a distortion of the figure rather than a dilation; the figure is no longer similar to the original.
- Multiplying the x- and y-coordinates by 1 is the identity transformation; you get the same figure you started with.

A copy of the pictures for Problems **3** and **7** is provided on Blackline Master 35 and Blackline Master 36, respectively.

On Your Own *(Student pages 390–392)*

These problems provide students with the opportunity for individual practice. See the lesson Planning Guide for homework recommendations.

PROBLEM 7 Blackline Master 37 provides a copy of the figure.

LESSON

Changing the Location of Things

Lesson Objective

Students use coordinates and vectors to translate figures about the plane.

Content Overview

Shapes are translated in the coordinate plane by performing arithmetic operations on the points that make them up. Students learn a new notation to describe arithmetic on points (both translations and dilations): $(x, y) \mapsto (ax + b, cy + d)$.

Planning Guide

Pacing	Activity	Materials	Homework Suggestions
Day 1	*Explore and Discuss* (SE p. 393) Activity: Pictures from Rules, Rules from Pictures (SE pp. 393–399)	graph paper	*On Your Own,* Problems 1 and 2
Day 2	Activity: Pictures from Rules, Rules from Pictures (SE pp. 393–399)	graph paper	*On Your Own,* Problems 3, 4, and 5 *Take It Further,* Problem 6

Program Resources

- *Connected Geometry* CD-ROM, Module 5: Investigations 5.9 and 5.10
- *Solution and Problem Solving Resource,* pages 411–414
- *Assessment Resources,* Quiz 5 Lesson 5, page 162

Preparation and Prerequisites

Students should be comfortable with performing arithmetic operations on variables.

Teaching the Lesson

Explore and Discuss *(Student page 393)*

If you have large pieces of graph paper or a graph board, you can have students demonstrate these problems and discuss the process as a class.

ACTIVITY

Pictures from Rules, Rules from Pictures *(Student pages 393–399)*

PROBLEM 1 Follow up with a class discussion on how to operate on coordinates to translate shapes in the plane.

Introduce notation such as $(x, y) \mapsto (ax + b, cy + d)$. Give a few examples like the following:

How would you write "add 4 to the first coordinate and 3 to the second coordinate?"

$$(x, y) \mapsto (x + 4, y + 3)$$

How would you write "multiply the first coordinate by 10 and the second coordinate by 75?"

$$(x, y) \mapsto (10x, 75y)$$

The two big ideas in this activity are translating figures by performing arithmetic operations on the coordinates of the points and the new notation. The notation is related to the previous lesson on scaling, and it will be used frequently throughout the rest of this lesson, so Problem **1** is particularly important.

PROBLEM 4 You may want to talk about negative scale factors and distortions, or you want to focus instead on the ideas of translation and dilation.

PROBLEM 5 Encourage each student to share at least one solution. Solutions for each picture should be presented. (Students may need some help with notation and with identifying equivalent rules.)

PROBLEMS 6–9 Have students work individually or in small groups and then finish these problems for homework.

You may want to spend some time talking about "equivalent rules," especially if students in your class generate equivalent but not identical solutions for some of the pictures in Problem **5.** For example, show two rules:

- $(x, y) \mapsto (2x + 4, 2y + 6)$
- $(x, y) \mapsto (2(x + 2), 2(y + 3))$

Ask, "What is the difference in the *process*? What is the difference in the *result*?"

PROBLEMS 7–10 In Problems **7** and **10,** there are subtle differences between scaling and then translating, or translating and then scaling. Ask students: "How can you tell from the written rule which is done first? In Problem **8,** which rules produced squares? Rectangles? Were there any rules that didn't produce a rectangle?"

On Your Own *(Student pages 399–400)*

These problems provide students with the opportunity for individual practice. See the lesson Planning Guide for homework recommendations.

Take It Further *(Student page 400)*

This problem will lead students in new directions or will challenge them to apply what they already know.

LESSON

Adding Points and Scaling Points

Lesson Objective

Students investigate the effects of adding and scaling points.

Content Overview

The main ideas of this lesson are:

- scaling a figure by operating on the coordinates of the points $((x, y) \mapsto \frac{1}{2}(x, y))$;
- scaling a figure with vectors;
- collinearity of all multiples of a point (cP, where c is a number and P is a point);
- an informal introduction to self-similar figures;
- translating a figure by adding a point to every point on the figure $((x, y) \mapsto (x, y) + (2, -5))$;
- translating a figure with vectors; and
- congruence of translated figures.

In this unit, the authors use "scaling a point" as a shorthand for dilating a point with the center at the origin.

Planning Guide

Pacing	Activity	Materials	Homework Suggestions
Day 1	*Explore and Discuss* (SE p. 403) Activity 1: Scaling Points (SE pp. 403–408)	graph paper	*On Your Own,* Problems 2 and 3
Day 2	Activity 2: Adding Points (SE pp. 408–413)	• BLM 38, p. 47 • graph paper	*On Your Own,* Problems 5, 6, and 7
Day 3	Activity 3: Vectors (SE pp. 413–417)	• BLM 39, p. 48 • BLM 40, p. 49 • BLM 41, p. 50 • graph paper	*On Your Own,* Problems 1, 4, and 8

Program Resources

- *Connected Geometry* CD-ROM, Module 5: Investigations 5.10, 5.11, and 5.12
- *Solution and Problem Solving Resources,* pages 415–432
- *Teaching Resources,* pages 47–50
- *Assessment Resources,* Quiz 6 Lesson 6, pages 163–164

Preparation and Prerequisites

The distance and midpoint formulas are used in some problems in this lesson. Similarity is discussed in several problems, but the discussion is relatively informal.

Teaching the Lesson

Explore and Discuss *(Student page 403)*

Students read the introduction aloud as a class or in groups. Have student volunteers act out the *Explore and Discuss* problems.

ACTIVITY 1

Scaling Points *(Student pages 403–408)*

As a class, discuss the collinearity of all multiples of a point and read about scaling with vectors.

PROBLEMS 5–6 After students finish these problems, ask the following:

- What happens to the individual points as they are scaled? (They move farther from the origin or closer to it, depending on the scale factor.)
- What happens to the individual points in relation to the shape they lie on? (They seem to "spread out" or get squeezed together, depending on the scale factor, and the shape itself gets either bigger or smaller as you have seen before.)

PROBLEMS 13–14 Students can work on these problems in the computer lab if you have access to it. End with a discussion on self-similar figures. The point of the discussion should be to tie ideas about the self-similar figures to the scaling that students have been doing. Adding the coordinate axes in Problem **13** shows students that scaling picture 1 by $\frac{1}{3}$ gives you exactly the leftmost piece of picture 2, and so on. Without the coordinate axes and the techniques of scaling points in this activity, the relationship might not be as clear.

PROBLEMS 12–13 These problems introduce self-similar pictures using two famous fractals: the Sierpinski triangle (or Sierpinski gasket) and the Koch curve. If your students have never seen fractals before, you may want to take a little time with these problems, talking about scale factors, developing Logo procedures to create them, and discussing what happens at many steps in the sequence. The "Mathematics Connections" section describes one way to develop the Logo programs, as well as some more advanced ideas about self-similar figures.

On stretching vectors, it may not be obvious that this trick doesn't always work. That is, you cannot stretch vectors for every scalar multiple of a vector. To stretch a vector, do the following:

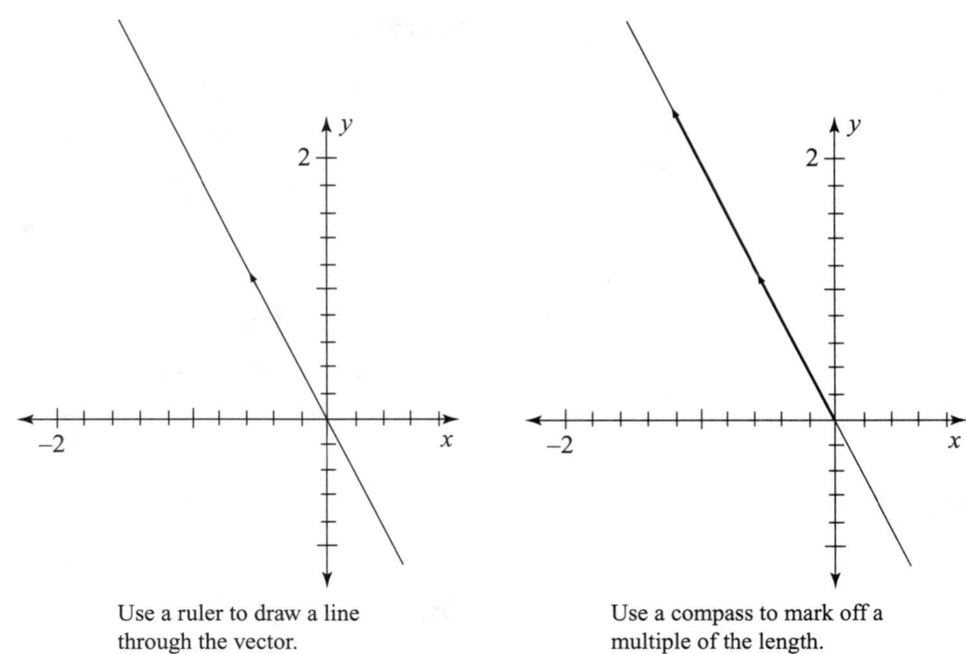

Use a ruler to draw a line through the vector.

Use a compass to mark off a multiple of the length.

But then again, it is not possible to exactly plot irrational multiples of points either.

This will clearly work for all whole number multiples (for negative multiples, you simply mark off the appropriate number of lengths on the opposite side of the origin). For rational multiples of the vector, the procedure is a little trickier. You have to construct $\frac{1}{2}$ (or $\frac{2}{3}$ or $\frac{5}{18}$) of the length and then stretch that new vector. For irrational lengths, stretching may not be possible.

ACTIVITY 2

Adding Points *(Student pages 408–413)*

Have a class discussion on how to find $A + B$ if you don't know any coordinates. (Methods may include the parallelogram rule if students know it or copying the length and direction of A, but starting at B instead of the origin.) Students then work on Problems **20–26.** Conclude class with a discussion about translating shapes by adding a point to each point on the shape, reversing a translation (by adding the negative of the point), and the identity transformation (adding the origin to any point).

This is the second example of an identity transformation. In the previous activity, you saw that scaling by a factor of 1 didn't change the shape either.

Students may need some help pulling the ideas together. In the discussion, ask questions like the following:

- Given two vectors A and B, how can you tell if combinations of scalar multiples $aA + bB$ will give you all of the points in the plane or just a line?
- Is there any time when these combinations will give you just a point? (Only if A and B are both at the origin)
- Would combinations of any two vectors—like (1, 2, 3) and (3, 7, 0)—give you all the possible points in three dimensions ($\mathbb{R}^3$)?
- If not, how many vectors would you need? What would combinations of the two vectors give you?

PROBLEM 27 A copy of the picture is provided on Blackline Master 38.

ACTIVITY 3

Vectors *(Student pages 413–417)*

This activity gives students another view of translating figures, this time using vectors.

PROBLEM 32 You may want to provide students with Blackline Master 39.

PROBLEM 36 A copy of the picture is provided on Blackline Master 40.

On Your Own *(Student pages 418–419)*

These problems provide students with the opportunity for individual practice. See the lesson Planning Guide for homework recommendations.

PROBLEM 8 Blackline Master 41 can be used with this problem.

Take It Further *(Student pages 419–420)*

These problems will lead students in new directions or will challenge them to apply what they already know.

Options and Extensions

Mathematics Connections

There are some simple and some difficult ideas behind self-similarity. You may want to stick with the simpler ideas in this lesson. The main idea behind the self-similar figures shown in the *Student Edition* is that, at stage 4 in Problem **12** (for example), if you cut off one piece and scale it up by the right amount, you will get a picture that looks just like stage 3. In general, if you look at stage n, cut off the right piece, and scale by the right factor, you get stage $n - 1$. You can use this idea to build up to recursive procedures for creating the two fractals shown in the *Student Edition.*

For the Sierpinski triangle, start by writing a procedure that will draw the stage 0 triangle:

```
to Tri0 :side
repeat 3 [fd :side  rt 120]
end
```

Students should be able to figure out the scale factor of $\frac{1}{2}$, either by recognizing the midlines in triangles in stage 1 or by trial and error.

For the stage 1, you want to draw one side of the big triangle, then draw one of the smaller triangles inside, and then repeat that procedure two more times. You can use the tri0 procedure to draw the smaller triangles:

```
to Tri1 :side
repeat 3 [fd :side  rt 120   tri0 :side/2 ]
end
```

The next stage has little stage 1 triangles in the corners, but that's an easy change to make:

```
to Tri2 :side
repeat 3 [fd :side  rt 120   tri1 :side/2 ]
end
```

Students can make as many of these programs as they want and thereby develop the Sierpinski triangle to any stage desired. However, you can create one procedure that does it all. Notice that each procedure calls the previous one, but they all look exactly the same. The exception is the stage 0 procedure, which stops the process of calling more and more procedures. The procedure can call itself, with sides scaled by $\frac{1}{2}$, as long as it knows when to stop. You can build in this stop condition by adding a second input, stage, that tells you how deep to go in the triangle:

```
to Tri :side :stage
if :stage=0 [stop]
repeat 3 [fd :side  rt 120   tri0 :side/2 :stage−1]
end
```

Notice that when Tri calls itself, it scales side by $\frac{1}{2}$ and decreases stage by 1.

A similar building up of procedures works for the Koch curve:

```
to Curve0 :length
fd :length
end

to Curve1 :length
curve0 :length/3  lt 60  curve0 :length/3
rt 120  curve0 :length/3  lt 60  curve0
:length/3
end
```

You can find the turning required by realizing that the middle segment is replaced by an equilateral triangle "hat." So the base angles both need to be 60°.

The procedure goes on, with the recursive program looking like this:

```
to Curve :length :stage
ifelse :stage=0 [fd :length]
[curve :length/3 :stage−1  lt 60  curve
:length/3 :stage−1  rt 120  curve :length/3
:stage−1  lt 60  curve :length/3 :stage−1]
end
```

You now have two sequences of shapes. When you pass the sequence to the limit, you get a fractal, a figure that is truly self-similar in that it can be divided into congruent subsets, each of which may be magnified by a constant factor to get the shape itself (not a "previous stage"). There is lots of mathematics here, but it is subtle. For students, it is best to think in terms of a sequence of shapes. For you, here are some interesting tidbits:

The "magnification factor" is how much you have to scale those pieces by to get back the original shape. It's the reciprocal of the scale factor used in the Logo programs.

- *Fractal dimension:* The most common definition of fractal dimension is

$$D = \frac{\log(\text{number of congruent pieces})}{\log(\text{magnification factor})}.$$

  The first of the two examples, the Sierpinski triangle, can be divided into three congruent pieces each of which must be scaled by 2 to get the original shape, so it has dimension $\frac{\log 3}{\log 2}$, which is less than 2. The Koch curve has four congruent pieces and a scale factor of $\frac{1}{3}$, so its dimension is $\frac{\log 4}{\log 3}$.

In the construction of the Sierpinski triangle, the authors "remove" the upside-down triangles at each stage, so they are not part of the figure. The limit is a totally disconnected set; hence, it has no area.

- *Perimeter and area:* The Koch curve has infinite length but contains a finite area (the lower bound is the original segment, the stage 0 curve). One way to see this is to realize that the length at each stage is $\frac{4}{3}$ the length at the previous stage. So the length of the curve (assuming you start with a unit length) is $\lim_{n\to\infty}(\frac{4}{3})^n$. This does not converge. The area, however, is completely contained by the triangle drawn around the first stage:

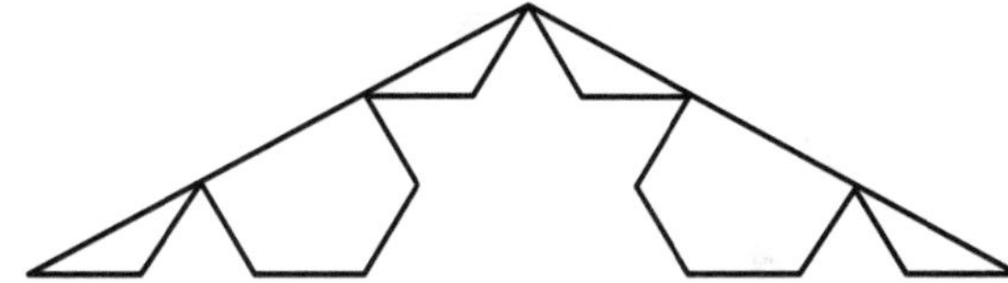

Similarly, the Sierpinski triangle has zero area and infinite perimeter.

For more about these ideas, see any of the books in the "Resources" section below.

Resources

If you want to study fractals further in your classroom, here are some good resources:

1. Abelson and diSessa, *Turtle Geometry* (MIT Press, 1980). This book includes, among other things, methods for developing recursive procedures like the ones suggested in "Mathematics Connections."
2. James Gleick's book *Chaos* (Penguin, USA, 1988) provides a wonderful history of the field and the personalities involved without too much sophisticated mathematics.
3. Mandelbrot's *The Fractal Geometry of Nature* (W.H. Freeman & Co., 1988) is the classic text, but only parts are accessible to high school students.
4. National Council of Teachers of Mathematics sells a book called *Fractals for the Classroom* by Peitgen, Jurgens, and Saupe.
5. Ivars Petersen's *The Mathematical Tourist* (W.H. Freeman & Co., 1989) is a great book for the general reader.
6. Clifford Pickover's book *Computers, Pattern, Chaos, and Beauty* (St. Martin's Press, 1991) has some very accessible chapters, as well as some more difficult chapters.

LESSON

The Algebra of Points

Lesson Objective

Students formalize ideas about adding and scaling points.

Content Overview

Students prove theorems about coordinates in this lesson, first by showing that specific points hold true and then by using generic points to prove the theorems. A couple of proofs are given, and students give reasons for each step. Students are also expected to develop their own proofs in some cases.

Planning Guide

Pacing	Activity	Materials	Homework Suggestions
Day 1	*Explore and Discuss* (SE p. 421) Activity 1: A Scaling Theorem (SE pp. 421–425)	graph paper	*On Your Own,* Problems 1 and 3 Activity 2, Problem 13
Day 2	Activity 2: An Adding Theorem (SE pp. 425–426)	• BLM 42, p. 51 • graph paper	*On Your Own,* Problems 2 and 4
Day 3	Activity 3: More on Scaling Points (SE pp. 426–428)	• BLM 43, p. 52 • graph paper	*On Your Own,* Problems 5, 6, and 7
Day 4	Activity 4: Parallel Lines (SE pp. 428–429)	graph paper	*On Your Own,* Problems 8, 9, and 12
Day 5	Activity 5: Properties of Points (SE pp. 429–430)	graph paper	*On Your Own,* Problems 10, 11, and 13

Program Resources

- *Connected Geometry* CD-ROM, Module 5: Investigations 5.13, 5.14, and 5.15
- *Solution and Problem Solving Resource,* pages 433–467
- *Teaching Resources,* pages 51–52
- *Assessment Resources,* Quiz 7 Lesson 7, page 165

Preparation and Prerequisites

Familiarity with adding and scaling points, the distance formula, congruent triangles, the Midline Theorem, and calculating midpoints is required.

Teaching the Lesson

Explore and Discuss *(Student page 421)*

Have students work independently through the problems. Then discuss the answers as a class.

ACTIVITY 1

A Scaling Theorem *(Student pages 421–425)*

Discuss "Ways to Think About It" and work through the proof of Theorem 5.3 with students. After discussing students' work on Theorem 5.3, hold a class discussion that will lead to a *new and improved* version of the theorem (*Checkpoint* Problem **12**).

ACTIVITY 2

An Adding Theorem *(Student pages 425–426)*

You may want to assign Problem **13** for homework the night before in preparation for the discussion of Theorem 5.4.

ACTIVITY 3

More on Scaling Points *(Student pages 426–428)*

PROBLEM 21 Have students explain their proof of Theorem 5.5 to a classmate. Select one or two students to present the theorem to the class, using only their own notes. This activity can be the basis for a class discussion on how to read a proof.

Students can then go on to complete Problems **22** and **23,** which ask them to prove other cases of Theorem 5.5. End class with several students presenting their solutions to these problems.

Part of reading a proof is working through the details, being sure you know the reason for moving from one step to the next. You can model this by working through some of the questions about Theorems 5.5 and 5.6.

These two triangles are similar according to the proof. Why? Well, both have a right angle, and they share the angle at the origin. They are therefore similar by AA.

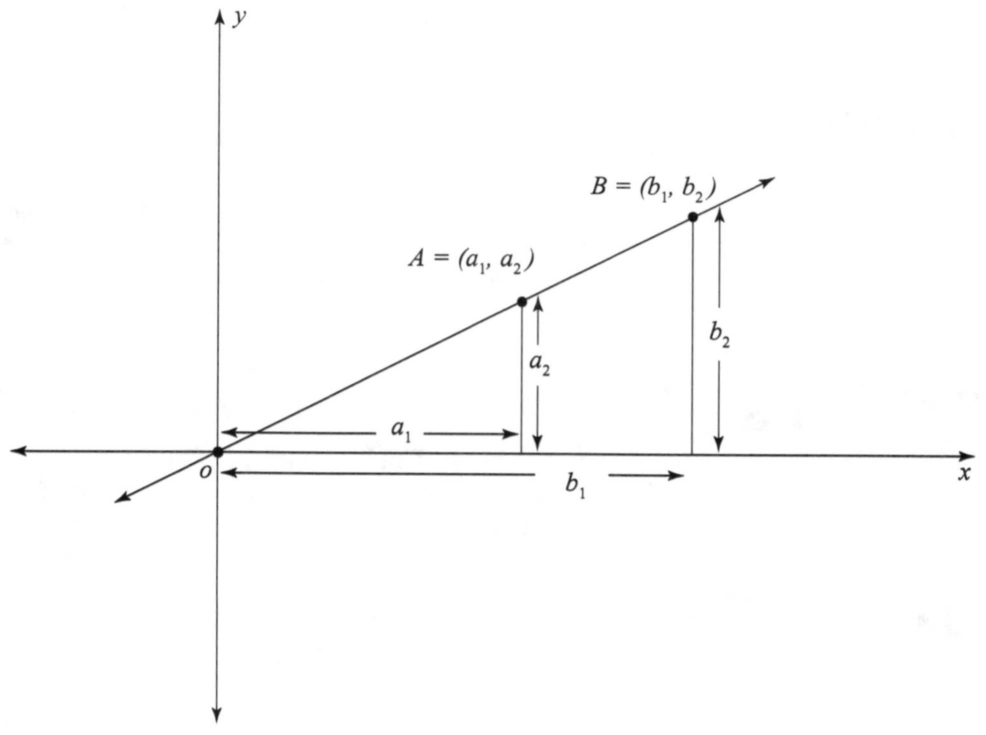

ACTIVITY 4

Parallel Lines *(Student pages 428–429)*

Encourage students to draw pictures while working through the proof of Theorem 5.7.

ACTIVITY 5

Properties of Points *(Student pages 429–430)*

PROBLEM 33 This problem asks students to prove the eight parts of Theorem 5.8. You may want to lead students through the first few properties so that they know what is expected. Then they can work individually or in groups to prove the remaining properties. Ask students to share their proofs of each property. The proofs should be short, and just one or two proofs for each property should suffice.

PROBLEM 35 Encourage students to draw pictures to help them generalize each property.

On Your Own *(Student pages 430–433)*

These problems provide students with the opportunity for individual practice. See the lesson Planning Guide for homework recommendations.

PROBLEMS 4–5 Blackline Master 42 and Blackline Master 43 are provided for these problems.

Take It Further *(Student page 433)*

These problems will lead students in new directions or will challenge them to apply what they already know.

LESSON

Vectors and Geometry

Lesson Objective

Students will learn more about vectors and use them to solve problems.

Content Overview

This lesson introduces students to the language and use of vectors. Students are asked to discover and apply several properties of vectors.

Planning Guide

Pacing	Activity	Materials	Homework Suggestions
Day 1	*Explore and Discuss* (SE p. 435) Activity 1: Vector Algebra (SE pp. 435–441)	• BLM 44, p. 53 • graph paper	*On Your Own,* Problems 1, 2, and 3
Day 2	Activity 1: Vector Algebra (SE pp. 435–441)	• BLM 45, p. 54 • BLM 46, p. 55 • graph paper	*On Your Own,* Problems 4, 5, 6, 13, and 14
Day 3	Activity 2: Head Minus Tail (SE pp. 441–446)	• BLM 47, p. 56 • BLM 48, p. 57 • graph paper	*On Your Own,* Problems 7, 8, 9, 10, 11, 12, 13, 14, 15, 16, and 17

Program Resources

- *Connected Geometry* CD-ROM, Module 5: Investigations 5.18 and 5.19
- *Solution and Problem Solving Resource,* pages 468–484
- *Teaching Resources,* pages 53–57
- *Assessment Resources,* Quiz 8 Lesson 8, page 166

Preparation and Prerequisites

Familiarity with coordinates, adding and scaling points, functions and function notation is required.

Teaching the Lesson

Students' ideas of vectors become more formal as they work through the activities in this lesson.

Explore and Discuss *(Student page 435)*

This quick activity provides an application of vectors and uses vocabulary given in the introductory paragraph of the lesson. Blackline Master 44 can be used with this activity.

ACTIVITY 1

Vector Algebra *(Student pages 435–441)*

PROBLEM 6 A copy of the picture is provided on Blackline Master 45.

PROBLEMS 8–14 By the end of this set of problems, students should be familiar with properties of vectors and the HEAD − TAIL technique of finding the "up-over" for vectors. Students should also be familiar with finding equivalent vectors by using the HEAD − TAIL rule. You may want to refer students back to their work on adding and scaling points to show that they were really just using vectors to accomplish these tasks. Blackline Master 46 can be used with Problem **8.**

ACTIVITY 2

Head Minus Tail *(Student pages 441–446)*

In this activity, students move vectors and figures to the origin by performing vector algebra. Students first see the HEAD − TAIL rule written in these problems.

PROBLEM 19 You many want to provide students with Blackline Master 47.

On Your Own *(Student pages 447–450)*

These problems provide students with the opportunity for individual practice. See the lesson Planning Guide for homework recommendations.

PROBLEM 10 A copy of the picture is provided on Blackline Master 48.

L E S S O N

Slope and Equations of Lines

Lesson Objective

Students relate ideas about vectors to slope and equations of lines.

Content Overview

In this lesson, topics include:

- testing for collinearity;
- a different form for the equation of a line;
- calculating slope; and
- finding points on a line, given its equation.

Planning Guide

Pacing	Activity	Materials	Homework Suggestions
Day 1	*Explore and Discuss* (SE p. 452) Activity 1: On the Line? (SE pp. 453–454)	graph paper	*On Your Own,* Problems 1, 2, 3, and 4
Day 2	Activity 2: Slope (SE pp. 454–456)	graph paper	*On Your Own,* Problems 5, 6, 7, and 8
Day 3	Activity 3: More About Equations of Lines (SE pp. 456–458)	graph paper	*On Your Own,* Problems 9 and 10

Program Resources

- *Solution and Problem Solving Resource,* pages 485–500
- *Assessment Resources,* Quiz 9 Lesson 9, pages 167–168

Preparation and Prerequisites

Students should be familiar with vector algebra.

Teaching the Lesson

Although the ideas of slope and equations of lines are probably familiar to students, do not rely on their previous knowledge. Approach these as new topics that are applications of what students know about vector algebra.

Explore and Discuss *(Student page 452)*

Read through the introductory material and the corresponding question. Discuss the solution given in the *Explore and Discuss* section as a class.

ACTIVITY 1

On the Line? *(Student pages 453–454)*

This activity presents students with a form for an equation of a line that they probably have not encountered before.

ACTIVITY 2

Slope *(Student pages 454–456)*

Students are probably familiar with the traditional definition of slope as "change in y over change in x." If students are working straight through these problems, be sure to stop them and have a brief discussion of why vertical lines must be ruled out in Problems **9** and **12.**

If students are not yet aware that vertical lines have no slope, you may want to spend a moment discussing this idea with them.

ACTIVITY 3

More About Equations of Lines *(Student pages 456–458)*

In this activity, students transform their equations into the traditional slope-intercept form and are introduced to the vector equation of a line.

On Your Own *(Student pages 458–460)*

These problems provide students with the opportunity for individual practice. See the lesson Planning Guide for homework recommendations.

Unit 5 Review

This unit review is intended to provide students with problems that will encourage them to look back at the unit as a whole. Students have one more opportunity to pull together, apply, and communicate the ideas they have developed by working on the activities throughout the unit.

It is especially important for students to have the opportunity to share their solutions with the class.

PROBLEM 1 This problem gives students a chance to practice plotting points, as well as to use the distance formula and slope to predict the correct vertices that will make the final figure a square.

PROBLEM 2 Often students are not consistent in their subtraction when using the distance formula. Given (x_1, y_1) and (x_2, y_2), be sure students are finding $(x_1 - y_1)$ and $(x_2 - y_2)$ and not $(x_1 - y_1)$ and $(y_2 - x_2)$.

PROBLEM 3 The sides of the square are not horizontal or vertical. Be sure students do not estimate to find the midpoint; instead, they should use the midpoint formula.

PROBLEM 4 Students need to recognize that the scale of the x- and y-axes is not 1. For example, the bottom left point is $(-3, 0)$, not $(-6, 0)$.

PROBLEM 5 Students should realize by now that **a** is a horizontal line and **b** is a vertical line.

PROBLEM 6 If students do not immediately remember that all of the x-coordinates are the same number on a vertical line, have them repeat this problem several times given other points.

PROBLEM 7 You may want to ask students what the equation of this line is.

PROBLEM 8 Ask students how the lines in Problems **7** and **8** compare.

PROBLEM 9 The four lattice points ((5, 0), (−5, 0), (0, 5), and (0, −5)) are easy for students to find. They may have to refer back to the lesson to remind themselves about circles.

PROBLEM 10 Students may want to refer to their 3-dimensional models or try to draw these points on paper. They should be looking for three numbers that, when applied to the distance formula, result in $\sqrt{25}$ or 5.

PROBLEM 11 This problem is a review of the distance formula in three dimensions.

PROBLEM 12 Students may simply state the distance formula in words or describe how to create a right triangle and use the Pythagorean Theorem.

PROBLEM 13 This problem is a review of the midpoint formula in three dimensions. Students may be expecting to be given two points and sometimes stumble over the term *origin*. If students are having difficulty, have them plot the points.

PROBLEM 14 Students should express the midpoint formula in their own words for part **a.** Encourage students to express their answer to part **b** algebraically.

PROBLEM 15 Students may need help setting up this problem to explain how the distance formula is derived from the Pythagorean Theorem. You might want to get them started with this picture.

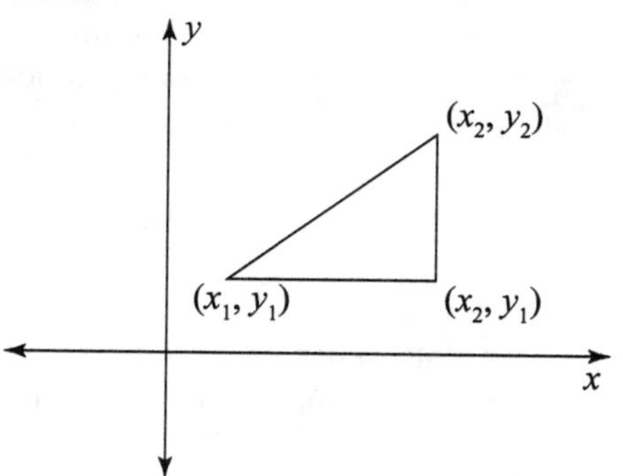

PROBLEM 16 The *Solution and Problem Solving Resource* gives one example of scaling by –2. Students should express an understanding of how to scale a figure by multiplying each coordinate by some value *k*. You might assign students to scale by various *k*s to get a variety of results.

PROBLEM 17 Supply some students with figures that are all in one quadrant and other students with figures that are in more than one quadrant. Have them generalize what happens.

PROBLEM 18 Encourage students to describe how to translate in all directions. Have them give more than one example.

PROBLEM 19 Provide graph paper so that students can check their answers by actually applying these rules to a figure.

PROBLEM 20 Encourage students to use algebra to simplify the expressions rather than apply the rules to a figure.

PROBLEM 21 You might assign different types of rules to different students. For example, ask one student to make up a rule that will slide a figure up. Another student might be assigned a rule that will reflect the figure over the *x*-axis, and so on.

PROBLEM 22 Make sure students consider cases in which *c* is not positive.

PROBLEM 23 This problem reviews Theorem 5.6 in Lesson 7.

PROBLEM 24 Students should describe how to add two points by adding their coordinates, as well as by using the vector method.

PROBLEM 25 This problem reviews the work done in Activity 1 in Lesson 8. A copy of the picture is provided on Blackline Master 49.

PROBLEM 26 Students should refer to Theorems 5.9, 5.10, and 5.11 for reference when solving this problem.

PROBLEM 27 This topic was not presented in Lesson 9, although students were given the opportunity to notice properties of parallel and perpendicular lines while working through the problems.

Optimization
A Geometric Approach

Unit Overview

This unit focuses on optimization problems—finding maxima and minima—but no calculus is used. Some algebraic manipulations are necessary, but most of the unit's problems can be solved with strictly geometric techniques.

Optimization problems are traditionally reserved for calculus. And yet, while most of the problems in this unit can indeed be solved with calculus, you may be surprised at how approachable they are with geometric methods and at how elegant the geometric solutions can be. Moreover, these problems are specifically designed to help students get at the big ideas behind optimization problems—thinking about extreme cases and boundary conditions and using a mixture of deduction, experimentation, and reasoning by continuity. Thus, they provide the context for the kind of thinking that teachers of mathematics (and of calculus specifically) want from their students. In the "Mathematics Connections" section of this guide, however, you will find that some of the notes about mathematical connections include connections to calculus.

Learning Goals

1. Find minimal distances from point to point (using a straight line), from point to line (using a perpendicular), and from point to a line or from other boundary to a second point (using the "reflection principle").
2. Know that, for a given perimeter, the square maximizes area over a rectangle and use cutting arguments or area calculations to compare areas of other figures.

3. Understand that contour lines are curves of fixed value for a function on the plane and explain how to use them and tangency to solve optimization problems.
4. Identify circles as curves of constant distance from a single point, ellipses as curves of constant distance from two points, and arcs of circles as curves of constant angle between two points.
5. Explain the idea of continuous variation in terms of "small changes in input produce small changes in output."
6. Reason about extreme cases or boundary cases in solving problems.
7. Pursue an extended investigation: Define a problem clearly, investigate it, make a conjecture, prove a result, and explore extensions.
8. Understand the difference between an initial conjecture, a conjecture supported by *a lot* of evidence, and a theorem that has been proven.
9. Follow a logical argument and, with guidance, construct original proofs.
10. Locate the Fermat point of a triangle and explain why, for most triangles, it minimizes the distance to the three vertices.

Assessment Opportunities

Quizzes and Informal Assessment

- Problems 2 and 3 from Lesson 1, Activity 1, make good assessments of whether students see the related geometry within slightly different contexts.
- Problem 17 from Lesson 3, *Take It Further,* is a relatively easy problem that asks students to extend the notion of contour lines to three dimensions. It serves as a good check of both students' concept of contour lines and their visualization.
- Problem 7 from Lesson 4, Activity 2, assesses understanding of what students are trying to prove and students' ability to interpret pictures and "put the words on them."
- Problem 14 from Lesson 5, *Take It Further,* is a good assessment of students' understanding and use of contour lines.

Journal Ideas

Students keep writing assignments in a journal. Possible assignments:

- Lesson 2, *On Your Own,* Problem 6. List strategies used to solve optimization problems.
- Lesson 3, *On Your Own, Write and Reflect,* Problem 1. Find ways in which contour plots are used by weather forecasters.
- Lesson 4, *On Your Own,* Problem 6. List characteristics of equilateral triangles, as well as all triangles.
- Lesson 5, Problems 27 and 34. Investigate Hoffman and Toricelli's proof.
- Lesson 5, *On Your Own,* Problem 6. Write about various topics related to proof.

Projects/Presentations

- **Lesson 4,** Problems 6 and 7 (Students work through two proofs of the solution to Rich's problem. They should be able to present one of the proofs to the class, explaining the details, answering questions, and so on. Students can work through the proofs and do their presentations in groups, and then each student should hand in an individual writeup.)
- **Lesson 5**
  - Present Hoffman's proof of the airport conjecture to the class.
  - Present a construction technique for the 120° spot (one given in the Student Edition or one devised by the students) and explain why it works.
  - Present the proof of the airport conjecture based on Rich's function.

UNIT 6 Planning Guide

Lessons	Learning Goals	Assessment Opportunities	Suggested Pacing	Materials
LESSON 1 *Making the Least of a Situation*	1	*Checkpoint,* Problem 6 Quiz 1, *Assessment Resources,* p. 202	2 days	• BLM 50, p. 59 • BLM 51, p. 60 • rulers • geometry software (optional)
LESSON 2 *Making the Most of a Situation*	2	*Checkpoint,* Problem 10 Quiz 2, *Assessment Resources,* p. 203	2 days	• BLM 52, p. 61 • rulers • scissors
LESSON 3 *Contour Lines and Contour Plots*	3, 4	*Checkpoint,* Problems 5, 9, 16, and 23 Quiz 3, *Assessment Resources,* p. 204 Mid-Unit Exam, *Assessment Resources,* pp. 207–210	4 days	• BLM 53, p. 62 • drawing tools • protractors • geometry software (optional)
LESSON 4 *Rich's Function*	5, 6	*Checkpoint,* Problems 5, 9, and 12 Quiz 4, *Assessment Resources,* p. 205	3 days	geometry software (optional)
LESSON 5 *The Airport Problem*	7, 8, 9, 10	*Checkpoint,* Problems 3, 19, 36, and 41 Quiz 5, *Assessment Resources,* p. 206	6–7 days	• BLM 54, p. 63 • maps • geometry software • other materials, depending on the models you build
UNIT 6 REVIEW		End-of-Unit Exam, *Assessment Resources,* pp. 211–214	2 days (including testing)	No special materials needed.

LESSON

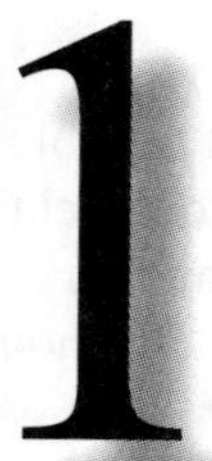

Making the Least of a Situation

Lesson Objective

Students find methods to minimize paths from point to point, from point to line, and along a path given certain constraints.

Content Overview

The outcomes of these problems, to be used frequently in later problems, should teach some basic minimizing principles in geometry:

- The shortest path from a point to a line is along the perpendicular from the point to the line.
- The shortest path between two points is along the segment between them.
- Every point on a perpendicular bisector is equidistant from the two endpoints.
- Reflecting a point over a line forms a segment for which the line is a perpendicular bisector.

There are several "framing problems" in this lesson that are revisited in later lessons and solved using more than one technique. These problems help students see connections between the various methods they are learning.

Planning Guide

Pacing	Activity	Materials	Homework Suggestions
Day 1	*Explore and Discuss* (SE p. 467)	• BLM 50, p. 59 • rulers	*On Your Own,* Problems 1, 2, 3 and 4
Day 2	Activity: Minimizing Distance (SE pp. 468–470)	• BLM 51, p. 60 • geometry software (optional)	*On Your Own,* Choose from Problems 5–13

Program Resources

- *Connected Geometry* CD-ROM, Module 6: Investigations 6.1, 6.2, and 6.5
- *Solution and Problem Solving Resource,* pages 508–523
- *Teaching Resources,* pages 59–60
- *Assessment Resources,* Quiz 1 Lesson 1, page 202

Preparation and Prerequisites

Students will encounter the terms *perpendicular* and *perpendicular bisector,* and they will need to be able to reflect a point over a line.

The reflection method will be used frequently in later problems.

Teaching the Lesson

Explore and Discuss (Student page 467)

After students work on these problems, there should be a short discussion in which ideas about shortest distance between two points and shortest distance from a point to a line are clarified.

You might point out to students that the word "distance" is not defined so rigorously in everyday life. When one talks about the distance from Boston to New York, one usually means the length of the shortest path that one can travel by car between the two cities. There may not be a road which follows the *actual* shortest path.

A copy of the parking lot picture is provided on Blackline Master 50.

ACTIVITY

Making the Least of a Situation (Student pages 468–470)

PROBLEM 1 The outcome of this problem is the "reflection principle:"

Take A and reflect it over the line to make A' so that the line is the perpendicular bisector of $\overline{AA'}$. Then, going from A to the line to B is the same as going from A' to the line to B, because $AP = A'P$ for any point P on the line. So, just connect A' to B and that's where you should put P.

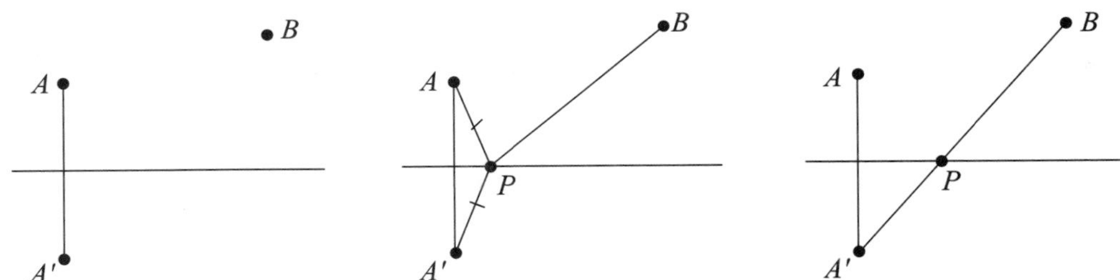

Getting to a conjecture in this problem depends on students asking themselves the right questions. If they try only the two examples given in the Student Edition, urge them to experiment with others, such as A being $\frac{1}{3}$, $\frac{1}{4}$, or $\frac{3}{4}$ as far from the riverbank as B.

PROBLEMS 15–16 These problems can be used to apply or develop the classical formulas that connect sizes of angles and the corresponding sizes of their intercepted arcs. (If P is outside the circle, the size of $\angle SPT$ is smaller than if P is *on* the circle.)

On Your Own (Student pages 470–472)

These problems provide students with the opportunity for individual practice.

There are quite a few *On Your Own* problems presented in this lesson. Choose a few for homework after Activity 1 from Problems **5–13.**

You may want to provide students with Blackline Master 51 for Problem **9.**

Take It Further *(Student pages 473–474)*

These problems will lead students in new directions or will challenge them to apply what they already know.

Options and Extensions

If students built a dynagraph for Problems **b–d** in *Explore and Discuss*, you can ask them to think about some way they might alter that setup to represent Problem **c** or Problem **d.** By taking the "inland" point (it was called L in that problem) and simply flipping it (by using the reflect command) over the shore into the water, students have the setup they need. (This action might also provide a key insight for making the theoretical analysis of the problem.)

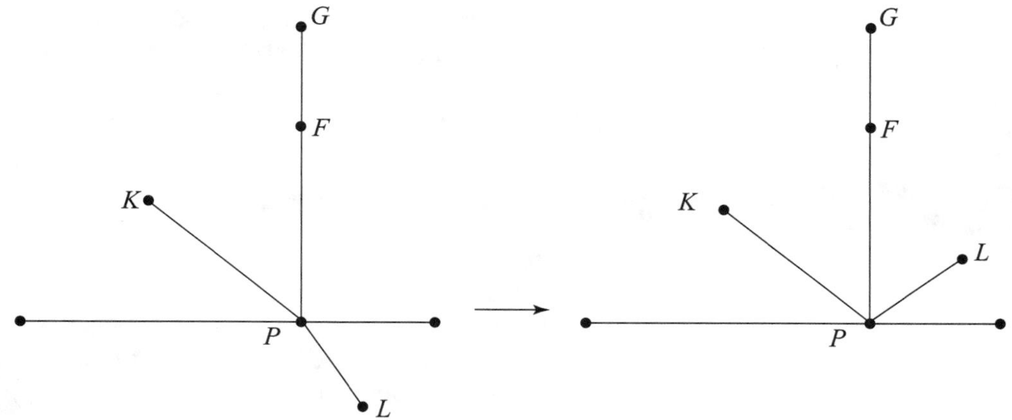

Relabeling and running the dynagraph, you get a picture like the one shown below.

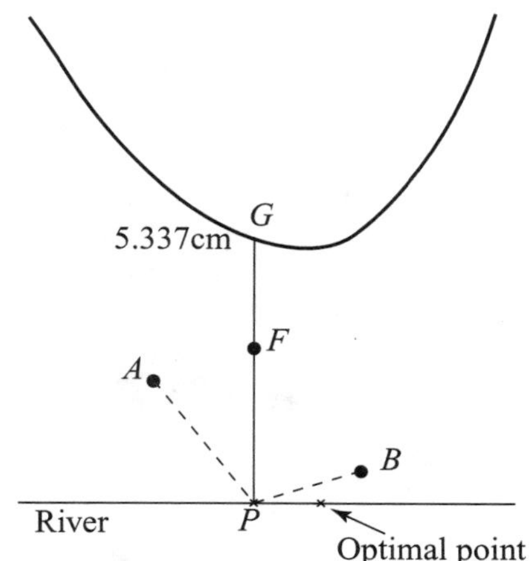

Without Technology

To model the situation in Problems **b–d** in *Explore and Discuss* with string and nails, use two nails and a stationary piece of string to represent the shoreline. Include a washer on that string to represent the point on the shoreline, and loop a second piece of string from point L through the washer to point K to represent the varying possible paths over land and in the water. The washer can be alternately fixed at several places with a thumbtack, and the length of the string needed to reach point K marked with different colored markers for each place fixed with the thumbtack.

Using Technology

If you model the situation in Problems **b–d** in *Explore and Discuss* in a geometry environment, you can drag P back and forth and observe how the total trip distance changes. To do this, you might want to measure $KP + LP$. Another way to model the situation is to build a *dynagraph* of the function $P \mapsto KP + LP$. For example, erect a perpendicular stick up from P and find points F and G so that $PK = PF$ and $PL = FG$.

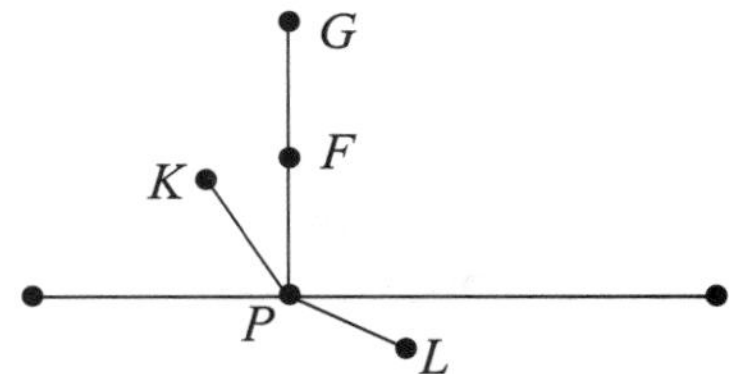

So, the total length of $\overline{PG}$ is the length of the trip. As you drag P back and forth, you can observe the height of G. The minimum trip will be at the point at which G is lowest. If you put a trace on G, dragging P back and forth will produce a graph of the function $P \mapsto KP + LP$.

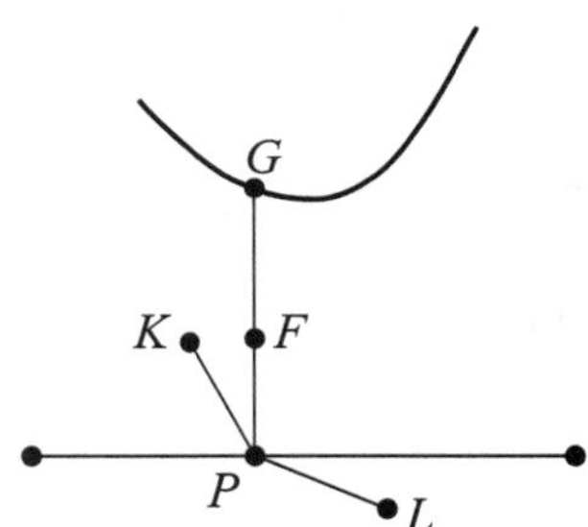

You can verify that the minimum point on the dynagraph occurs when K, P, and L are collinear. What happens if you put a trace on F? See the "Mathematics Connections" section for further scenarios applicable to this problem.

Mathematics Connections

PROBLEMS 1–2 The graph of the function can, of course, be generated without geometry software. Students who have done some work with coordinate geometry and the requisite algebra can write the analytic description of the distance as a function of *P*'s position, starting with a diagram like the one below:

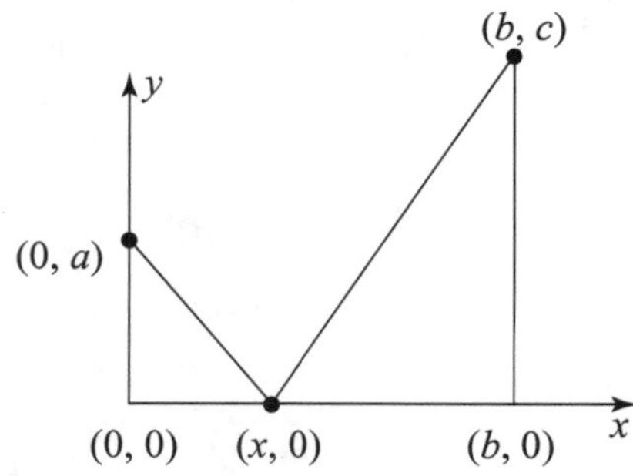

The distance from $(0, a)$ to $(x, 0)$ is $\sqrt{a^2 + x^2}$, and the distance from $(x, 0)$ to (b, c) is $\sqrt{(b - x)^2 + c^2}$. Thus, the total distance $D(x)$ is $\sqrt{a^2 + x^2} + \sqrt{(b - x)^2 + c^2}$.

Sometimes people who have physical handicaps that don't allow them to run very fast can swim very fast instead.

You might want to discuss other optimization scenarios relevant to the *Explore and Discuss* problem or to Problems **1** and **2.** For the *Explore and Discuss* problem, for example, suppose you can run faster than you can swim. Then any line segments through the water have a different "cost" (or "weight" or "angle") than do line segments over the land. An analagous situation arises in optics, when a light beam traveling in air "bends" (direction is *refracted*) when it enters water. The description of this phenomenon is given in Snell's Law.

You might ask a science teacher to come into your class and discuss Snell's Law. (In France, Snell's Law is known as "Descartes' Law.")

Field-tester/teacher Jane Gorman posed the burning tent problem to her class. Several students observed that if you want to get to the tent in as short a *time* as possible (time is crucial if your tent's on fire), then you might want to take into account the fact that you can probably run faster with an empty bucket. Where should you hit the river in this case? It turns out that if you can run *r* times as fast when the bucket is empty, the best place to land is at the spot at which the cosines of the angles of incidence and reflection have ratio *r*. This problem will come up later (see Problem **8** of Lesson 3 in *On Your Own*), at which time students will use contour lines to obtain a qualitative solution. But the authors thought you would enjoy seeing a simple solution that uses calculus and that generalizes the "unweighted" case nicely.

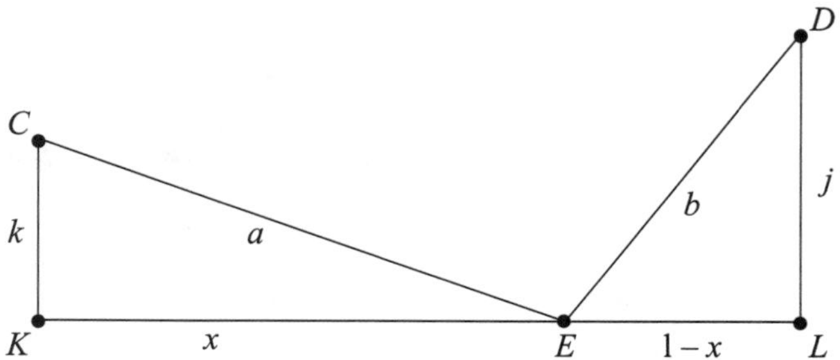

Suppose the lengths are given in the figure (there's no loss of generality in assuming that $KL = 1$). Notice that k and j are constants but that a and b depend on x. Suppose that you can run $\frac{1}{r}$ times as fast from E to D (the tent) as you can from C to E. So, r might be 2 or 3 or any other number greater than or equal to 1. Then, if $s = a + rb$, s is a positive constant times the total time taken to get to the tent, so you want to minimize s.

If your rates are r_1 empty and $\frac{r_1}{r}$ full, then the time it takes to get to the tent is $\frac{a}{r_1} + \frac{rb}{r_1}$.

Since everything depends on x,

$$\frac{ds}{dx} = \frac{da}{dx} + r\frac{db}{dx}.$$

Since

$$a^2 - k^2 = x^2$$

and

$$b^2 - j^2 = (1 - x)^2,$$

you have

$$2a\frac{da}{dx} = 2x$$

and

$$2b\frac{db}{dx} = 2(x - 1).$$

So,

$$\frac{da}{dx} = \frac{x}{a}$$

and

$$\frac{db}{dx} = \frac{x - 1}{b}.$$

Substituting, you have

$$\frac{ds}{dx} = \frac{x}{a} + r\frac{x - 1}{b}.$$

But a dynagraph experiment shows that s is one of those functions that has a minimum when its derivative is 0.

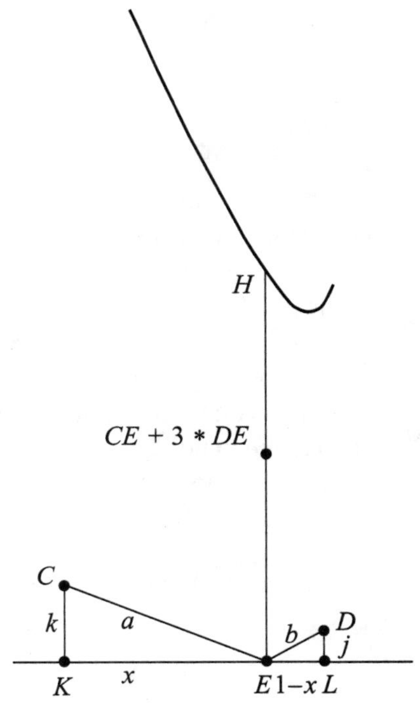

So, you have

$$0 = \frac{x}{a} + r\left(\frac{x-1}{b}\right),$$

or

$$\frac{x}{a} = r\left(\frac{1-x}{b}\right).$$

But in terms of trigonometry, this just says that

$$\cos \angle CEK = r \cos \angle DEL.$$

For example, if you can run with a full bucket $\frac{1}{3}$ times as fast as you can run with an empty one, you should land at the spot at which

$$\cos \angle CEK = 3 \cos \angle DEL.$$

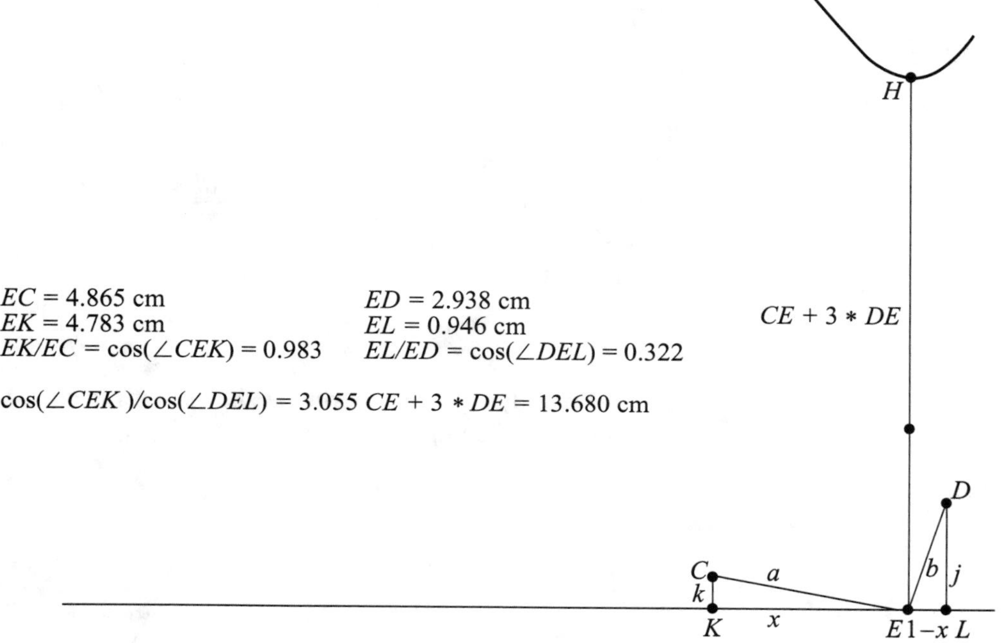

Notice that if $r = 1$ (as was intended in the original burning tent problem), you recover the fact that the angle of incidence wants to be the same as the angle of reflection.

If this problem comes up in your class discussions before students get to contour lines, you might suggest (if they don't) that if you run half as fast on the last leg of the trip, you really want to minimize the sum of the distances from You to the River and *twice* the distance from the River to the Tent. This insight can be a nice digression into rate, time, and distance. It also makes the problem more adaptable to experimentation with geometry software.

This experiment requires geometry software.

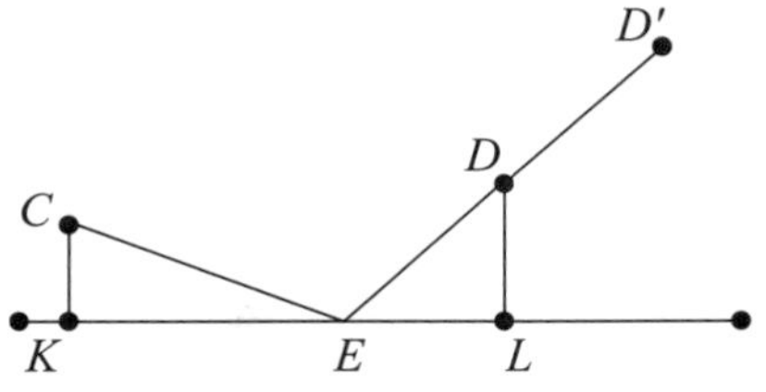

Minimize $CE + ED'$ as a function of E

It comes as a surprise to many students that the best spot isn't simply the one that minimizes the amount of bucket carrying time (that would be at the foot of the perpendicular from the Tent to the River), but it is just a bit off from this position. Wrestling with this counterintuitive fact can be very productive. In any case, you will want to help students make as much progress as they can, stating as many conclusions as possible, without saying too early that the complete solution to the problem requires more mathematics than they have right now.

By the way, the same solution applies to the "weighted" version of the run-and-swim problem in Lesson 3, *Take It Further,* Problem **14.**

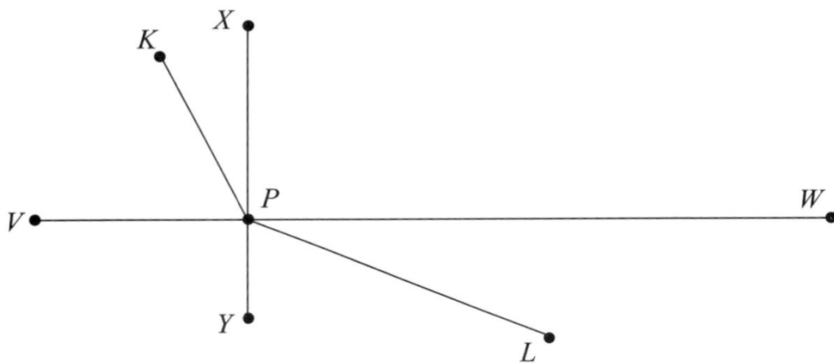

If you can run r times as fast as you can swim, then you should land at a spot at which

$$\cos \angle WPL = r \cos \angle KPV.$$

This is analagous to the situation in which a light beam travels from L through water at P, is *refracted,* and then travels on to K. In optics, Snell's Law says that

$$\frac{\sin \angle YPL}{\sin \angle KPX} = r,$$

where r is the "index of refraction." Is this equivalent to the authors formulation?

PROBLEM 13 Consider $\triangle ABC$. Let $\angle 1 = \angle AXM_1$, and let $\angle 2 = \angle M_2XC$. Recall from the burning tent problem that because X is the point which makes path $\overline{M_1X} + \overline{XM_2}$ as short as possible, you know that $m\angle 1 = m\angle 2$.

First, assume that X is the midpoint of $\overline{AC}$; thus, $AX = XC$. Since X is a midpoint, it follows that $\overline{XM_1}$ and $\overline{XM_2}$ are midsegments of $\triangle ABC$. Then apply the following theorem:

Theorem *A midsegment of a triangle is parallel to the third side of the triangle.*

This theorem tells you that $\overline{XM_1}$ and $\overline{BC}$ are parallel, as are $\overline{XM_2}$ and $\overline{AB}$. This implies that

$$m\angle 1 = m\angle M_2CX$$

and

$$m\angle 2 = m\angle M_1AX,$$

respectively. Therefore, since $m\angle 1 = m\angle 2$, you have

$$m\angle M_2CX = m\angle M_1AX.$$

This result allows you to conclude that $\triangle ABC$ is isosceles.

For the other half of the proof, assume that $\triangle ABC$ is isosceles. Show that X is the midpoint of $\overline{AC}$. Since the triangle is isosceles, you know that

$$m\angle M_1AX = m\angle M_2CX$$

and that

$$\overline{AM_1} = \overline{CM_2}.$$

Since $m\angle 1 = m\angle 2$, you see that $\triangle AM_1X$ and $\triangle XM_2C$ are congruent. Therefore,

$$\overline{AX} = \overline{XC}.$$

So, X is the midpoint of $\overline{AC}$.

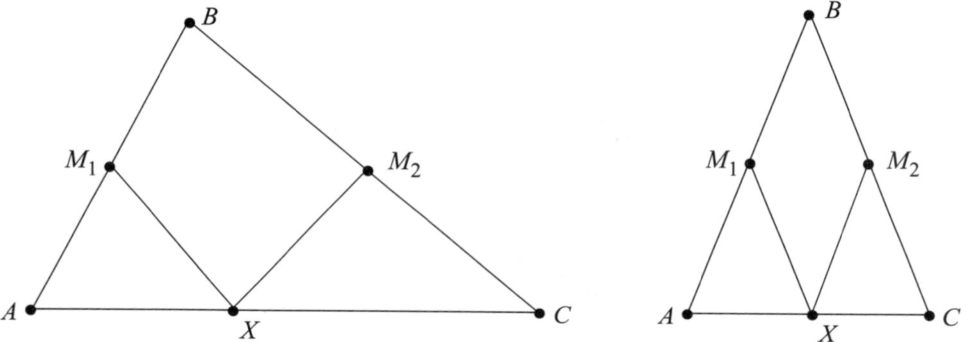

Shortest distance exists when $m\angle AXM_1 = m\angle CXM_2$. Triangle ABC (on the right) is isosceles.

LESSON

Making the Most of a Situation

Lesson Objective

Students find methods to maximize the areas of given figures with fixed perimeters.

Content Overview

The main ideas in this lesson include:

- For all rectangles of fixed perimeter, the square has the greatest area.
- In general, for a polygon with a given number sides and fixed perimeter, the regular shape encloses the greatest area.
- For fixed perimeter and regular polygons, increasing the number of sides increases area.
- Properties of angles that are inscribed in circles.

Planning Guide

Pacing	Activity	Materials	Homework Suggestions
Day 1	*Explore and Discuss* (SE p. 479) Activity: Some Maximization Problems (SE pp. 479–481)	• BLM 52, p. 61 • rulers • scissors	*On Your Own,* Problems 1, 2, and 4
Day 2	Activity: Some Maximization Problems (SE pp. 479–481)	• rulers • scissors	*On Your Own,* Problems 3, 5, 6, 7, 8, 9, and 10

Program Resources

- *Connected Geometry* CD-ROM, Module 6: Investigations 6.3 and 6.5
- *Solution and Problem Solving Resource,* pages 524–539
- *Teaching Resources,* page 61
- *Assessment Resources,* Quiz 2 Lesson 2, page 203

Preparation and Prerequisites

Students need to have some general notions about area, as well as some area formulas—for triangles and rectangles—and methods for approximating other regular polygons. Some algebraic manipulations, using variables in perimeter and area calculations, are necessary as well.

Teaching the **Lesson**

Explore and Discuss *(Student page 479)*

You may decide to use geometry software and allow students to explore several shapes. Although these questions ask about all possible shapes, this lesson concentrates on the maximum area of a rectangle with fixed perimeter.

ACTIVITY

Some Maximization Problems *(Student pages 479–481)*

PROBLEMS 1–3 Students will need either geometry software or graph paper to compare areas of various figures.

These problems are closely related, and the similarities should be made clear to students. If they can solve Problem **1,** they can solve Problem **2** by thinking about parallelograms as two congruent triangles joined at one of their identical sides (the diagonal of the parallelogram).

PROBLEM 4 This problem is important and deserves a lot of attention. Ask students to present the argument orally (or do so yourself). Students can work on the three parts of the problem in class and as homework. The next day, ask them to present their solutions for part **c.**

PROBLEM 5 This problem generalizes Problem **4.** Students may need some guidance with the algebra, but the point is to understand the cutting argument.

PROBLEMS 8–9 These problems involve a different kind of optimization—maximizing angle measurement rather than area.

On Your Own *(Student pages 482–484)*

These problems provide students with the opportunity for individual practice. See the lesson Planning Guide for homework recommendations.

PROBLEM 2 Blackline Master 52 provides a copy of the polygons.

Take It Further *(Student pages 484–485)*

PROBLEM 11 In this problem, students may end up faced with comparing the areas of three polygons: a square with sidelength 210, a regular pentagon with sidelength 168, and a regular hexagon with sidelength 140. You can ask students to *approximate* the areas of each of these figures. They are different enough (rough calculations show areas of about 44,000, 49,000, and 51,000, respectively) so that students can see that the hexagon wins. The situation is similar for Problem **12.**

Options and Extensions

Using Technology

PROBLEM 3 Here is a way to approach the problem using geometry software.

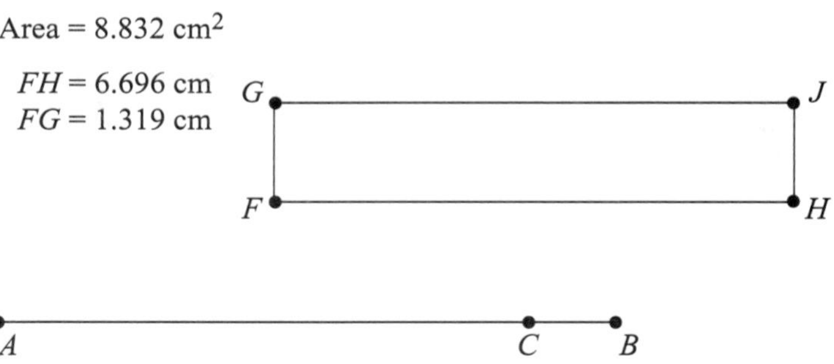

The figure above is a scale drawing of the house, in which *AB* is half the perimeter (its measure is 8 cm in the sketch). Point *C* is a movable point on $\overline{AB}$. The rectangle is constructed to remain a rectangle, so $FH = AC$ and $FG = CB$. When you measure *FH* and *FG* and calculate their product, the values can be displayed on the computer screen. As *C* slides back and forth across $\overline{AB}$, the rectangle changes—its area changes—but its perimeter stays at about 16 centimeters.

Area = 10.498 cm²

FH = 1.649 cm
FG = 6.366 cm

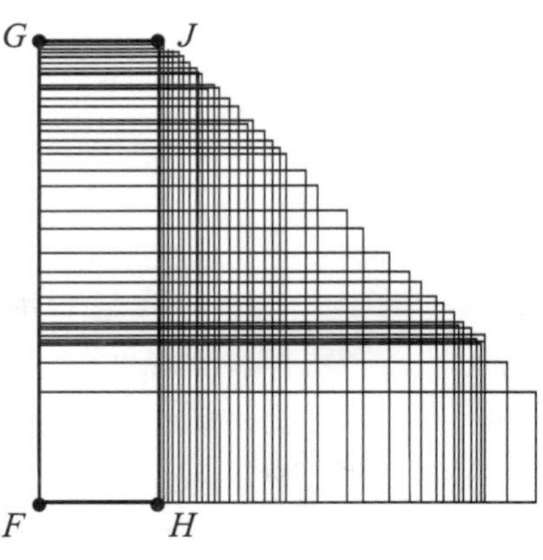

On one axis, copy a length equal to FH. On the other, copy a length equal to FG • FH.

A more elaborate way to visualize the situation is to make a dynagraph of the situation as in the figure on the next page.

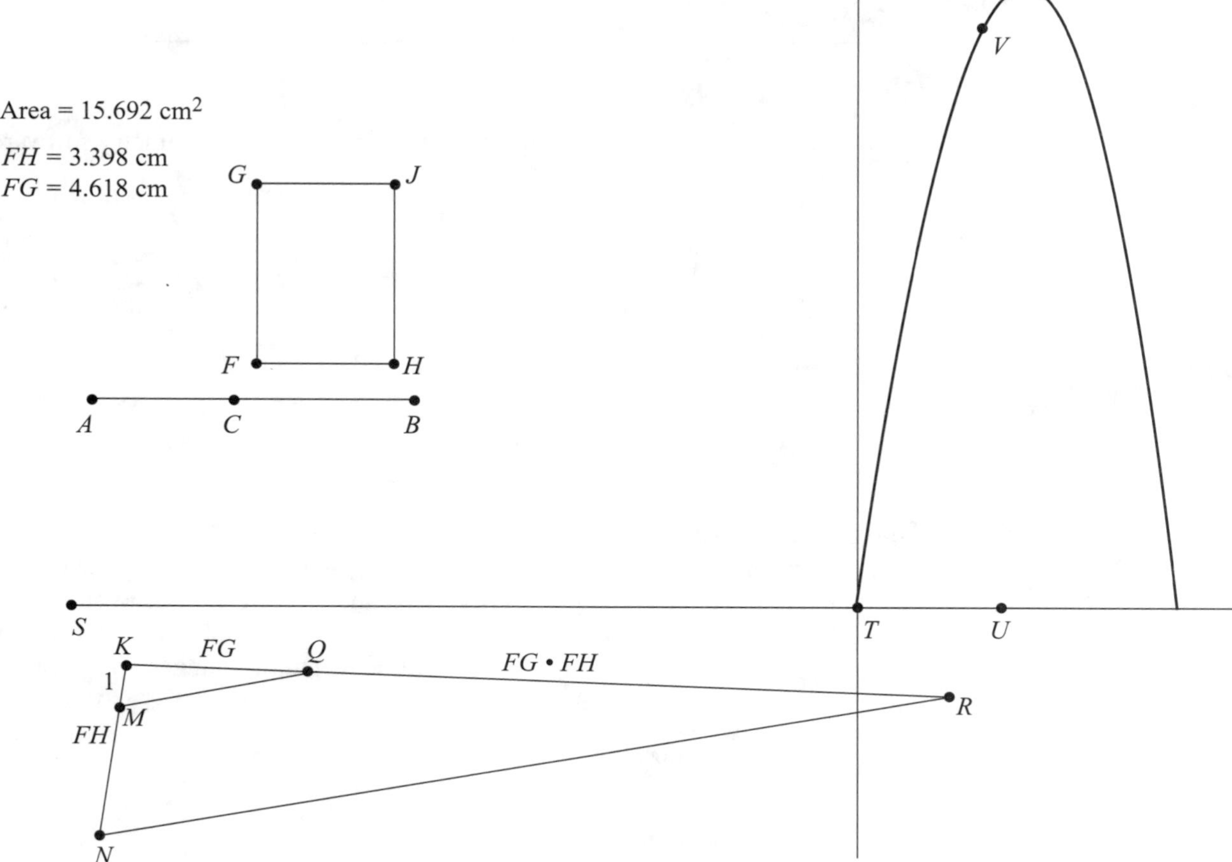

Depending on your software, you may have to construct the length $FG \times FH$ using the Euclidean method for multiplying lengths.

Mathematics Connections

PROBLEM 5 Another proof uses a result that comes up over and over in mathematics: the *arithmetic-geometric mean inequality.* It says that if a and b are positive real numbers, then

$$\sqrt{ab} \leq \frac{a+b}{2}.$$

Can the geometric mean ever equal the arithmetic mean?

The arithmetic mean of two numbers a and b is their average. It is the number m that makes the sequence

$$a, m, b$$

an *arithmetic* sequence ($m - a = b - m$). The geometric mean of two numbers a and b is the number r that makes the sequence

$$a, r, b$$

What would be a good definition for geometric mean of three numbers?

a *geometric* sequence, so that $\frac{a}{r} = \frac{r}{b}$. The arithmetic-geometric mean inequality says that the geometric mean is never bigger than the arithmetic mean. To establish the arithmetic-geometric mean inequality, argue like this: If a and b are real numbers, then

$$(a - b)^2 \geq 0$$

because the square of any number is never negative. Therefore,

$$a^2 - 2ab + b^2 \geq 0$$

and so

$$a^2 + 2ab + b^2 \geq 4ab.$$

(This comes from adding $4ab$ to both sides.) Therefore,

$$\frac{(a + b)^2}{4} \geq ab.$$

An entire book has been written about ideas associated with the arithmetic-geometric mean inequality, Pi and the AGM, *by Jonathan M. Borwein and Peter B. Borwein (John Wiley, NY, 1987).*

Since both sides are nonnegative, you can take square roots, yielding the arithmetic-geometric mean inequality.

Now, looking back at the rectangle problem, you have:

$$\begin{aligned} \text{area of rectangle} &= ab \\ &\leq \left(\frac{a + b}{2}\right)^2 \\ &= \text{area of square,} \end{aligned}$$

where the inequality is obtained by squaring the AGM.

PROBLEM 9 The *Solution and Problem Solving Resource* provides a proof that, given a fixed volume, the cube minimizes surface area for all rectangular boxes. That proof makes use of the arithmetic-geometric mean inequality, and some students may wish to see such a proof.

It turns out that, in order to prove the arithmetic-geometric mean inequality for three variables, it is easier to first prove it for four variables and then use that case in the proof for three variables.

You first want to prove that, if a, b, c, and d are positive integers, then

$$\sqrt[4]{abcd} \leq \frac{a + b + c + d}{4}.$$

The idea for this proof is credited to the French mathematician Augustin Cauchy (1789–1857).

Make substitutions for the variables a, b, c, and d, keeping track of what happens at each step. Therefore, substitute the following:

$$a \rightarrow \frac{a + b}{2}$$

$$b \rightarrow \frac{a + b}{2}$$

$$c \rightarrow c$$

$$d \rightarrow d.$$

Notice that, after making these substitutions, the sum of the variables is still the same:

$$\frac{a + b}{2} + \frac{a + b}{2} + c + d = a + b + c + d.$$

The product, however, has increased or remained the same. To see this, apply the inequality in two variables to a and b and get

$$\sqrt{ab} \leq \frac{a+b}{2}$$

$$ab \leq \left(\frac{a+b}{2}\right)^2.$$

Thus,

$$abcd \leq \left(\frac{a+b}{2}\right)\left(\frac{a+b}{2}\right) cd.$$

Make a series of further substitutions. At each step, the same reasoning shows that the sum stays the same, while the product increases or remains the same.

Next, make these substitutions:

$$\frac{a+b}{2} \to \frac{a+b}{2}$$

$$\frac{a+b}{2} \to \frac{a+b}{2}$$

$$c \to \frac{c+d}{2}$$

$$d \to \frac{c+d}{2}.$$

Then make the substitutions:

$$\frac{a+b}{2} \to \frac{a+b+c+d}{4}$$

$$\frac{a+b}{2} \to \frac{a+b}{2}$$

$$\frac{c+d}{2} \to \frac{a+b+c+d}{4}$$

$$\frac{c+d}{2} \to \frac{a+b}{2}.$$

Finally, substitute:

$$\frac{a+b+c+d}{4} \to \frac{a+b+c+d}{4}$$

$$\frac{a+b}{2} \to \frac{a+b+c+d}{4}$$

$$\frac{a+b+c+d}{4} \to \frac{a+b+c+d}{4}$$

$$\frac{a+b}{2} \to \frac{a+b+c+d}{4}.$$

Denote the quantity $\frac{a+b+c+d}{4}$ by T. Since at each step the sum of the four terms stays the same while the product increases or stays the same, you have

$$abcd \le (T)(T)(T)(T)$$
$$abcd \le T^4$$
$$\sqrt[4]{abcd} \le T$$
$$\sqrt[4]{abcd} \le \frac{a+b+c+d}{4}.$$

So, you have the inequality in four variables. Now for the proof in three variables. Suppose that a, b, and c are positive integers. You want to show that

$$\sqrt[3]{abc} \le \frac{a+b+c}{3}.$$

Apply the inequality for four variables to a, b, c, and $\sqrt[3]{abc}$:

$$\sqrt[4]{abc\sqrt[3]{abc}} \le \frac{a+b+c+\sqrt[3]{abc}}{4}$$

Try using the argument to establish an AGM for eight numbers, and then use it to derive an AGM for seven numbers.

The left-hand side above is actually equal to $\sqrt[3]{abc}$ (this is easiest to see if you convert everything to fractional exponents and simplify). Thus,

$$4\sqrt[3]{abc} \le a + b + c + \sqrt[3]{abc}$$
$$3\sqrt[3]{abc} \le a + b + c.$$

You have shown that

$$\sqrt[3]{abc} \le \frac{a+b+c}{3}.$$

Be careful: The "bases" of the two figures look the same length, but they aren't quite equal.

PROBLEM 13 This problem asks students to compare the areas of half a regular octagon of side 30 and half a regular hexagon of side 40. If your students know some trigonometry, this problem requires some very nice calculation (the half-hexagon is made up of three equilateral triangles of side 40, and the half-octagon is made up of four isosceles triangles, each with base 30 and a 45° vertex angle). If students don't know the necessary trigonometry, you might ask them to do a cutting experiment.

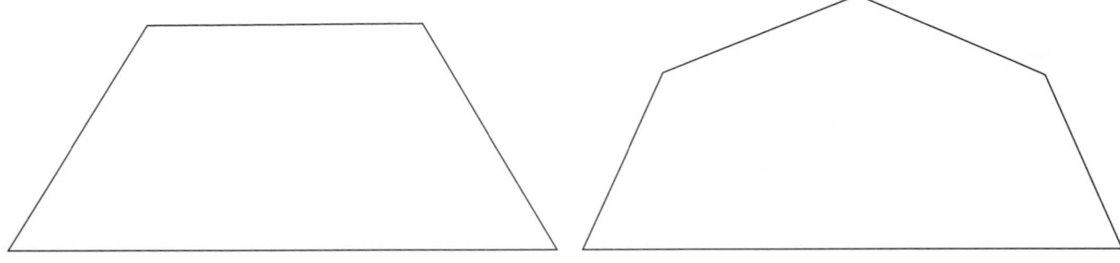

Teacher-to-Teacher

The hockey problem: A hockey player skates toward the goal net along a line perpendicular to the net, but off to the side, so that the skating path doesn't intersect the segment between the ends of the net. What is the best place from which to take a shot?

Jon Choate, a teacher at Groton School in Connecticut who also coaches hockey, says that players develop an intuition for finding the place that maximizes the angle between the puck and the goal ends. Jon has thought about the following situation.

When players warm up, they skate out on various lines that are perpendicular to the goal. If each player shoots from his or her "best" spot, what is the locus of these shooting positions?

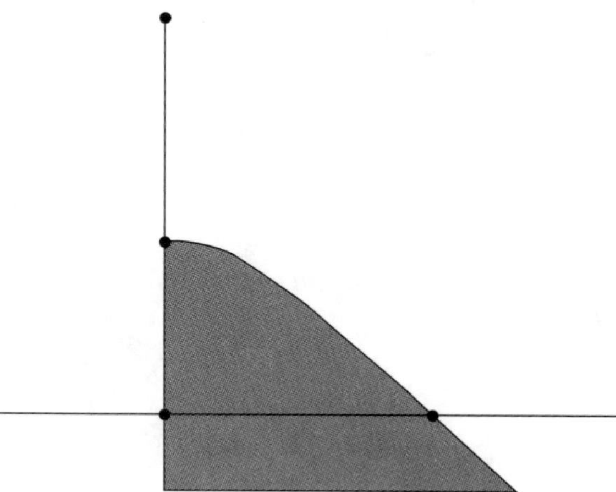

Can you describe the curve? The area beneath this shooting curve is referred to as the "gray area" by hockey enthusiasts.

LESSON

Contour Lines and Contour Plots

Lesson Objective

Students explore functions on the plane ($\mathbb{R}^2 \to \mathbb{R}$) and use contour lines to find minimal values for these functions along a path.

Content Overview

The idea of function is central to this lesson. Other key ideas include:

- Contour lines represent all of the places with the same value for a function ("equally good/equally bad places").
- The minimal value for the function along a path is at its tangent point to the contour line with the smallest value.
- Circles are contour lines of constant distance from one point.
- Ellipses are contour lines of constant distance from two points.
- Arcs of circles are contour lines of constant angle.
- Surface plots are 3-dimensional plots of contour lines. They show the value of the function along a contour line by their distance from the x-y plane.

Planning Guide

Pacing	Activity	Materials	Homework Suggestions
Day 1	*Explore and Discuss* (SE p. 487)	drawing tools	Finish *Explore and Discuss* activity
Day 2	Activity 1: Interpreting Contour Plots (SE pp. 487–488) Activity 2: A Contour Plot for Soccer (SE pp. 488–489)	• BLM 53, p. 62 • protractors • geometry software (optional)	*On Your Own,* Problems 3, 4, 5, and 7
Day 3	Activity 3: Contour Lines and Functions (SE pp. 490–491)	No special materials needed.	*On Your Own,* Problems 2, 9, 10, and 11
Day 4	Activity 4: Revisiting the Burning Tent Problem (SE pp. 492–495)		*On Your Own,* Problems 1, 6, 8, 12, and 13

Program Resources

- *Connected Geometry* CD-ROM, Module 6: Investigations 6.4 and 6.5
- *Solution and Problem Solving Resource,* pages 540–555
- *Teaching Resources,* page 62
- *Assessment Resources,* Quiz 3 Lesson 3, page 204

Preparation and Prerequisites

Several problems from Lesson 2 are revisited here. This gives students another way to look at minimization problems. Vocabulary and ideas about functions are introduced, particularly in the "Ways to Think About It" reading. So, your students do not need to know about them previously.

Teaching the Lesson

Explore and Discuss *(Student page 487)*

Ask students to read the introductory reading aloud in class so that they can ask questions as they go along.

ACTIVITY 1

Interpreting Contour Plots *(Student pages 487–488)*

PROBLEMS 1–2 These problems are important for the rest of the lesson and require some focused class time. If students do not understand the answers, they will have difficulty with the rest of the lesson.

PROBLEM 3 This problem is a good assessment to see if students can reinterpret the map in a new context. Blackline Master 53 provides a copy of the map.

PROBLEM 4 The fact that points A and B cannot be included on the contour plot may be missed by many students.

ACTIVITY 2

A Contour Plot for Soccer *(Student pages 488–489)*

PROBLEMS 6–9 These problems focus on arcs of circles as curves of constant angle. This idea may be unfamiliar to most students, and the early problems might be difficult. Marking points of constant angle with the model described in "Without Technology" or with software described in "Using Technology" can provide key insights.

ACTIVITY 3

Contour Lines and Functions *(Student pages 490–491)*

The "Ways to Think About It" reading introduces the concept of function and ties it to what students have been doing. It should be read carefully and discussed.

PROBLEM 11 This problem is one that students have already solved—the circle as constant distance from a point—but phrased in the language of functions. It is important for students to make the connection between this problem and Problem **4.**

ACTIVITY 4

Revisiting the Burning Tent Problem *(Student pages 492–495)*

Activity 4 is a good way to tie together minimization strategies that students learned in Lesson 2 and work with contour lines.

PROBLEM 23 This problem serves as a mechanism to help those students having trouble with some of the ideas in this lesson, such as the difference between lines that are tangent to and lines that cross contour lines.

On Your Own *(Student pages 495–498)*

These problems provide students with the opportunity for individual practice.

PROBLEMS 10–11 These problems are particularly challenging. If students are having difficulty with Problem **10,** ask them to solve the special case in which $\angle C$ is a right angle.

Take It Further *(Student page 499)*

These problems will lead students in new directions or will challenge them to apply what they already know.

Options and Extensions

Without Technology

You do not need to build all of the string-and-nails models yourself. Your students can do the building during class one day. Even the stiff angles described below can be made by students in class using cardboard, protractors, and good scissors.

Students can also perform the experiment in Problems **6–8** with physical manipulatives, using a stiff *angle* (a plastic triangle or a carpenter's L) and two nails in wood. Slide the *angle* around with its sides against the nails. The vertex traces out a circular arc.

Using Technology

PROBLEMS 6–8 Students may use geometry software to find the points experimentally. They can set up two points as goal posts and a third point as the player. Measuring the appropriate angle, they can move the player to some location at which the angle is 40° and mark that position softly on their computer screen (or a transparency taped over the screen) with an erasable marker. After they have found and marked enough such points, they may be ready to make a conjecture. If everybody uses goal posts the same distance apart, their transparencies may be superimposed to combine the data.

Alternatively, students may use Trace Locus to leave a trace of the player's position as they move it while watching vigilantly to keep the measured angle between 39.9° and 40.1°. Even with this technique to capture the data, students may want to transfer their results (with a felt tip marker) to a transparency or tracing paper.

By varying the position of the player while maintaining a constant angle, students are generating the arc in which all of those angles are inscribed.

Drawing Curves with Geometry Software

This section is quite long. You may want to come back to it when you need it or just skip it if you're already familiar with these software packages.

In this lesson and for the rest of the unit, students will be asked to construct contour lines for various functions $f: \mathbb{R}^2 \rightarrow \mathbb{R}$. The authors encourage you and your students to devise mechanical devices for constructing such curves (the famous pin-and-string construction for an ellipse is such an example).

Powerful media like Mathematica®, which have built-in facility for drawing contour plots, may or may not be available to you. Essentially, there is a primitive (it's called ContourPlot in Mathematica) that takes a function defined by you (usually in algebraic notation) and several other parameters, and then produces a contour plot for the function.

You can write your own program to produce a contour plot for a function in Logo. One easy way is to instruct the computer to scan the screen, pixel by pixel; at each data point to evaluate the function at hand on the coordinates of the pixel; and then to color it accordingly. This tedious process (tedious for the computer, not for you) pieces together local information about the function and produces a picture of the global behavior of the function. For example, if you have four colors, color the pixel red if the value of the function is less than 3, blue if it is greater than or equal to 3 and less than 10, yellow if it is greater than or equal to 10 and less than 100, and black if it is greater than or equal to 100. You end up with "contour bands," and you can then go back to adjust the intervals to get better pictures. The boundaries between bands are contour lines.

Another method—one that really builds habits of algorithmic thinking, performing thought experiments, reasoning by continuity, and visualization—is to use geometry software to generate contour lines. This cannot always be done, and the capabilities will vary from system to system. Simply being able to answer the question "Can I figure out how to make the software generate the contour lines for this function?" is a valuable skill for students to develop. In the rest of this section, various methods are discussed for generating curves described by various geometric constraints, using common features of many geometry software environments.

The idea is to bring back the old notion of "locus of a point": If a point moves in such a way that it satisfies certain constraints, what path does it trace out? Geometry software environments allow students to set up the constraints and then to trace the path of a point that is subject to them. This "tracing point" moves as a result of the direct manipulation of one or more features of a sketch; in other words, it is a *function* of these features. When students construct such sketches, they are constructing computational models for functions, and the behavior of such functions can be *experienced* in a very kinesthetic way when students experiment with their creations. In addition, some geometry software allows students to gather the image points of such functions into a *set* that can be manipulated by other functions. Setting up the constraints involves functional thinking in the sense of constructing algorithms. Manipulating the sketch involves functional thinking in the guise of reasoning by continuity. Gathering the points in the path into an object that itself depends on parameters in the sketch is a good example of abstraction.

Start with the typical construction of an ellipse. Given a positive constant k and two points A and B, the ellipse with foci A and B and major axis k is the set of points P such that $PA + PB = k$. Draw $\overline{CD}$ with length k. Place a "slider point" E on $\overline{CD}$ that breaks the segment into two parts. The sum of the lengths of these two parts is always k.

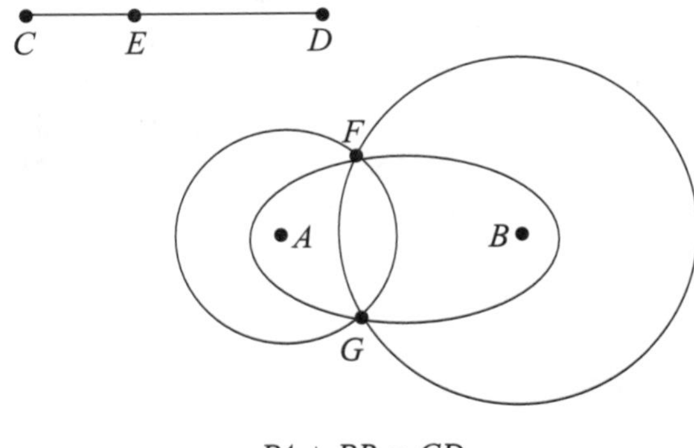

$PA + PB = CD$

Circles of radius CE and ED are constructed with centers A and B. As E is slid back and forth along $\overline{CD}$, points F and G (the intersections of the two circles) trace out the upper and lower halves of an ellipse with foci at A and B and whose major axis has length CD. Why?

This slider point method is the computational equivalent of the pin-and-string construction of an ellipse, which is made easier with the aid of a small ring:

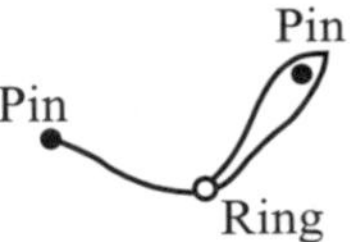

Tie the string to one pin, lace it through the ring and around the second pin, and tie it to the ring. Now trace the curve by putting a pencil in the ring.

This "slider point" method is quite general. For example, rather than looking at all of the points P such that $PA + PB$ is constant, students can construct functions that produce the set of points P such that $PA + 2PB$ is constant.

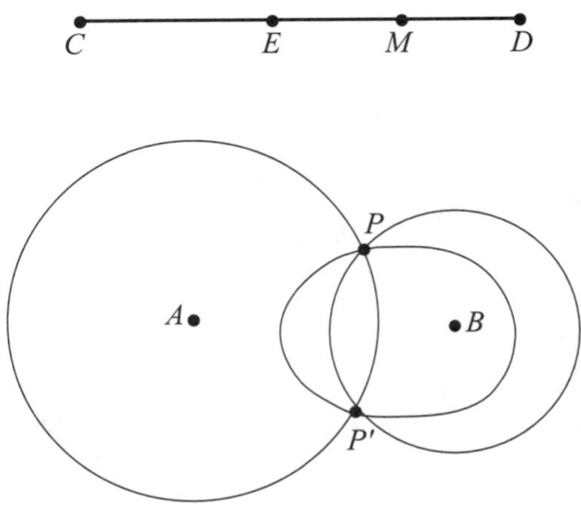

$PA + 2PB = CD$

In the sketch on the previous page, points P and P' are functions of E that are constructed in the following way: Circles of radius CE and $EM = \frac{1}{2}ED$ are drawn around A and B respectively, intersecting at P. As E is dragged along $\overline{CD}$, P moves in a way such that $PA + 2PB = CD$ is constant.

The slider point breaks a segment into two parts, the sum of whose lengths is constant. These parts can be used to generate figures other than circles; the set of possible loci that students can build depends only on the available primitives. In Cabri Geometry II™, for example, conic sections are built-in primitives so that loci defined as intersections of conics are possible. For example, "a generalized ellipse with three foci," the locus of points P so that $PA + PB + PC$ is constant, can be obtained from the intersection of an ellipse and a circle.

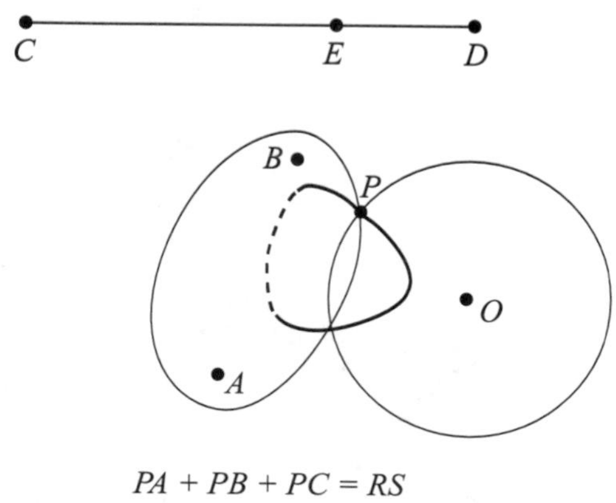

$PA + PB + PC = RS$

To generate the locus, slide E back and forth along $\overline{CD}$.

In the sketch above, $\overline{CD}$ is divided at E. An ellipse with major axis ES is constructed on foci A and B, and a circle with radius $\overline{ED}$ is constructed with center O. P is the intersection of the ellipse and the circle.

This encapsulation of isolated events into objects that can then be input to higher-order processes is a fundamental abstraction mechanism in mathematics.

The continuous dependence of the locus on the "sliding" point E in the above examples is just the beginning. Once the locus is obtained, students can ask how *it* depends on the parameters in the sketch. In most dynamic geometry environments, it is possible to "encapsulate" loci into objects that can be manipulated via other functions. For example, the pictures below show families of ellipses, "quasi-ellipses," and "generalized ellipses" that grow and shrink as a function of the "length of the string."

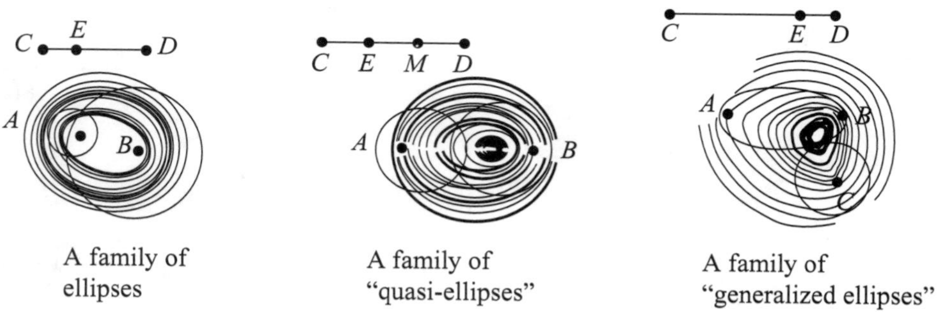

A family of ellipses

A family of "quasi-ellipses"

A family of "generalized ellipses"

You can make a dynamic sketch of this example, in which k is the length of some segment in the sketch. By changing k, the lines on either side of l move closer and farther away.

One final class of examples: In all of the examples so far, you have been worrying about the distances between points. If you include distances between points and lines as part of the allowable constraint definitions, you get different kinds of contour lines.

The simplest example: Suppose l is a line. If f is the function that measures the distance from its input to l, then the contour line for $f(P) = k$ is the union of two parallel lines, each k away from l, on either side of it.

Assume f is defined on the interior of the angle and f(P) = r + s. For which point P is f(P) = k?

How about this one: Given $\angle BAC$ and a positive number k, what is the locus of points P in the interior of the angle so that the sum of the distances from P to the sides of the angle is k?

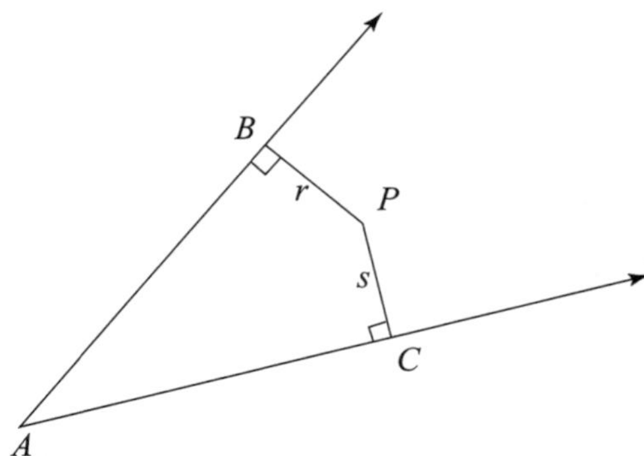

You can generate the locus by using the slider-point method. Take a segment of some fixed length k and break it into two pieces of lengths r and s with a slider point. Then make two parallels to $\overrightarrow{AB}$, each a distance of r away, and make two parallels to $\overrightarrow{AC}$, each a distance of k away. These four constructed lines will intersect once inside the angle. Call that intersection point P. Put a trace on P and move the slider back and forth.

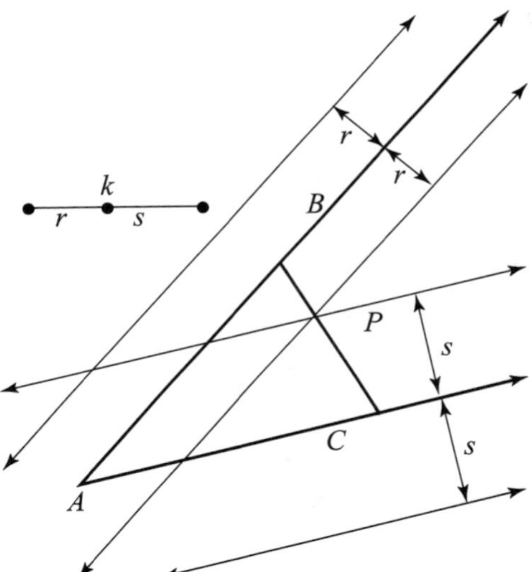

Does P trace out a line segment?

It looks like P traces out a line segment. Is that true? One way to locate some possible values of P is to imagine what happens if r or s is very small. If r is small, P is close to $\overrightarrow{AB}$; and, in the limiting case, P is right on $\overrightarrow{AB}$ at the spot at which the distance from P to $\overrightarrow{AC}$ is k.

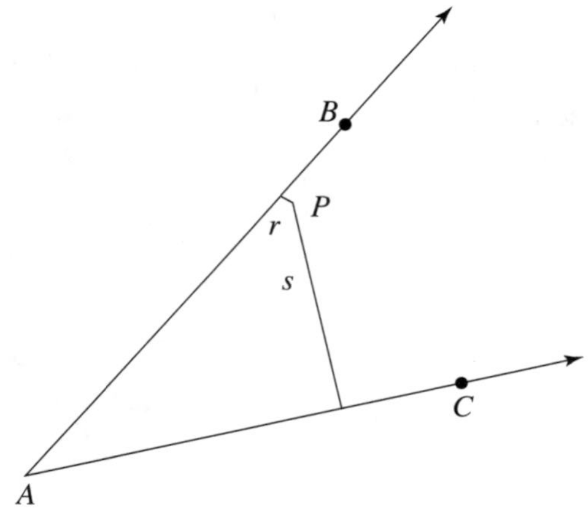

r is almost 0; s is almost k

Another special case is at the other extreme.

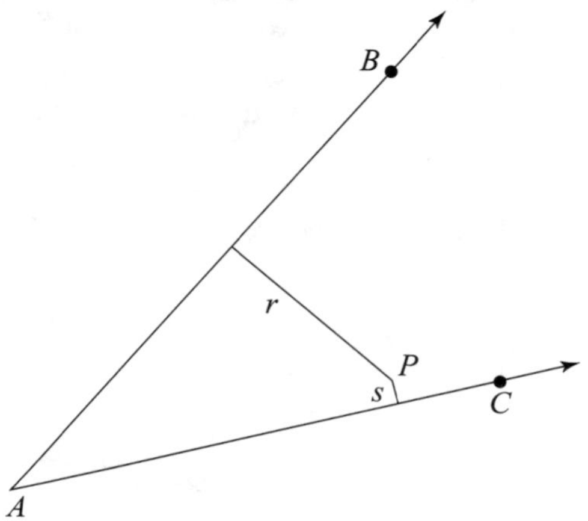

s is almost 0; r is almost k

This gives two points, L on $\overrightarrow{AB}$ (a distance of k from $\overrightarrow{AC}$) and a corresponding point M on $\overrightarrow{AC}$ (a distance of k from $\overrightarrow{AB}$):

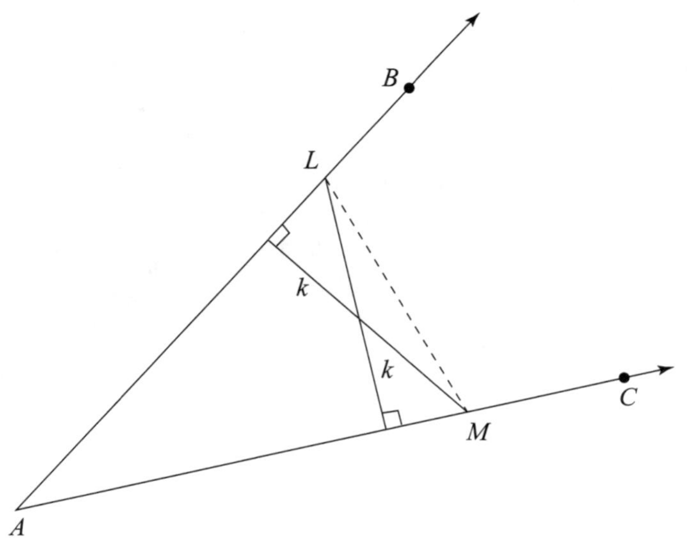

Notice that $\triangle LMA$ is isosceles. From this figure, it's straightforward to prove that a point P in the interior of the angle is on $\overline{LM}$ if and only if the sum of the distances from P to the sides of the angle is k.

A theorem about quadrilaterals: "A quadrilateral whose diagonals are congruent and bisect each other is a rectangle."

The sides of angles are rays. But suppose you extend the rays to get two intersecting lines. What is the locus of points, the sum of whose distances from two lines is constant? Work the argument above across the interiors of the four angles that are formed, use some theorems about quadrilaterals, and you have a surprising (to the authors, anyway) theorem:

Theorem *The locus of points whose sum of distances to two fixed lines is constant is a rectangle.*

In this figure, how could you locate the value of the constant sum?

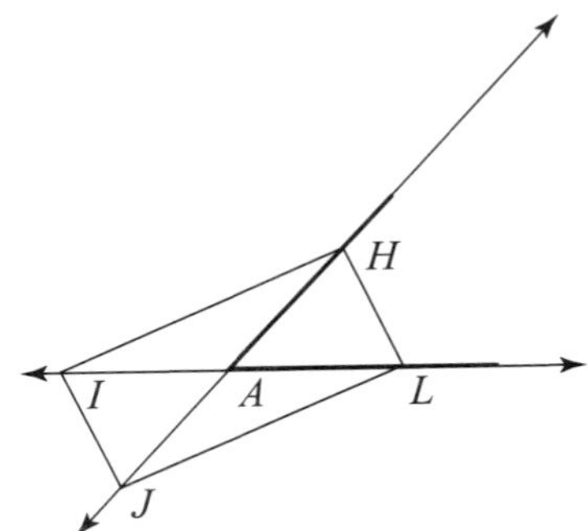

Finally, applying the slider-point method again, you can generate the locus of points the sum of whose distances from *three* fixed lines is constant.

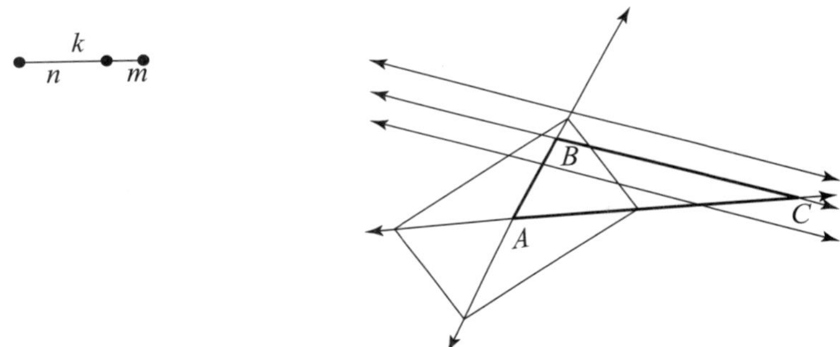

When the running path is not parallel to the posts, the graph of the angle change is not symmetric. Below is a picture (generated in The Geometer's Sketchpad®*) of the change.*

$\angle AUB$

Distance of U to the right of O along l

121.847°
B
A
O
U
l
2.131 cm

In the picture above, a segment of length k is broken into segments of lengths n and m with a slider point. A rectangle is constructed—the rectangle of points the sum of whose distances from $\overleftrightarrow{AB}$ and $\overleftrightarrow{AC}$ is n, as is the pair of parallels, each k away from $\overleftrightarrow{BC}$. This pair of parallels will intersect the rectangle at different points (depending on the position of the slider). Put a trace on each of these, move the slider, and watch what happens.

Mathematics Connections

PROBLEM 8 In a full investigation of this problem (in Activity 2), students will find the maximum value for the kicking angle at the point of tangency between the player's running line and a contour line. The notion of tangency of contour lines maximizing or minimizing some value is revisited often in mathematics. The horizontal tangent to the curve that students study in calculus is an example of this idea. Horizontal lines are contour lines along which the value of y does not change as x changes. Where a horizontal line is tangent to the graph of $y = f(x)$, you see local (or global) maxima or minima of $f(x)$. Here you see circles performing the same function. Circles are the contour lines along which the value of $\angle AUB$ does not change as U changes. Where a circle is tangent to some path that U might take, $\angle AUB$ is at its maximum.

This idea reappears again in Problem **10,** where the contour lines will be ellipses. In the escape-from-the-strange-pool problem (Activity 1, Problem **4**), the level curves were concentric circles with the swimmer's original position at their center. All points along any circle are equally distant from the swimmer. The smallest circle that is just tangent to the pool determines the direction by its point of tangency. Larger circles that are tangent to other parts of the pool show local minima—swimming to their point of tangency is shorter than swimming to other points near that point of tangency—but are not the global minimum identified by the smallest tangent circle.

This problem refers to Problem 10 in the On Your Own *section.*

PROBLEM 10 If your class can use a little trigonometry, you can reinforce a major idea by using a special case in which $\angle C$ is a right angle.

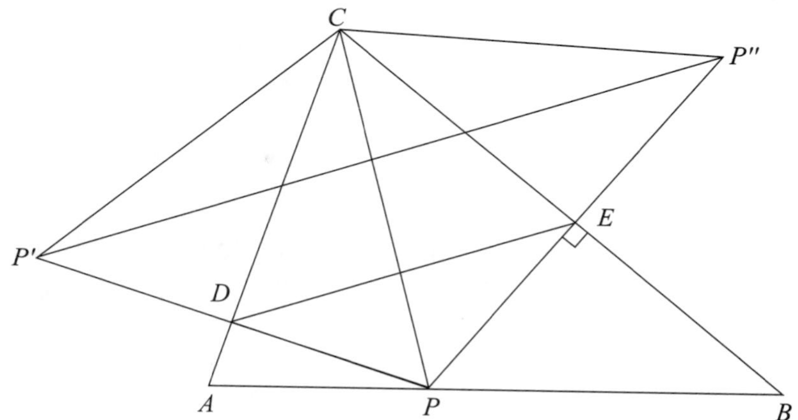

Let $DE = x$ and $CP = y$. Then $P'P'' = 2x$ and $CP' = CP'' = y$. Use the Law of Cosines on $\triangle CP'P''$ to obtain

$$(2x)^2 = y^2 + y^2 - 2 \cdot y \cdot y \cdot \cos\angle P'CP''$$

$$4x^2 = 2y^2 - 2y^2 \cos 2\angle ACB$$

$$2x^2 = y^2 (1 - \cos 2\angle ACB).$$

x and y are positive, so taking square roots is allowed.

If $m\angle ACB = 90°$, then $\cos 2\angle ACB = -1$. So, $2x^2 = 2y^2$, and $x = y$. This is the special case of a right angle. Simplifying further, you get

$$x = y\sqrt{\frac{1 - \cos 2\angle ACB}{2}}.$$

Using the half-angle formula for angles in quadrants I and II, you get

$$\sin\left(\frac{\theta}{2}\right) = \sqrt{\frac{1 - \cos\theta}{2}}.$$

The authors bet that there is an easier way to see that x = y sin∠ACB without all the gymnastics shown at the right. If you find such a way, send it to them.

Thus, you have

$$x = y \sin \angle ACB.$$

So, since $\sin \angle ACB$ is a positive constant (it is 1 when $\angle ACB$ is a right angle), x is a minimum when y is a minimum.

For fun, try graphing x against y on a Cartesian graph.

LESSON

Rich's Function

Lesson Objective

Students learn about functions, constant functions, similar triangles, equilateral triangles, and inequalities.

Content Overview

This lesson introduces Rich's problem, describes his method of "reasoning by continuity" to solve the problem, and develops two proofs of the result that the sum of the distances from any point inside an equilateral triangle to the sides of the triangle is equal to the length of the triangle's altitude. Students are asked to come up with variations on Rich's problem by changing one or more of the elements of the problem.

Planning Guide

Pacing	Activity	Materials	Homework Suggestions
Day 1	*Explore and Discuss* (SE p. 500) Activity 1: Reasoning by Continuity (SE p. 501)	geometry software (optional)	*On Your Own,* Problems 1, 5, and 6
Day 2	Activity 2: Proving Rich's Function Is Constant (SE pp. 502–504)	geometry software (optional)	*On Your Own,* Problems 7 and 8
Day 3	Activity 3: What if the Triangle Isn't Equilateral? (SE pp. 504–505)	geometry software (optional)	*On Your Own,* Problems 2, 3, 4, 9, and 10

Program Resources

- *Connected Geometry* CD-ROM, Module 6: Investigations 6.7, 6.8, and 6.10
- *Solution and Problem Solving Resource,* pages 556–566
- *Assessment Resources* Quiz 4 Lesson 4, page 205

Preparation and Prerequisites

Students need to use the Pythagorean Theorem to calculate the height of an equilateral triangle. To complete the proof of the generalization of Rich's function, students need to know that in a triangle, the longest altitude goes from the smallest angle to the smallest side. This fact can be developed when needed.

Teaching the Lesson

Rich's problem is not itself an optimization problem, but extensions to it—changing the triangle from equilateral and moving the point outside the triangle, for example—generate optimization problems. The way Rich solved the problem—using a combination of deduction and reasoning by continuity, along with some test-taking skill—is a very useful habit of mind for solving optimization problems.

Explore and Discuss *(Student page 500)*

Give students ample time to play around with this problem without looking at the solution. You never know: You might have a Rich in your class!

ACTIVITY 1

Reasoning by Continuity *(Student page 501)*

This activity leads students through Rich's method of reasoning by continuity to solve the given problem and asks students to find the correct answer.

ACTIVITY 2

Proving Rich's Function Is Constant *(Student pages 502–504)*

PROBLEM 6 It is important that students see the potential power of mathematics in doing something like calculating area in more than one way. In this particular case, they can use the technique to prove that the sum of the distances to the sides of the triangle from *any* spot inside the triangle is equal to the height of the triangle. They may use such a technique, again, for any number of other purposes.

ACTIVITY 3

What if the Triangle Isn't Equilateral? *(Student pages 504–505)*

The central mathematical message in this activity is that seeing what goes wrong in a proof when the hypotheses are relaxed gives you some insight into how the statement of the result needs to be modified. But there is another mathematical connection here: Students see that, if the triangle isn't equilateral, the function always assumes values between the shortest and longest heights of the triangle (as long as you stay inside the triangle).

What if these two heights are the same? Then, on one hand, the triangle is equilateral; on the other hand, the function is constant on the triangle's interior, recovering the student's original result. So often in mathematics, a result is noticed in a special case, and an explanation is constructed that makes use of the features of the special case. This leads to a consideration of more general cases, and experimentation shows how the result must be modified to accommodate more generality; new conjectures arise. Then the actual *methods* used to establish the special result can be studied, and, with a little perseverance, one can modify the arguments to establish more general results. These general theorems, in turn, *imply* the original result that motivated the whole activity, providing deeper insights into it and placing it in a more general context.

On Your Own *(Student pages 506–508)*

These problems provide students with the opportunity for individual practice. See the lesson Planning Guide for homework recommendations.

Take It Further *(Student page 509)*

These problems will lead students in new directions or will challenge them to apply what they already know.

Options and Extensions

Mathematics Connections

Rich's function is another example of a function defined on the plane (in this lesson, you look at only the interior of a triangle): The function calculates the sum of the distances to the *sides* of the triangle. The fact that the function is constant on the triangle's interior is quite surprising, but this can be proved by calculating the area of the triangle in more than one way. You can move the point outside the triangle and see that the function is no longer constant. Can you think of an "ordinary" function, that is, $y = f(x)$, "number-in number-out," that is constant for awhile and then starts growing? In the language of calculus, such functions cannot be differentiable at the points at which things start growing. In this case, it happens on the sides of the triangle. The surface plot of the function looks like the diagram shown below.

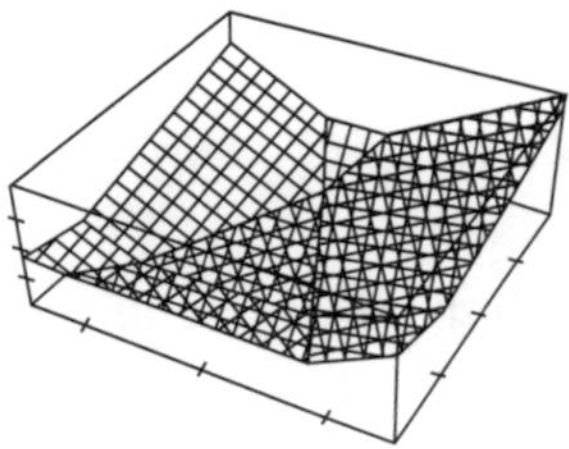

So, there are distinct folds where there are no well-defined tangent planes.

LESSON

The Airport Problem

Lesson Objective

Students explore possible "best spots" for building an airport and learn about continuous change.

Content Overview

- In Activity 1, students explore the possible "best spots" for the airport. One of the possibilities, finding a place that minimizes the total length of road that must be built, is selected as the theme for this activity. This goal can be stated in mathematical language: Given three points A, B, and C, for what point D is the sum $DA + DB + DC$ as small as possible?

  In the process of beginning the activity, students will learn about continuous variation, specifically the system of $\triangle ABC$ with its internal, continuously-varying point D.
- Activity 2 presents three ideas for investigating and developing a conjecture about the airport problem:
  1. Look at simpler problems and special cases.
  2. Look at a mechanical model.
  3. Use a computer.
- Activity 3 presents two proofs of the airport conjecture, one worked out carefully and one left for students to work through. The first proof is used to give an algorithm for locating the Fermat point. Its construction also sheds some insight on why the Fermat point is not the best spot for the airport if one angle of the triangle is bigger than 120°. (The Fermat point falls outside the triangle in these cases.) This proof sets up a construction in which the airport's location is found by drawing a segment between two points in order to minimize the distance between them. This useful habit of mind is reminiscent of many shortest path problems from Lesson 2.
- Activity 4 connects the airport problem to Rich's function, which gives the sum of the distances to the sides of an equilateral triangle. The idea here is for students to see connections between the two results.

Planning Guide

Pacing	Activity	Materials	Homework Suggestions
Day 1	*Explore and Discuss* (SE p. 510)	maps	Finish *Explore and Discuss* problems and *On Your Own,* Problem 1
Day 2	Activity 1: The Environmental Solution (SE pp. 511–512)	Materials will depend on the models you choose to build.	*On Your Own,* Problem 2
Day 3	Activity 2: Special Cases and Models (SE pp. 512–516)	• BLM 54, p. 63 • colored pens • geometry software	*On Your Own,* Problems 3 and 4
Day 4	Activity 2: Special Cases and Models (SE pp. 512–516)	• colored pens • geometry software	*Checkpoint,* Problem 19
Day 5	Activity 3: Establishing the Conjecture (SE pp. 517–522)	geometry software (optional)	*On Your Own,* Problems 5, 6, and 7
Day 6	Activity 3: Establishing the Conjecture (SE pp. 517–522)	geometry software (optional)	*On Your Own,* Problems 8, 9, and 10
Day 7	Activity 4: The Airport Revisited (SE pp. 523–524)	No special materials needed.	*On Your Own,* Problems 11 and 12

Program Resources

- *Connected Geometry* CD-ROM, Module 6: Investigations 6.11–6.21
- *Solution and Problem Solving Resource,* pages 567–586
- *Teaching Resources,* page 63
- *Assessment Resources,* Quiz 5 Lesson 5, page 206

Preparation and Prerequisites

- Problem **2** asks students to explain how to find the airport location if they want the airport to be equidistant from the three cities. This location is the circumcenter of the triangle. Students need not know about circumcenters ahead of time, but a small discussion about what they are and how to find them may be appropriate either before or after students work on this problem.
- Familiarity with geometry software.
- Knowledge about the following topics is needed for understanding the proofs: equilateral triangles, angles about a point (especially vertical and straight angles), facts about congruence (rotating a triangle produces a congruent one, for example), and measures of inscribed angles. Any of these topics can be developed or postulated (for later analysis) during the course of this lesson without creating a serious detour.

Explore and Discuss *(Student page 510)*

Students should work in pairs or small groups on this activity. Give each group a map. Ask students to mark their cities. Give them time as a group to discuss where the airport will go. You can end with a class discussion about the decisions made and what features students took into consideration.

In the discussion of the definition of "best," several possibilities will probably emerge. In addition to the fairness one mentioned in the Student Edition, make sure to include:

- *Economy:* The total cost of the roads built from the cities to the airport should be as small as possible.
- *Pollution reduction:* There should be as little total driving as possible in order to reduce exhaust emissions and traffic.

Students should understand that, in working on this activity, they are not expected to come up with the "right" conjecture at this point. The idea is to come up with something reasonable to explore and refine during Activity 1.

ACTIVITY 1

The Environmental Solution *(Student pages 511–512)*

The important idea in this activity is that point D can be thought of as a *moving* point, and, as it roams around the plane, it carries with it a process ("calculate the sum of the distances to the vertices of the triangle") that produces a *value* (the actual number you get when you sum the distances). This process view of mathematical functions is something that many high school students never develop. Using the language of functions and processors in a context like this, in which students never actually write down an explicit formula for the process, can help them begin to see functions as machines.

ACTIVITY 2

Special Cases and Models *(Student pages 512–516)*

Overviews of each idea mentioned on page 238 follow.

Idea 1: Look at Simpler Problems and Special Cases

Students use ideas about continuous change. Special cases are investigated. If there are only two cities, the airport can go anywhere between them. If there are three collinear cities, the airport should be located in the middle city. If the middle city is moved off the line between the other two by just a little, the ideal spot for the airport shouldn't move by very much. If one city is very far from the other two, the airport should be close to the segment containing the two close cities. If the cities form an equilateral triangle, the airport should go at the "center."

The authors realized while writing this activity that the first model gives a simple way (that is completely analogous to the pin-and-string construction of the ellipse) to draw the contour lines (the curves on which the sum of the distances to the cities is constant) for the airport function.

Idea 2: Look at a Mechanical Model

Three devices are suggested that allow students to invent and check conjectures. These models have the potential to help students think about the "sum of the distances function" as a continuously-varying system. They also help convince students that there is a unique best spot for the airport. The three devices are:

- a circle of nails in a wooden board (or a circular geoboard), with string to model the total distance between three cities and a fourth point modeled with a small metal ring;
- soap films;
- holes drilled in a board, with string passing through the holes and pulled taut with weights.

Idea 3: Use a Computer

Students use geometry software to model the airport problem. Essential to this technique is the building of a dynagraph that allows students to observe the sum of the distances to the airport both numerically and geometrically. The model is also used to approximate the contour lines for the airport function.

Depending on your class, on the materials available, and on the time you want to spend, you may want to do one, two, or all of these ideas. The authors have found in field tests that students are often convinced of their conjecture after just one experiment, and they don't see the point of performing another one to come up with the same conjecture.

If you have the resources, you may want groups of students to investigate just one of the ideas, making sure that each idea is covered by at least one group. One day of class presentations should be enough for everyone to get some knowledge of the other ideas and to see that they all come up with similar conjectures through different methods.

Alternatively, you may want students to investigate either the mechanical model or the computer model in class and complete the "Simpler Problems and Special Cases" problems as homework assignments. Teaching suggestions for each idea follow.

Teaching Idea 1 The focus of these problems is to get students to see the continuity in the given situation and to use it in developing a conjecture.

PROBLEM 8 This problem is a good place to bring up the transition from one case to another. With three collinear cities, the airport is best located at the center city. In an equilateral triangle, the airport goes in the "center." If you start with three collinear cities, with one city at the midpoint of the other two, and gradually move the middle city out along the perpendicular bisector of the segment between the other cities, at what point does the airport "leave" the middle city and move into the triangle's interior?

PROBLEM 9 Students might argue something like this: "If you move D closer to A, the distance to A gets shorter, but the distances to B and C each get bigger by a bit. So things won't change by much." That's the appropriate level of precision for this problem. As students build mechanical and computational models in the next activities, their feeling for the continuous nature of this problem should strengthen, and you may want to revisit this problem.

PROBLEM 10 This problem is difficult. In the section "Look at a Mechanical Model," students might develop a plausible argument for their position. Over the course of this unit, students *prove* the existence of a unique minimum and show how to locate it.

Teaching Idea 2 This idea should be done in groups; it is too difficult to handle the models on an individual basis. After students have built the first model, they should try several combinations of three cities, keeping track of their data with different-colored pens or on separate sheets of paper.

Teaching Idea 3 Students should first draw the three cities, connect each to a movable point *D*, and then sum the three distances to *D*. This sum can be seen visually with a dynagraph, but the idea can also be seen just by watching the numbers. As students move *D* around, they should notice that the sum changes continuously—there are no big changes in the sum for small changes in the location of *D*. That's useful for approximating the best location. Once students think that they have found the best spot for *D* for a given configuration, they should change the triangle and start moving *D* again.

Students will probably need guidance to know when to change D and when to change the triangle.

To make a conjecture, students will need to keep track of the best locations of *D* for various configurations. This tracking can be done with printouts or by placing tracing paper on the computer screen and copying the final setup.

ACTIVITY 3

Establishing the Conjecture *(Student pages 517–522)*

Depending on the time available, you may want some groups to present Hoffman's proof and others to present Toricelli's. Those presenting Toricelli's have more of the proof to construct on their own, but they will also have the benefit of working through another proof first.

On Your Own *(Student pages 524–528)*

These problems provide students with the opportunity for individual practice. See the lesson Planning Guide for homework recommendations.

PROBLEM 3 Copies of $\triangle ABC$ are provided on Blackline Master 54.

Take It Further *(Student page 528)*

These problems will lead students in new directions or will challenge them to apply what they already know.

Options and Extensions

This lesson focuses on an extended investigation of one problem and its variations. The problem has a long and interesting history; some readings about it are included here and in the student materials.

As stated, this problem is not yet an optimization problem, but the direction that the lesson takes—trying to find the spot that requires the minimal amount of new roadwork (with the admittedly-problematic assumption that no existing roads are being considered) turns it into one. In teaching this lesson, the authors have found that some students really enjoy the purely-mathematical exploration of minimizing distance in this pretend world. Others are annoyed by the detachment from reality. They prefer to work with a real map and take existing roads, lakes, and other potential obstacles into account. A real-world problem may be a much more difficult problem.

In Activity 2, as engaging and enlightening as these "analog gadgets" are for many people, there are two caveats that need to be made explicit:

- Many students (and adults) have a difficult time dealing with mechanical devices. They get bogged down in the details of the string and pins, and they have a difficult time manipulating the physics of the situation. For these students, descriptions of the mechanical devices are sometimes more effective, as are computer simulations like the one in Activity 3. Students can then conduct thought experiments to get at the essential messages that the physical experiments are trying to convey.

- Although the authors have much anecdotal evidence from their own classes, they are unaware of conclusive research that shows that devices like these help students construct the essential mathematics involved in the continuity properties of functions.

There is a long-standing tradition in graduate schools of mathematics for graduate students to study famous proofs of theorems and then present the proofs to classmates. This tradition is very beneficial. Just as studying a piece of music is an important ingredient in developing skill at composition, studying the proofs of others helps one develop skill at constructing proofs. Simply memorizing the proof presented in Activity 3 is useless, but reworking it and presenting it in your own words can be quite valuable. An especially important exercise is to give some scenarios that might have led Hoffman and Toricelli to the *invention* of these proofs in the first place.

Using Technology

You may want students to use geometry software while working through Hoffman's proof. While not essential, the use of such software is *very* effective, especially if done on an overhead projector screen.

Mathematics Connections

PROBLEMS 9–10 These problems get at some important and subtle mathematical ideas. Problem **9** asks students to argue that the airport function is continuous on the plane. The precise definition in this case demands that you can make two values of the function—that is, two different sums of distances to the vertices from two different points—as close as you like (on the number line) by making the points at which you calculate the sums close enough on the plane. So, by making two airport locations close enough, you can make the associated sums of distances as close as you like—making their difference less than $\frac{1}{1,000,000}$. In analysis classes in college, students spend their time calculating things like just *how* close you would have to make the airports in order to make the sums of distances to the vertices within $\frac{1}{1,000,000}$ of each other. (To complicate matters, the answer to this question probably depends on where you are on the plane relative to the cities.)

Unit 6 Review

This unit review is intended to provide students with problems that will encourage them to look back at the unit as a whole. Students have one more opportunity to pull together, apply, and communicate the ideas they have developed by working on the activities throughout the unit.

It is especially important for students to have the opportunity to share their solutions with the class.

PROBLEMS 1–2 These problems review work done in Lesson 1 on minimizing distance.

PROBLEM 3 Students have encountered the burning tent problem several times in this unit and should be able to describe it either in the context of a burning tent or generically.

PROBLEM 4 This problem reviews the fact that students learned in Lesson 2—that a square with fixed perimeter will maximize area. Encourage students to share their proofs with classmates.

PROBLEM 5 Students never proved that the circle has the largest area for a given perimeter but you may want to spend time exploring this idea now. See the *Connected Geometry* CD-ROM, Investigation 6.18, for further activities on this topic.

PROBLEMS 6–7 These problems review the general idea of contour lines presented in Lesson 3.

PROBLEM 8 Students can refer to Lesson 3, Activity 3, *Contour Lines and Functions,* to review concepts needed to answer this question.

PROBLEM 9 Students learned about reasoning by continuity while studying Rich's function in Lesson 4. Ask them to review Rich's function and apply his technique to this problem.

PROBLEM 10 Throughout their study of *Connected Geometry,* students have been making many conjectures and should be able to explain how they differ from theorems.

PROBLEM 11 Students should be able to describe not only the point at which the distance is minimal, but also the triangles in which this situation is possible.

PROBLEM 12 This problem asks students to describe the Fermat point and recognize that not all triangles will have such a point.